C000193563

Science About Us

A complete course for CXC Integrated Science

Alec Farley, BA, MS, Dip. Adv. Studies Ed.
Former Head of Science, New Amsterdam Multilateral
School, Guyana

Winston King, BSc (Hons), MEd, PhD, MI Biol.
Lecturer in Science Education, School of Education, UWI
Cave Hill, Barbados

Norman Lambert, BSc (Hons), Dip. Ed., Dip. Soc. Ethics
Queens Royal College, Port of Spain, Trinidad

Vilma McClenan, BSc (Hons), Dip. Ed.
Project Officer, UWI Distance Teaching Experiment
UWI, Mona, Jamaica

Heinemann Educational Books

London   Kingston   Port of Spain

Heinemann Educational Books Ltd

22 Bedford Square, London WC1B 3HH
175 Mountain View Avenue, Kingston 6, Jamaica
27 Belmont Circular Road, Port of Spain, Trinidad

LONDON   EDINBURGH   MELBOURNE   AUCKLAND
HONG KONG   SINGAPORE   KUALA LUMPUR   NEW DELHI
NAIROBI   IBADAN   JOHANNESBURG
PORTSMOUTH (NH)

© Heinemann Educational Books 1985
First published 1985

British Library Cataloguing in Publication Data

Science about us: a complete course for CXC
 integrated science.
 1. Science
 I. Farley, Alec
 500   Q161.2

ISBN 0-435-98302-4

Filmset in 11/12 Times by
BAS Printers Limited, Over Wallop, Hampshire, UK
Printed and bound in Great Britain by Cambus Litho, East Kilbride

Contents

Part 4 Science in transport

Acknowledgements

Acknowledgements for permission to publish photographs are due as follows:

J Allan Cash pages 85, 123, 146, 152, 157, 168, 169, 183, 185

All-Sport Photographic Ltd pages 155, 156, 159, 182

Anne Bolt pages 79, 86 (pylons), 104, 107, 110, 116, 117, 170, 202

Camerapix, Hutchinson Library page 147 (net fishing)

Colorsport page 201 (Carl Lewis)

Daily Telegraph Colour Library page 186

Department of Environment page 201 (crashed car)

Alec Farley page 90

Armet Francis page 23

Guyana High Commission page 181 (bridge)

Philip Harris Biological Ltd page 10 (chromosomes)

Health Education Council (UK) page 130

Neil Hokan page 22

John and Penny Hubley pages 150, 175

Val Millington page 159 (cricket)

National Maritime Museum, Greenwich page 183 (ship)

National Meteorological Library pages 89, 191

Oxfam page 36

Oxford Scientific Films pages 84, 99, 108, 194, 195

Philips Welding Ltd page 87

Science Photo Library page 109 (solar cells)

Arthur Smith/Jamaica Information Service page 147 (fish farm)

TALC page 28

Tropix Photographic Library pages 109 (solar panels), 183 (radar), 193

Tupperware page 106

Vicky Unwin page 100

WASA page 80

C James Webb pages 9, 10, 30, 31, 38, 60, 61, 72, 76, 78, 113, 121, 129, 132, 142, 160, 163

Text illustrations drawn by Donald Bason, Sam Denley, Illustrated Arts, John Plumb, Despina Savva

Cover photographs by R. Hibbert (top left), All-Sport/ Adrian Murrell (top right), Alec Farley (bottom right), Anne Bolt (bottom left)

Cover design by Chris Gilbert

To the teacher

Science plays an important part in our daily lives and it is reasonable to expect that it will increasingly affect our lives in the years ahead. As such, science should be an integral part of our general education courses.

Science About Us was written primarily for those students who are entering the fourth form and who wish to pursue a science course as part of their general education, and for those who can pursue only one science course at this level.

This book was written according to the rationale, aims and objectives of the Caribbean Examinations Council Integrated Science (Single Award) syllabus. It caters for both the General and Basic Proficiency Levels. The work is organized around four themes:

Science in the home
Science in the workplace
Science in sport and recreation
Science in transport

The material is also organized into spreads so that each spread or half spread deals with a specific idea.

This book is more than a reader. The authors have paid due attention to the varied facets of science—science as product, science as process, and how science serves society. It is hoped that you can use it as a basis for constructing your own course.

To the student

Most people consider science an important part of general education because decisions are made each day which require some knowledge of science.

Science is many things. It is information about and explanations for natural phenomena. It is a way of thinking and of solving problems. By using scientific knowledge we gain mastery over the environment, we improve our health, live longer, make life more comfortable, free ourselves from the burdens of excessive manual labour and increase our leisure time and range of recreational pursuits. Unfortunately, there are those who use scientific knowledge to harm their fellow men. And that is a real tragedy.

This book is concerned with science in the home, science in the workplace, science in recreation and science in transport—in short, this book is concerned with *Science About Us*. It consists of a number of spreads or articles, each one dealing with a specific idea or topic. The spreads give information, offer explanations, raise questions and suggest experiments and other activities that you should do. Remember to exercise care and obey the safety rules while using apparatus, chemicals and other materials.

Science is fun. Do enjoy *Science About Us*.

When you pursue a science course, you must pay due attention to matters of safety.

Accidents do arise in the home, the workplace and even in recreation. An understanding of science should help us become aware of potential hazards as well as procedures to be adopted to prevent accidents, and how to give first aid.

Respiratory hazards

Artificial respiration

A person's lungs may fail as a result of **suffocation, electric shock, gas poisoning,** or **drowning.** The resultant **lack of oxygen** to the brain causes **death** after two to four minutes, so artificial respiration must be carried out **immediately** the patient is discovered.

Artificial respiration or resuscitation is the first aid action to take if a person has stopped breathing, that is, their **lungs have failed.**

The method of artificial respiration illustrated here is called the **Kiss of Life** and **must not be used in some cases of poisoning** due to the dangers of contamination.

Kiss of Life method

Ensure an open airway to the lungs (see the diagram, left).
1 Support the back of the neck with a rolled-up coat.
2 Push the forehead backwards.
3 Pull the chin downwards to open the mouth.
4 Remove anything obstructing the back of the mouth, e.g. swallowed tongue, vomit.

Now ventilate the patient's lungs in the following way:
5 Take a deep breath.
6 Pinch the patient's nostrils closed.
7 Seal your mouth around the patient's mouth.
8 Blow as much air into the lungs as possible.
9 After removing your mouth from the patient's, watch the chest return to normal.
10 Repeat stages **5, 6, 7, 8 and 9** above.
11 Give the patient about 4–5 ventilations in this way, one every 4 seconds.
12 Check that the heart is beating or that there is a pulse.
13 Try to get someone else to call for an ambulance.

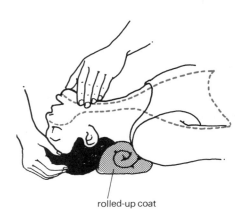

rolled-up coat

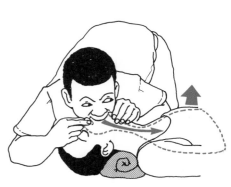

The iron lung

The iron lung is an artificial aid to breathing. It is used by patients who can no longer breathe normally, e.g. when a disease like polio has paralysed the necessary muscles. The patient cannot leave the iron lung for much longer than he can hold his breath without suffering brain damage.

Combustion hazards

Fires can be started by the careless use of household appliances. An electric iron left 'on' at a high setting can overheat and start a fire. Using water to fight such fires can give electric shocks to those fighting the fire,

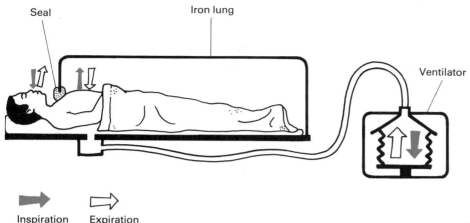

Seal   Iron lung   Ventilator

Inspiration   Expiration

The pressure inside the iron lung forces the chest and lung to pump air

since water conducts electricity. If there is a delay in lighting gas burners or gas cookers after the gas tap has been opened, a flare up or explosion may result.

If a person gets burnt, cool the burned area at once by plunging it into cool water or by applying a sterile cloth soaked in cool water. **Never** apply butter or grease to the burn! Never try to remove any burnt skin, or try to burst blisters, and do not use antiseptics or disinfectants on the burnt part. Cover the burn with a clean dry cloth, seek medical help, and treat the person for shock.

When fuels, e.g. kerosene oil, are burned, toxic fumes can be given off. This burning therefore should be done only in properly ventilated areas.

Hazards to eyesight

Lights that are too bright or that contain ultraviolet rays can burn the retina of the eye. Welders and those watching welding should therefore wear special *approved* goggles to protect their eyesight. Lighting that is too dim, whether at school or at the workplace, can produce eye fatigue since the iris of the eye has constantly to work to keep the pupil wide open.

Eye injuries can also be caused by liquids splashing into the eye, or from solid particles being lodged against the surface of the eyeball. This latter causes considerable pain and irritation, while liquids usually cause pain and a burning sensation.

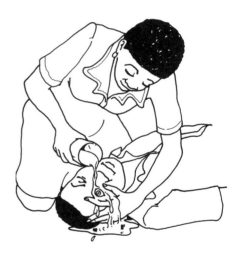

Treatment involves irrigating the eyes with a gentle stream of cold water for about 15–20 minutes, with the eyelids held open throughout. If you are treating yourself, plunge your face into a basin of water, with your eyes open, and *your breath temporarily held*. Do this several times until the eye is properly washed.

Bleeding

Shock is a state of collapse which occurs when a lot of blood has been lost as a result of injury; the brain thus receives an inadequate blood supply. The person looks pale, with profuse sweating and blurred vision, and finally collapses.

Treatment involves laying the person flat on the back, with the legs propped 20–30 cm above the body in freely circulating air. Artificial respiration should be given if necessary, and any bleeding stopped by using a clean cloth to apply pressure. The person should be reassured **while medical help is sought**.

Nose bleeding results when fine blood vessels in the nasal region are damaged. Treatment involves tilting the person's head slightly forward (to prevent him from inhaling blood) and pinching the nostrils shut, while the person breathes through the mouth. Instruct the subject **not to blow their nose**. Have good ventilation and apply a *cold* water compress to the bridge of the patient's nose and to the nape of the neck for about 10 minutes to stop the bleeding.

1

The structure of living organisms

Muscle cells

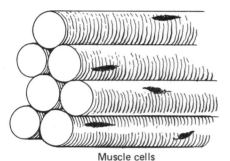
Onion cells

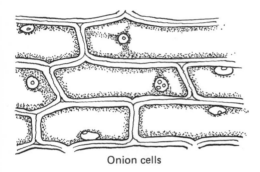
Xylem cells

Cells, tissues and systems

Your body, like every other living organism, is made up of **living cells**. However, the numbers and types of cells vary in different organisms. Each cell is a structural and functional unit which may work alone or in conjunction with other similar cells. Similar cells which are grouped together and perform similar functions form a **tissue**. **Bone**, **muscles** and **blood** are animal tissues; the tough, woody **xylem** of a tree trunk, and the softer, green **parenchyma** of stem and leaves are also tissues.

Various tissues are grouped together as **organs**. The heart, for example, contains muscle tissue, blood and other connective tissue, nervous tissue and covering tissue. A leaf is made of conducting tissues (xylem and phloem) as well as covering and packing tissue (parenchyma).

Several different organs can be linked to each other and so work together as a **system** within the organism's body. For example, the respiratory, digestive and nervous systems are found, among others, in the human body.

Activities

1   Find out who Robert Hooke was. How did he help us to understand about the structure of cells?
2   Get a clean slide and place a drop of water on it. Wash your index finger clean, then *very gently* use it to scrape off some of the lining of your cheek, inside your mouth. The whitish substance you will get under your fingernail will probably contain some flattened cells similar to those shown in the photograph. Place this whitish mass of cells in the drop of water; place a cover glass over it; then look at the cells under a microscope. Can you identify the parts?
3   Make a large labelled drawing to show the general structure of a cell.
4   List the essential differences between animal and plant cells.

Chromosomes—the threads of life

The nucleus is the central 'motor' of each cell. It tells the cell which specific functions it must perform, and also when to perform these functions. It can do so because of the special information contained in code form in each nucleus. The dark, granular appearance of the nucleus is produced by the tightly coiled threads called **chromosomes**. Chromosomes are frequently referred to as the 'threads of life' because they contain all the information a cell needs to perform its function, and, moreover, they bear the **genes** (the sites of the encoded information) which control inherited traits or characteristics. Each gene is located at a definite place along the chromosome. Each gene affects a certain trait, e.g. how tall you are, the colour of your skin, eyes or hair. The number of chromosomes in each body cell is the same. In humans, a bone cell has 46 chromosomes; each nerve cell or blood cell also has 46 chromosomes in its nucleus. Similarly, each cell in the leaf, root or stem of the pea plant has 14 chromosomes inside its nucleus. This is what makes it easy to recognize humans as different from any other living organism.

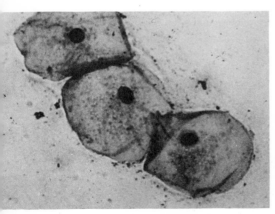
Cells from human cheek lining × 1000

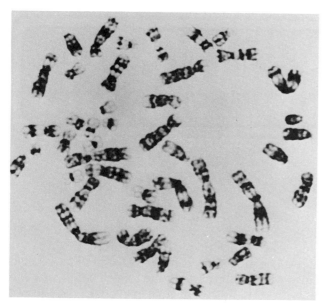

Complete set of human chromosomes (normal male) very highly magnified

Cell division

Ordinary cell division

When a cell has grown to a mature size the coded information in the chromosomes within the nucleus of the cell can direct it to divide. During cell division the plasma membrane and the entire cytoplasm separate into two equal parts and, most important of all, the chromosomes are duplicated. Thus, two new cells, alike in every way, are formed from the original cell. All the genetic information has been passed in the chromosomes from parent cell to the new daughter cells.

This type of ordinary cell division or **mitosis** goes on within each organism, causing that organism to grow in size and complexity.

Cell division with a difference

Cells that result from mitosis have a complete or **diploid** set of chromosomes. Inside the male and female reproductive organs of all living animals and plants a special type of cell division, **meiosis**, occurs periodically. It results in the formation of male and female **sex cells**—the **sperms** and **eggs**. Because of the chromosome behaviour during meiosis, each sex cell has only half or the **haploid** number of chromosomes in the parent cell. Each human sperm, and each egg, therefore contains only 23 chromosomes, while every other human cell contains 46 chromosomes.

Since one egg and one sperm fuse at **fertilization**, the new organism formed by this process has a complete (diploid) set of chromosomes, and receives information from two sources, that encoded in the chromosomes of the sperm and of the egg. This information tells the new cell how to grow, what functions to perform and ultimately determines what that new organism looks like. It is for this reason that people can say: 'You look very like your mother, except you have your father's eyes!'

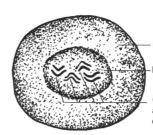

Cytoplasm
Nucleus
Chromosomes already divided

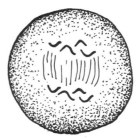

Chromosomes move apart

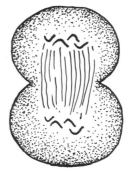

Cytoplasm divides

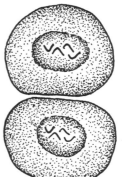

Two new cells formed

Stages in mitosis of a cell

Questions

1 State two important differences between mitosis and meiosis.
2 Explain why meiosis is also called 'reduction division'.
3 In your own words, explain the value of meiosis to living organisms.
4 Do some research in your library and then write about the work of Gregor Mendel and how it contributed to our understanding of genetic inheritance.

Asexual reproduction

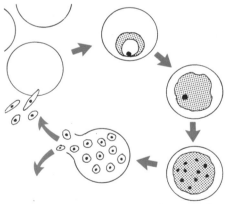

Asexual reproducion of Entamoeba

Reproductive cycle of Plasmodium in red blood cells

Mitosis

When mature cells divide by mitosis, they **reproduce** by forming new **daughter cells**. These daughter cells are genetically alike, because of the way the chromosomes behaved during mitosis.

Simple **unicellular** (one-celled) organisms such as *Entamoeba* (which causes Amoebic dysentery) reproduce themselves regularly in this way. When a mature size is reached, the unicell stops moving. The nucleus divides, the cytoplasm also divides, and finally the unicell splits into two new organisms, alike in every way. Both cells then grow to mature size.

This is the simplest form of reproduction. It is called **asexual reproduction**, because it involves only one parent, and there is no fusion of male and female sex cells.

Many lower animals and plants reproduce asexually. *Plasmodium*, which causes malaria, and bread mould *Mucor* reproduce in this way.

The malaria parasite, *Plasmodium*

After a mosquito has bitten its victim, it injects a substance into the blood stream to stop the blood clotting. If the mosquito is carrying *Plasmodium*, this microorganism is also passed into the blood stream. The malaria parasite then reproduces asexually by repeated mitosis, first in the liver, then in the red blood cells. As the number of asexual divisions increases, red blood cells are destroyed and anaemia results. As each red blood cell dies it bursts, releasing toxins into the host's body. These cause a high fever, with temperatures of 38–40 °C.

This ability of disease-causing microorganisms to perform rapid asexual reproduction must be constantly borne in mind since

(a) they could become established quickly in the host's cells, or in unhygienic surroundings where they find ideal living conditions;
(b) their rapid rate of increase often makes an effective cure time-consuming.

Bread mould, *Mucor*

Bread mould or *Mucor* is a plant. It belongs to a group of plants, the fungi, whose cells do not contain chlorophyll. They are therefore unable to make their food by the process of photosynthesis. Fungi derive nutrients by absorbing them from the dead or living substances or **substrates** upon which they grow.

If you leave a slice of slightly damp bread in a dish in the lab or at home for about a week, what happens to it? When you examine it you'll probably see a white, cottony web of fine threads speckled with little black dots, growing over the surface of the bread. When you look at it more closely using a hand magnifier, you will notice that the black dots stand up from the surface of the bread, on very fine threads.

This cottony growth is the fungus, *Mucor*. The whole growth you see is the body or **mycelium** of the fungus, made of fine tube-like, fungal threads called **hyphae**. This mycelium has grown from a single, asexually produced cell called a **spore**. When a spore falls upon moistened bread, or on fruit, it divides repeatedly by mitosis and produces the mycelium.

Each black dot is a spore case or **sporangium**. Mitotic cell division occurs within it, resulting in the production of a mass of unicellular, asexual spores. When the sporangium is mature the wall bursts open and the spores are released into the atmosphere. Spores are blown about and eventually, when each lands on a suitable organic substrate, it will germinate, divide by mitosis, and establish its own mycelium. By this means of asexual reproduction the organism rapidly establishes itself wherever there are adequate nutrients and favourable living conditions.

Mould will grow on foods and other substances in our home and surroundings, if conditions are favourable. However, it is possible to prevent mould from causing damage. Wet shoes, books and clothing, for example, should be thoroughly dried before they are put away since moulds and many other microorganisms cannot thrive in the absence of moisture. Damp cupboards and drawers should be opened periodically so that air can circulate in them to dry them out. Foods such as bread and biscuits should not be left in the open but should be stored in a dry, covered container where fungal spores cannot enter.

Asexual reproduction in higher plants

Many higher plants also carry out asexual reproduction:

(a) where there are favourable conditions for growth;
(b) after a period of dormancy, to re-establish the aerial parts.

In such cases, there is no fertilization, and no seed production. Instead, buds on stems, leaves and roots grow by mitotic cell division (mitosis), forming new plants. The process is called **vegetative propagation**. Because these new plants are produced asexually, their genetic make-up is exactly the same as the parent's. This similarity has distinct advantages; e.g., when a particular variety of potato is being grown for its flavour, size, texture etc., it is reproduced asexually to ensure that *all* new plants have the exact traits of the parent plant.

Some examples of vegetative propagation are given in the table below.

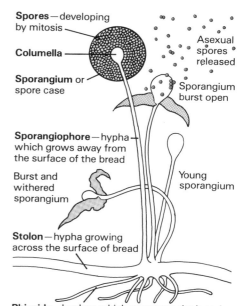

Stages in mitosis of mucor spores × 700

Plant Organ	*Method of Vegetative Propagation*
STEM STRUCTURES	
(a) Bulb	An underground, reduced stem surrounded by fleshy, close-set leaf bases. Lateral buds grow into new plants, using the food reserves in the leaf bases, *Onion, Spider lily.*
(b) Corm	Short, vertical underground stem, swollen with stored food. Two or three corms may be present together. Lateral buds produce new corms, while terminal bud gives rise to the flowering shoot, *Coco (Colocasia), Eddoes, Dasheen.*
(c) Rhizome	Horizontal underground stem, swollen with stored food. Aerial shoots formed from lateral or terminal buds, *Ginger, Canna lily.*
(d) Runner	Lateral branches which arise close to the ground, grow along the surface, and eventually separate to form new plants, *Strawberry, African violets (Episcia).*
(e) Stem tuber	Swollen tip of underground lateral stem. Buds on the tuber produce many new plants, *Irish potato.*
(f) Sucker	Shoots which arise from underground parts of plants grow upwards and become established as new plants, *Banana.*
ROOT STRUCTURES	
(a) Root tuber	Swollen fibrous root or tap root capable of forming new plant which develops from bud at tip, *Sweet potato, Carrot.*
LEAF STRUCTURES	
(a) Leaf bud	Buds in the notches along the leaf margin of a succulent leaf form new plants, *Bryophyta.*

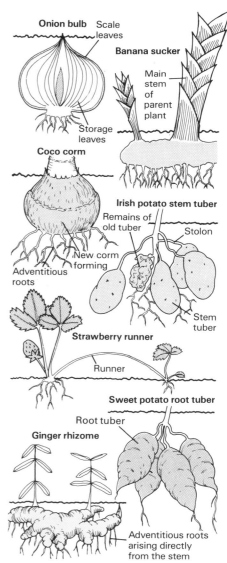

Finding out more

Read all you can about Alexander Fleming and his discovery of the uses of a type of mould called *Penicillium*.

Sexual reproduction in higher plants

What do flowers do?

You have probably seen thousands of flowers, of different sizes, shapes and colours. But have you ever really looked closely and carefully at a flower? What parts does a flower possess? What does a flower do?

Flowers are the organs of sexual reproduction of higher plants, and are necessary for the production of seeds.

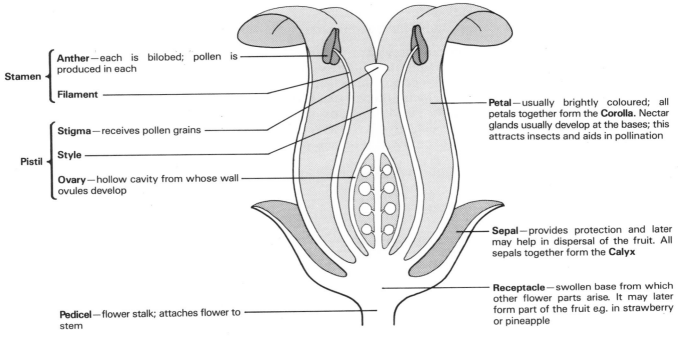

Stamen
- **Anther**—each is bilobed; pollen is produced in each
- **Filament**

Pistil
- **Stigma**—receives pollen grains
- **Style**
- **Ovary**—hollow cavity from whose wall ovules develop

Petal—usually brightly coloured; all petals together form the **Corolla**. Nectar glands usually develop at the bases; this attracts insects and aids in pollination

Sepal—provides protection and later may help in dispersal of the fruit. All sepals together form the **Calyx**

Receptacle—swollen base from which other flower parts arise. It may later form part of the fruit e.g. in strawberry or pineapple

Pedicel—flower stalk; attaches flower to stem

Vertical section showing parts of a typical flower

Parts of a flower

Although flowers may vary in many ways, most flowers have the following easily identified parts (see the diagram above):

anther, filament, stigma, style, ovary, pedicel, petal, sepal, receptacle.

Protective parts of the flower

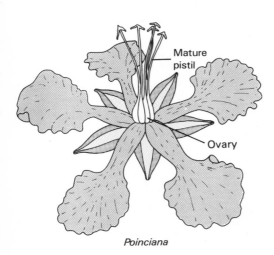

Mature pistil

Ovary

Poinciana

Look at a flower from the Poinciana tree, and identify the parts described here. The bottom of the flower is surrounded by five green structures called **sepals**. Sepals are a special kind of leaf which protect the young flower when it is folded up in a **bud**. Most sepals are green and leaf-like. You can also find green sepals at the base of the red Hibiscus and the yellow Allamanda flower. In other flowers the sepals are large and brightly coloured, e.g. Barbados Pride.

The **petals** are the flower parts immediately inside the sepals. They too are a special kind of leaf. The petals in the Poinciana and Hibiscus are red; they may also be pink (Oleander), yellow (Allamanda), or blue (Plumbago). Many petals are white (orchids and roses). Both the sepals and the petals protect the sexual organs of the flower while they are developing. Petals are also useful in attracting insects to the flowers, thus aiding pollination.

The number of sepals and petals in a flower varies greatly. Some, like the Poinciana, Hibiscus and Allamanda flowers, have only a few petals. How many petals does a rose or a sunflower have?

In some flowers the sepals and petals cannot be distinguished as two separate sets of flower parts. In this case, the combined flower part is called the **perianth**. If you look at flowers from the Lily family, you can see the perianth parts are in multiples of three.

Reproductive parts of the flower

The organs of sexual reproduction are the **stamens** and the **pistil**, which are located inside the circle of petals. Most flowers have both stamens and pistil and are **hermaphrodite**. In some flowers there are only stamens or a pistil, but not both. These flowers are **unisexual**.

The stamens are the male reproductive organs and produce special male sex cells called **pollen**. There are usually several stamens, which are easily recognized in mature, fully-opened flowers by the yellow powdery **pollen grains** they produce in the **anthers** at their tips.

The pistil is the female reproductive organ. There is usually only one pistil, located in the centre of the flower. A pistil consists of three parts: the **stigma** at the top, the tubular **style** in the middle, and the **ovary** at the bottom.

Inside the ovary are one or more **ovules**. Each ovule contains the female sex cell, or **ovum**, and several other nuclei.

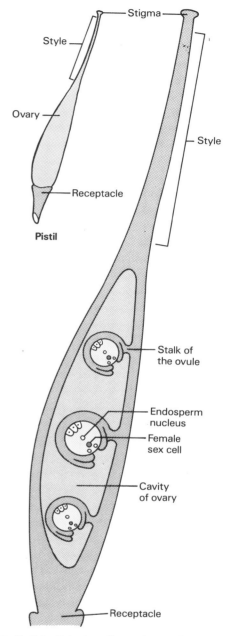

Pistil of the Poinciana flower (vertical section)

Questions

1. Where in flowers does meiosis occur?
2. Explain what is meant by an 'incomplete' flower.
3. (a) What is meant by the words: 'Male guinep (or ackee) tree' or 'male paw-paw tree'?
   (b) How do such trees reproduce sexually?

Activities

1. Look at the bud of a Poinciana flower. What parts can you identify on the unopened bud?
2. (a) At what time of the year does the Poinciana tree flower?
   (b) Describe the appearance of the tree at different times during the year.
3. (a) Examine a Poinciana flower carefully with a hand magnifier.
       (i) How many stamens are there?
       (ii) Describe how the stamens are arranged.
   (b) Carefully pick off one stamen and examine it; notice how the anther is attached. Make a labelled drawing to show the parts of the stamen.
   (c) Pick off all the floral parts so that only the pistil remains. Identify the stigma, style and ovary.
   (d) Lay the pistil flat on the table and, using a sharp razor blade, carefully cut it in two lengthwise, going from the receptacle upwards to the tip. Separate the two halves and examine them with a hand magnifier. Make a labelled drawing of the pistil in vertical section.
4. Use a hand lens to examine a flower. List the differences between this flower and a Poinciana flower.

Formation of fruits and seeds

Pollination

For sexual reproduction to occur in plants, pollen must be transferred from the anthers to the stigma. The transfer of mature pollen grains from the anthers where they are formed to the stigma of a flower of the same species is called **pollination**. Pollination often occurs when bees, ants and butterflies move from flower to flower in search of pollen and nectar. Birds and other animals also aid in pollination. Pollen can also be blown from anther to stigma by the wind.

There are two types of pollination, self-pollination and cross-pollination (see below).

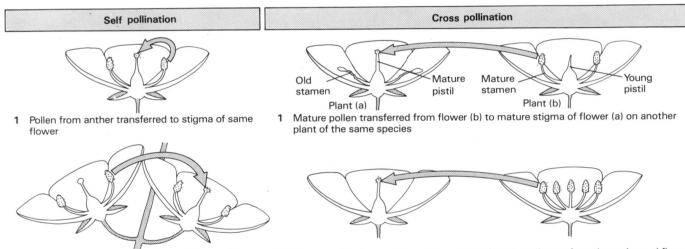

Self pollination	Cross pollination

1 Pollen from anther transferred to stigma of same flower

1 Mature pollen transferred from flower (b) to mature stigma of flower (a) on another plant of the same species

2 Mature pollen from anther of one flower transferred to stigma of another similar flower on same plant

2 Mature pollen from unisexual flower transferred to stigma of another unisexual flower on another plant of the same species

Cross-pollination is more advantageous to plants since it allows new genetic material to be introduced, thus improving the viability of the species and producing stronger, healthier plants.

Self-pollination is a form of inbreeding; it leads to smaller plants which are less resistant to disease and less able to withstand unfavourable growth conditions. In good agricultural practice farmers prevent self-pollination. This is done by removing the stamens before they ripen, and then transferring pollen from other flowers onto the stigma left in each flower. Crop yields are thus improved, and seeds are more viable.

Fertilization

What happens to the pollen grain after it lands on the stigma? After successful pollination, the following events occur.

1 The pollen grain germinates by pushing out a pollen tube, which may be attracted by sugary secretions on the stigma (stage (a), *left*).
2 The nuclei move into the pollen tube; the first nucleus guides the growth of the tube down through the soft tissue of the style (stage (b), *opposite*).
3 The pollen tube grows down to the ovule which it enters through a tiny opening called the **micropyle**. The first nucleus then dies (stage (c), *opposite*).

(a)

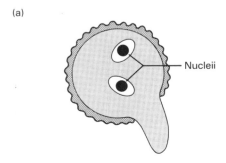

Nucleii

4 Once inside the ovule, the second pollen nucleus divides into two **male nuclei**. One fuses with the nucleus of the egg cell to form a **zygote**; the other male nucleus fuses with two other nuclei in the ovule to form the **endosperm cell**. This **double fertilization** process takes place within each ovule.

How are fruits and seeds formed?

After double fertilization has occurred, most of the flower parts, particularly the petals and stamens, wither away as they have served their purpose. Often the sepals remain and become dried and wing-like, while the style may develop into hooks. Such structures later assist the dispersal of the fruit or the seed. The receptacle and the ovary wall also change to form the fruit wall and fruit stalk. The ovary wall may become fleshy and succulent, and differentiate into two or three layers. Alternatively, it may dry out, harden, and increase considerably in size.

The transformed ovary and its contents together form the **fruit**. The fruit shows the scar or remains of the style at one end, and is attached to the plant by the former flower stalks.

Changes also occur within the ovule which transform it into a **seed**. The zygote develops into an **embryo** by mitotic division. The embryo develops a small, but distinctly recognizable **plumule**, **radicle** and **cotyledon(s)**.

(b)

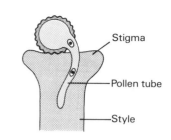

(c)

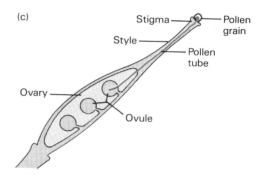

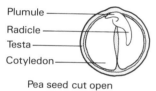

Pea seed cut open

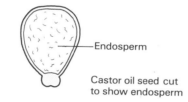

Castor oil seed cut to show endosperm

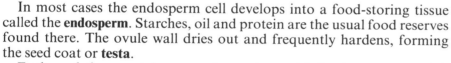

In most cases the endosperm cell develops into a food-storing tissue called the **endosperm**. Starches, oil and protein are the usual food reserves found there. The ovule wall dries out and frequently hardens, forming the seed coat or **testa**.

Each seed thus contains an embryo plant with food reserves, and is attached to the fruit wall by the former ovule stalk.

Activities

1 Examine the following: (a) poinciana or pea pod; (b) a plum. List the differences between the fruits and the seeds.
2 List the changes you observe in the following plants as the pistil becomes a fruit after fertilization.
   (a) poinciana (or pigeon/gungo peas)
   (b) tomato or orange
   (c) mango or plum.

Questions

1 List in correct order of occurrence the steps in sexual reproduction in flowering plants.
2 Name three different agents of pollination.
3 What is the significance/importance of pollination?

5

Red pea seed

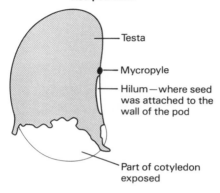

- Testa
- Mycropyle
- Hilum—where seed was attached to the wall of the pod
- Part of cotyledon exposed

Seed cut open

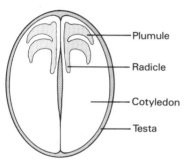

- Plumule
- Radicle
- Cotyledon
- Testa

Structure of a red pea seed

Inside a seed

The poinciana seed has a tough seed coat or testa, so it is not easy to see what is inside. However, the insides of a red pea or kidney bean can easily be examined because the red seed coat is softer and can be stripped off easily.

Not all seeds are like the red pea. Some have only one cotyledon, e.g. corn (maize), members of the 'grass' family (rice, wheat), and the lily family. In pea and poinciana seeds the endosperm tissue is not well developed, unlike that of the castor oil seed (*Ricinus*).

Finding out more

What reserves of food do you think are stored in the **endosperm** of a castor oil seed? Do you think the food reserve in the **non-endospermic** red pea seed or rice grain is the same as that in the castor oil seed? To find the answer to these questions, carry out the following food tests.

Starch test
Add one drop of iodine solution to the crushed cotyledons or to the endosperm of seeds such as: red peas, castor oil seeds and corn seeds. If starch is present the brown iodine will react with it and stain it a blue-black colour.

Test for fats/oils
1 Rub the cut surface of the seed on a clean sheet of paper and hold the paper up to the light. If you see a translucent area which does not dry out, it shows that some fat was rubbed from the seed into the paper.
2 Add a small amount of water to the crushed tissues of the cotyledons or endosperm, then add a small amount of the red dye Sudan III and shake the mixture. Any floating oil droplets will be stained red while the water remains colourless.

Protein test
There are two different tests for protein that can be done, depending on the chemicals that are available in school.
1 Crush up the cotyledons of the red pea seed and put them in a test tube. Crush some endosperm tissue from a castor oil seed and put it in a different test tube. Add a small amount of water to each test tube and mix the contents so that you have about 5 mm depth of plant tissue extract in each. Add about 5 mm depth dilute sodium hydroxide solution. (Remember that even this dilute solution is caustic, and can burn.) Then add 5 mm depth copper sulphate solution and mix well. If protein is present the mixture will turn a purple colour.
2 Add a few drops of dilute nitric acid to the crushed material. (Be careful—nitric acid is also caustic, and can burn your skin.) Gently heat the mixture by passing the test tube back and forth over a flame. Now add one drop of dilute ammonium hydroxide solution. If protein is present the mixture turns yellow-orange.

Dispersal of seeds

How can plants avoid overcrowding, when they must compete for soil, water, nutrients, sunlight and sufficient space in which to grow and develop properly? This situation would surely occur if all the seeds produced by one plant fell onto the ground below and around that plant, and germinated there. A single poinciana tree may produce up to twenty seeds in each pod. There are 200–400 pods on each tree after the flowering season. Each tree has a life span of about 40 years. Can you imagine how many plants there would be in a small space if all the seeds from one tree were to germinate each year during that tree's lifetime?

Fortunately, most plants have some way of ensuring that their seeds are scattered or **dispersed** to a situation *away from the parent plant* to reduce the competition for survival. In addition, some seeds die or are eaten by insects or other animals. Others fail to germinate because they are carried to an area where the soil is unsuitable for their growth.

Some fruits help in the dispersal of their seeds. For example, the coconut's streamlined shape minimizes turbulence as it passes through water; it has a fibrous, and well aerated fruit wall, so that it floats easily and can be carried great distances by water currents. Some plants have pods (e.g. poinciana and peas) or capsules (e.g. castor oil), which split open with an explosive force and a twisting movement when they dry. This flings the seeds a good distance away from the parent plant.

Animals, including man, also help seed dispersal when they eat the sweet, succulent pulp of the fruit and discard the seeds. These thus germinate away from the parent plant. Other seeds are eaten with the fruit wall, but are later passed out of the animal's body, quite unharmed, in the faeces. The tough protective coat these seeds possess means that they are not digested by the enzymes of the alimentary tract. Such seeds may be carried many miles in the animal's body before being deposited on the ground. Many small fruits and seeds develop hooks and spines which catch on to clothing or body hairs. The seed can be carried long distances before it simply drops off, or is brushed or rubbed off onto the ground where it germinates.

Light, small seeds and seeds with hairs or wings can be easily dispersed by the wind. Wings on seeds are usually flattened (e.g. *Triplaris* or *Petrea*), with a streamlined shape which helps them to act as *aerofoils*. A winged fruit or seed thus falls to the ground slowly and before it reaches the ground, has probably been blown by wind currents away from the parent plant. Look at the fruit of *Triplaris* or *Petrea* and note how they spin, like propellers, as they fall.

Questions

1 Look at these diagrams of seeds and fruits. How are their seeds dispersed?
2 For each type of dispersal mentioned, name a plant whose seed is dispersed in that way.

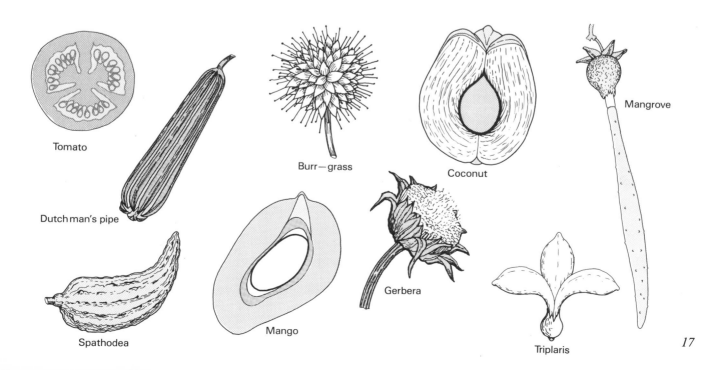

Tomato

Dutchman's pipe

Burr—grass

Coconut

Mangrove

Gerbera

Mango

Spathodea

Triplaris

Germination and growth

Germination of seeds

Germination is a growth process, in which a mature seed begins to develop into a young plant or seedling.

During growth some foods are broken down by enzymes and used to form new protoplasm; other foods are used in cellular respiration to produce the energy needed for this growth to occur. All these activities occur in a watery medium within the cells, and will only take place at temperatures which will not damage or destroy the organism protoplasm and its enzymes.

What do seeds need to germinate?

Because germination is a growth process, a seed will not germinate unless the conditions normally required for growth are present. These conditions are not required to the same extent by all seeds. To find out the conditions, we need to **experiment**. That is, we need to control **variables** that may affect the germination process.

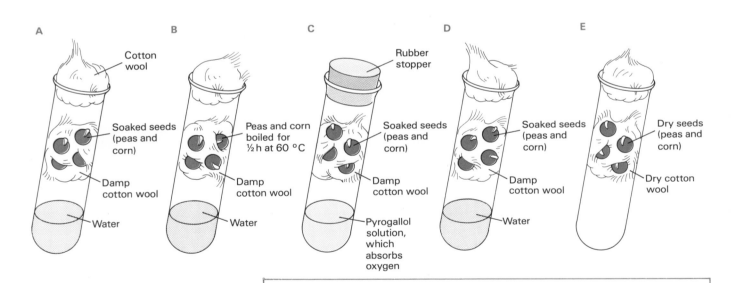

A — Cotton wool / Soaked seeds (peas and corn) / Damp cotton wool / Water

B — Peas and corn boiled for ½ h at 60 °C / Damp cotton wool / Water

C — Rubber stopper / Soaked seeds (peas and corn) / Damp cotton wool / Pyrogallol solution, which absorbs oxygen

D — Soaked seeds (peas and corn) / Damp cotton wool / Water

E — Dry seeds (peas and corn) / Dry cotton wool

Experiment A: To determine the conditions necessary for germination

What you do

1 Set up five test tubes as shown in the diagrams above. Try to use seeds from the same fruit, and use the same amount of liquid in each. Put tubes A, B, C and E in a warm place and put tube D in a refrigerator or freezer.

2 Observe the test tubes over the course of one week. Record your observations.
  (a) What variables are being investigated for their effect on germination?
  (b) In which tube do you predict that germination is most likely to occur? Give reasons for your answer.
  (c) How do you think boiling will affect the seeds in tube B?

Experiment B: To observe the effect of water on the germination of seedlings

Seedlings of corn, all the same age, were planted in similar sized pots containing the same amount of soil and were then left to grow under the same conditions of sunlight, temperature and air. Only the amount of water added each day, over a three-week period, varied as shown in the table.

   Examine the information given in the table and then answer the questions on the basis of that information *only*.

	POT 1	POT 2	POT 3	POT 4	POT 5	POT 6
Amount of water added daily	Nil	3 cm³	6 cm³	12 cm³	24 cm³	48 cm³
Growth of seedlings	None	None	Slow, or none	Very good	Good	None

(a) In which pot(s) could the soil have been too dry for germination to occur?
(b) What is the optimum amount of water for growth of these seedlings?
(c) Why do you think there was no growth in pot 6?

Types of germination

If you observe seeds from different plants during their germination you will notice that

(a) their rates of growth vary considerably;
(b) their water, oxygen and temperature requirements differ;
(c) the sequence in which the parts appear is not always the same.

This last point is used to differentiate between two distinct types of germination.

   Epigeal germination occurs in dicotyledonous seeds such as the poinciana, sunflower and castor oil. The cotyledons **emerge from the seed coat** (testa), rise above the ground, develop chlorophyll and begin to perform the functions of green leaves. They continue to do so until the first true foliage leaves grow out of the plumule, turn green, and themselves begin to photosynthesize. At this point, the cotyledons shrivel up, die, and drop off.

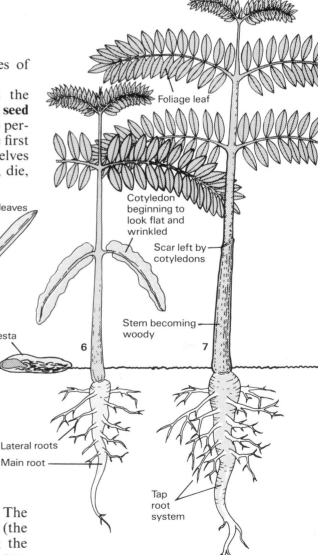

Stages in the germination of a Poinciana seed (epigeal germination)

   Hypogeal germination occurs in seeds such as the broad bean. The cotyledons **remain below ground**, while the stem above the cotyledon (the epicotyl) lengthens and pushes through the soil surface, pulling the plumule out of the cotyledons as it does so. Above ground the stem straightens and the foliage leaves unfold.

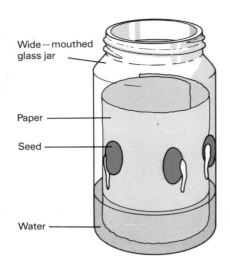

Wide—mouthed glass jar

Paper

Seed

Water

Experiment C: To observe the stages in germination of various seeds

What you need

Red (kidney) peas, broad beans, sunflower seeds, castor oil seeds, corn seeds—at least 3 of each type. A set of wide-mouthed jars (e.g. mayonnaise bottles) or gas jars. Blotting paper or paper towels.

What you do

1 Soak the seeds in water overnight (this will help to speed up germination).
2 Pour about 1 cm depth of water in each jar, then line them with the paper.
3 Place the seeds between the glass and the paper, about 3 cm from the bottom. Put each type of seed in a different jar. Make sure the seeds are not in the water (this would make them rot).
4 Write the date and your name on the outside of each jar. Leave the jars where they will not be disturbed. Add water periodically.
5 Check the appearance of the seeds each day. Keep careful written and diagrammatic records of all your observations as the seeds begin to germinate, and then grow into seedlings. Note any changes in the length of both plumule and radicle; the position of the cotyledon(s), development of root hairs, lateral roots, and leaves.

   What type of germination do (a) red peas, (b) corn show? (Base your answers on your experimental observations.)
6 Plot the rate of growth, as indicated by increase in height, for different types of seeds over the same period.

   (a) Can you predict the height of any one type of seedling at (i) three weeks old, (ii) five weeks old?
   (b) Try to verify your predictions, using the same seedlings.

Growth in plants

One of the characteristics of living organisms is that they grow. During growth the organism

(a) takes in materials from its environment and transforms them into its own living protoplasm;
(b) produces new cells, which later become specialized for certain purposes, by mitosis.

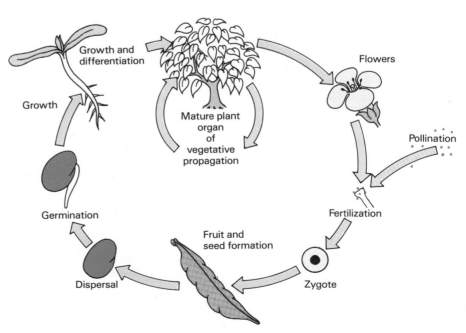

Stages in the life cycle of higher plants

20

Growth may not be continuous; it may be confined to set periods in the life cycle, or else to specific body parts. Eventually all growth ceases and death occurs. Before it dies the organism usually reproduces during one of the active growth periods, either asexually or sexually.

This sequence of events is known as the **life cycle** of the organism. The stages in the life cycle of higher plants may be represented as shown on the opposite page.

For growth to occur, each plant must have adequate water, carbon dioxide and mineral salts to make food, and enough oxygen for its respiratory needs. The right habitat conditions, such as good soil, optimum temperature and adequate sunlight, are also necessary.

Growth substances

All the activities of growth in plants are controlled by growth substances called **auxins**. Auxins are produced mainly in the stem and root tips and readily diffuse to the other cells, whose growth they influence. They can stimulate or suppress growth, according to their concentration in these cells. Growth substances cause plant parts to show **growth responses** to the directional stimuli of **light**, **water** and **gravity**. An example of a growth response is shown in the diagram on the right.

Growth substances actively influence the growth of the plumule and radicle during germination, causing the radicle to grow down into the soil and the plumule up towards the light. This happens regardless of the position in which a seed falls onto soil when it is dispersed from the fruit.

Some practical considerations

When planting seeds, either as crops or for ornamental purposes, it must be remembered that they need water, oxygen and an optimum temperature. The soil should be well watered prior to planting; if possible the seeds can be soaked for about 24 hours beforehand.

Many seeds will fail to germinate if they are buried deep in the soil, where there is a limited supply of oxygen. Remember that atmospheric oxygen may penetrate the soil too slowly for the seeds to get enough for their germination.

If temperatures become too cold, many seeds cease their activities altogether and enter a period of **dormancy**. When the soil warms up to the optimum growth temperature, these seeds will become active again and start to germinate. This ability of seeds to remain dormant enables them to be dried, packaged and kept for long periods. This allows humans to grow many plants long after the original parent plants have died.

Growth in animals

Growth substances or **hormones** are also present in animals. Later, you will learn how these substances affect growth and metabolism in your body, and also regulate the reproductive process.

In humans there are distinct periods of growth that occur between birth and death. These growth periods can be represented on a graph by a curve known as a **growth curve**.

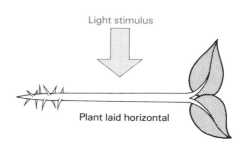

Plant laid horizontal

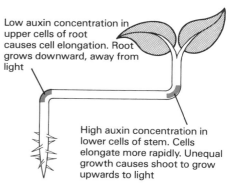

Low auxin concentration in upper cells of root causes cell elongation. Root grows downward, away from light

High auxin concentration in lower cells of stem. Cells elongate more rapidly. Unequal growth causes shoot to grow upwards to light

Auxins influence the shoot to grow towards the light and the root away from it

A generalized growth curve for girls from birth to age 25

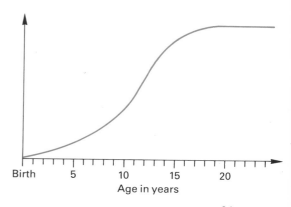

Activities

1 Construct a bar graph to show the variation of height with age for
   (a) the girls in your class;
   (b) the boys in your class.
2 Compare the two graphs. What can you infer about the connection between growth rate and age for (a) boys, (b) girls?
3 Repeat the activity, but this time use boys and girls in your school between the ages of 11 and 12.
4 Compare your results. Are there any general differences between the two age groups?

7 Puberty and adolescence

For about the first ten years of life, boys and girls differ in their external genital organs, but are very much alike in their internal body functions or physiology. In particular, their reproductive organs remain undeveloped and non-functional. At the age of about 10, as shown in the growth curve on page 21, there is an active period of growth and development which culminates in sexual maturity.

Puberty marks the onset of secondary sexual development and is heralded by certain changes which are distinctive for males and females. These changes are the body's response to the chemical stimulus of **hormones**. The **pituitary gland** secretes hormones which stimulate the ovaries and testes so that they begin to produce sex cells (sperm and eggs), as well as their own reproductive hormones. It is the interaction of the pituitary and reproductive hormones which causes the changes described below.

In girls

Breasts begin to develop fairly rapidly. Fat accumulates around the hips and the pelvis widens, producing the typical female shape. Hair grows under the armpits and around the genital area. There is a regular monthly **menstruation**, i.e. the girl 'starts her period'.

In boys

The corresponding changes may start later in boys than in girls. The 'Adam's apple' or voice box enlarges, and the voice begins to 'break' as it changes to a deeper tone. The body becomes more muscular and the chest widens, to give the characteristic male shape. Hair grows under the armpits, around the genitals, and on the chest and face. The penis and testes enlarge and there may be frequent emission of **semen** (the fluid containing sperm) during sleep ('wet dreams').

All the above changes are accompanied by heightened sexual awareness among the young males and females. This is often accompanied by anxiety or discontent about the physical changes which are occurring.

There is a tendency for **adolescents** (young adults) to develop spots, bumps, excessive oiliness and skin discolorations, especially if too many sweets and starches are included in the diet. Characteristic odours also become apparent in all mammals experiencing secondary sexual development. Many of these are associated with attracting the males to the females, particularly at the time of **ovulation**, i.e. when a mature egg is being released from the ovary. Adolescent humans must give special attention to personal hygiene to avoid the unpleasant odours (e.g. nervous perspiration when talking to the opposite sex) associated with that period of maturing.

Puberty is thus the period in which the physical and physiological changes associated with the transformation of a child into a young adult (adolescent) capable of sexual reproduction take place.

Adolescence begins with puberty, and ends on the completion of the 'teen' years. It is a transitional period in which the values, attitudes and mental outlook, as well as the physical attributes, of the adult are becoming established. It is the stepping stone from child to adult, and is a characteristic of development in humans, more so than in other mammals.

8

Sexual reproduction in mammals

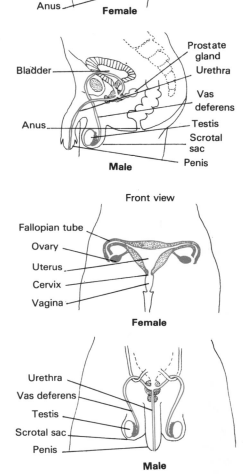

Male and female reproductive organs

You have already discovered that higher plants have male and female reproductive organs, and can therefore reproduce sexually.

What about mammals? How do they reproduce themselves?

All mammals, including man, reproduce sexually. The sexes are always separate, and they have highly specialized reproductive organs. The diagrams on the left show these organs in humans.

Each part of the reproductive system is specially adapted to the functions it must perform. For example, the muscular uterus (womb) can enlarge considerably to accommodate the developing foetus.

The sexual cycle

The production of eggs and sperm is carefully controlled by hormones. Mature eggs develop in the ovaries on a regular basis. In humans usually only one egg or ovum matures each 28 days. Other mammals normally produce between 2 to 8 eggs at set times.

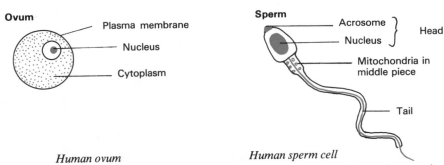

Human ovum

Human sperm cell

The testes continuously produce sperm. These pass into the seminal vesicles where they are stored temporarily, and a viscous seminal fluid is added.

In most mammals there is a distinct **breeding season** during which males produce sperm, and females 'in heat' ovulate and are receptive to copulation. Outside the breeding season these animals are sexually inactive.

There is no breeding season for humans, so fertilization and conception can occur in an ovulating female at any time during the year. The monthly formation of mature eggs is referred to as the **menstrual cycle** in humans, and the **oestrus cycle** in other mammals.

The external sign of the menstrual cycle is the monthly discharge of blood through the vagina. But accompanying this are internal changes which occur in the ovaries and the uterus. These changes result from the interaction of pituitary and reproductive hormones.

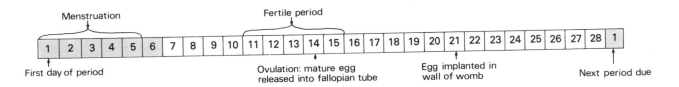

The menstrual cycle. Dates are based on a standard 28–day cycle. Many women have longer or shorter cycles but ovulaion takes place 14 days before the first day of the next period, whatever the length of the cycle

The menstrual cycle usually spans 28 days. Day 1 is counted as the first day of menstrual bleeding, which usually lasts 5 to 7 days. During menstruation the thickened, highly vascular uterine wall comes away (hence the pain) and passes out of the vagina along with a degenerated, unfertilized egg. During Days 6–14 which follow menstruation, the uterine wall repairs itself. During this time changes also occur within the ovary. An immature egg cell completes its development inside the **Graafian follicle**. This growth is controlled by **follicle-stimulating hormone**, a pituitary secretion which reaches the ovaries via the blood stream.

On, or near, Day 14, ovulation occurs under the stimulus of another pituitary secretion, **luteinizing hormone**. Between Days 14 and 28 the uterus wall thickens considerably and develops many blood vessels in preparation for a possible pregnancy. This is controlled by the hormone **progesterone**.

If fertilization occurs, the menstrual cycle is interrupted and there is no monthly discharge of blood until after the end of the pregnancy. If the ovum is not fertilized, that cycle ends at Day 28. On the next day, Day 1, a new menstrual cycle starts, with the onset of bleeding.

Fertilization

Because humans have no breeding season, sexual intercourse or copulation can occur at any time. During sexual intercourse the man's erect penis is inserted into the woman's vagina. The pleasurable sensations of intercourse cause a reflex response—the ejaculation of sperm into the vagina. Sperm are thus deposited near to the **cervix** at the entrance to the uterus. About 300 million tiny sperm are deposited during a single ejaculation of semen.

Using their whip-like tails, the sperm move through the cervix and up to the **Fallopian tubes**. Their passage may be aided by the uterine contractions which happen during orgasm, since these help to suck semen into the tubes.

In the tubes, sperm move about randomly. Several sperm may contact the egg, but only one will use its **acrosome** to penetrate the egg membrane. The sperm nucleus then passes into the egg, fusing with the egg nucleus in the process of fertilization. In mammals a single internal fertilization occurs. The resultant zygote has genetic information from both parents encoded in its chromosomes.

After fertilization

Every mammal (including you!) begins life as a single, fertilized egg cell or **zygote**. Immediately after fertilization the zygote performs a series of mitotic cell divisions in a process called **cleavage**. This is essentially similar to the divisions which occur in the ovary of flowers as an embryo is formed after fertilization.

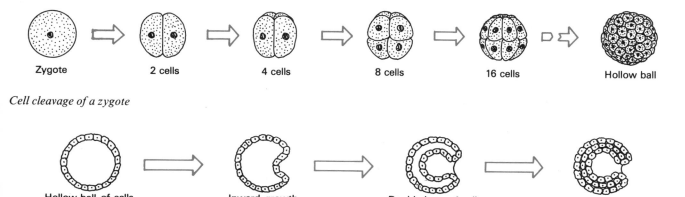

| Zygote | 2 cells | 4 cells | 8 cells | 16 cells | Hollow ball |

Cell cleavage of a zygote

| Hollow ball of cells | Inward growth | Double layer of cells | Three layers of cells |

Cell divisions and layers of an embryo

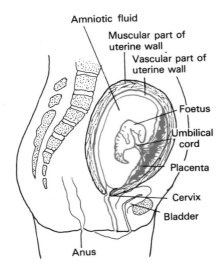

Amniotic fluid
Muscular part of uterine wall
Vascular part of uterine wall
Foetus
Umbilical cord
Placenta
Cervix
Bladder
Anus

The uterus after conception

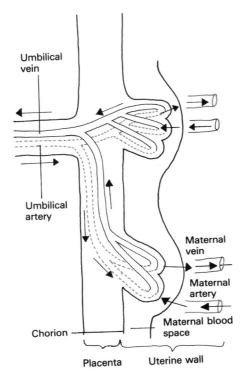

Umbilical vein
Umbilical artery
Maternal vein
Maternal artery
Chorion
Maternal blood space
Placenta
Uterine wall

Close-up of the placenta on the uterus wall. The mother's blood supplies the embryo with food, oxygen and water via the umbilical vein and carries away carbon dioxide and nitrogenous waste from the embryo via the umbilical artery

Cleavage results in the formation of a hollow ball of cells, one layer thick. This hollow ball is called the **embryo**. It is surrounded by two layers of cells, then a third layer forms between the existing two layers by further cell divisions. All the tissues—skin, muscle, bone, blood, nervous tissue— and eventually all the organs of the body are formed from these three layers of cells in the embryo. The outside layer forms skin and the nervous system. The middle layer forms muscles, bone, blood and blood vessels, and the reproductive organs. The inside layer of cells forms the lining of the digestive and respiratory tracts.

While these cleavage divisions are occurring the embryo travels along the Fallopian tube to the uterus. There it digs into the thick uterine wall and continues its development. The embedding of the embryo in the uterine wall is called **implantation**.

The uterus also undergoes specific changes to facilitate and ensure the subsequent growth and development of the embryo. Immediately after implantation an organ called the **placenta** develops from embryonic tissues. It forms a series of projections into the wall of the uterus where embryonic and maternal tissues fuse. Within the placenta the embryo's blood vessels associate closely with the mother's blood. Because it is highly folded the placenta has a relatively large surface area for exchange of foods, gases and wastes.

After a few weeks, the embryo changes shape and begins to show a human form. It is now about 2·5 cm long and is known as the foetus. Through the placenta the foetus obtains soluble nutrients and oxygen from its mother's blood, and gives up its nitrogenous wastes and carbon dioxide for later excretion by the mother. The **umbilical cord** is the link between the foetus and the placenta. Blood vessels pass from the foetus, through the umbilical cord, and branch in the placenta. Although the foetal and maternal blood are very close, they do not actually mix since they are separated by three thin membranes.

Embryonic membranes

As the foetus grows, the fluid-filled sac, which formed around it during early cleavage divisions, grows to fill up the whole of the uterus (or womb). This sac, or **amnion**, and the **amniotic fluid** it contains protect the foetus, and cushion it against sudden jerks or movements. The foetus also has space in which it can stretch its limbs and move about as it grows.

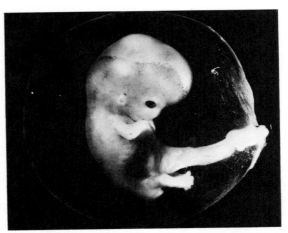

Magnified photo of human embryo at six weeks. It is about two cm long, has a large umbilical cord and is enclosed in the protective amnion

Gestation

The foetus grows and develops inside the uterus for roughly nine months to ensure that all organs and systems are adequately formed before birth. During this period the mother's mammary glands enlarge and begin to produce a watery fluid, called colostrum, which contains protein, fat and sugar. By the end of this nine-month period of **gestation** the foetus is about 50 cm long, weighs about 3 kg, and is lying as shown in the diagram, with its head just above the mother's cervix.

Pre-natal care is very important if the mother is to remain well and produce a normal healthy baby. Drugs should only be taken as prescribed by a doctor. Smoking, and drinking alcohol and coffee should be reduced or cut out altogether. X-ray pictures must not be taken of the mother as the radiation can damage the foetus. Contact with ill persons, especially those with German measles, is forbidden, especially during the first 3 months of pregnancy, since if the mother catches the disease it can cause abnormalities in the developing foetus. A proper diet containing extra calcium, vitamin D and proteins is particularly important at this time to ensure that bones and other foetal tissues are properly formed.

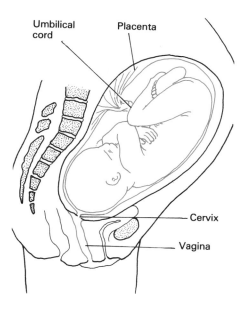

Full term pregnancy at 40 weeks

Parturition

This is the process of birth. Parturition occurs at the end of the period of gestation. Under the stimulus of hormones the uterus wall begins to contract forcefully, and at regular intervals. The amnion may burst so that the amniotic fluid passes out, or the 'show', a plug of blood and mucus, may announce the imminent birth of the child. The muscular cervix dilates until it is about 9 cm wide, and further powerful contractions force the foetus, head first, out of the uterus, through the cervix and vagina (now referred to as the **birth canal**) and out of the mother's body. Following the birth, the placenta or 'afterbirth' is also expelled by further uterine contractions.

As the placenta is expelled, it is torn away from part of the maternal tissue which causes some bleeding. In humans the placenta is disposed of hygienically; other mammals eat their placenta while cleaning themselves and their new-born young.

The umbilical cord is cut near to the baby. The stub of the cord soon withers and heals, leaving a scar called the **navel**.

Care of the young

Mammals are so called because they possess **mammary glands** or breasts in which a milky secretion is produced. These glands are used to feed or **suckle** the young. Humans have one pair of breasts; other mammals may have up to four pairs, to accommodate a larger number of offspring.

The offspring of all mammals have a strong sucking reflex, and feed voraciously for the first few weeks. Between feeding they sleep and make stretching movements.

Post-natal care of the young is well-established among mammals, and involves cleaning the 'nest' or home, cleaning and grooming the young, and feeding and playing with them.

In humans breast-feeding should be continued for at least the first six months of the child's life. Breast milk contains carbohydrates, proteins, fats, vitamins and minerals already 'mixed' in the proportions that best promote the baby's growth and development. Also, human milk contains **antibodies** which help to protect the baby from disease as it builds up its own immune system. Research and observation have shown that babies who are held and cuddled by their mother during breast-feeding are happier, better-adjusted babies.

Some of the dangers associated with bottle-feeding a baby are:

1 Risk of diseases such as gastro-enteritis, which may start when bottles, nipples and formula are not sterilized properly.
2 Risk of constipation, upset stomach, obesity and thirst when extra milk powder added to the feed makes it too strong.
3 Risk of malnutrition when the feed is mixed too weak in an effort to make the milk powder last longer.

Questions

1 Explain why a human egg does not have a hard shell, nor a large store of yolk.
2 Your teacher will show you a dissection of a small mammal. Try to identify the parts of the reproductive system.

9

Population control

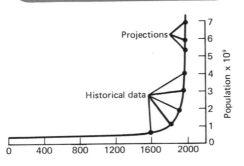

Graph showing projected world population growth (in thousands of millions) by the year 2000 AD

A **population** is a group of organisms of the same species, which are capable of interbreeding. Two examples of populations are a nest of ants and a stand of coconut trees. However, on these pages a population will be taken to mean all the people living in all the countries of the world.

The population of a country can be determined by taking a **census**. Census data are used, along with data about **birth rate**, **death rate** and **reproductive rate**, to make predictions about the future growth of that population. Current data predicts world population may grow to 6000 or 7000 million by the year 2000 AD, unless there is **drastic control of the birth rate**! This applies especially to peoples in developing and underdeveloped countries, for example in Africa, India, Latin America and the Caribbean.

If the size of a population is to remain constant, the birth rate must equal the death rate. In animal populations this is normally achieved by: (a) disease; (b) predators; (c) availability of food. However, such natural checks do not exist, to any significant extent, for human populations.

(a) **Disease** no longer claims large numbers of lives. The death rate has been lowered considerably over the last fifty years, because of:
   (i)   improved pre- and post-natal care of babies;
   (ii) the widespread availability of vaccines and other drugs;
   (iii) increased scientific knowledge.

(b) **Predators** of humans are few, if there are any at all! Humans no longer live 'in the wild', but have built massive cities and domesticated many former animal enemies. Possible predatory animals have little access, and new drugs are quite successful in preventing infection by disease-causing parasitic organisms.

(c) The **food supply** presents some threat to the unhindered growth of human populations. Today, more than half of the world's population suffers from malnutrition and associated diseases such as kwashiorkor and marasmus. Although it has been systematically attempted to increase world food production, it is doubtful whether it is possible to produce the increased amounts of food that will be needed to feed the present 'population explosion'. At the present rate of population increase, what will be the death rate from starvation, especially if babies continue to be born at the present rate?

Methods of birth control

Since the natural population checks are no longer sufficiently effective, widespread use of available **birth control methods** is needed to stem the increase in the world's population. The various methods of birth control aim to prevent either the fertilization of the egg, or the implantation of a fertilized egg in the uterus. Of course, there are numerous arguments about the morality or ethics of the practice of birth control. Many argue on religious grounds that the use of contraceptives is against the natural law of God; others argue that it is immoral to bring more children into an already over-populated world, which contains insufficient food, housing and educational facilities. So each individual must make his or her own choice . . . a choice based on sound knowledge and complete understanding of the implications of their actions.

Some of the methods of birth control are described here.

1 Abstention from sexual intercourse is especially recommended for the

This child is suffering from marasmus caused by lack of energy foods

young, who are themselves immature and financially unable to take care of children. Abstention during the fertile period of the menstrual cycle (see Section 8) is recommended for those who do not wish to use other methods of birth control.

2 The condom, sheath or 'french letter' is made from thin, surgical rubber, lubricated with oil. It comes in a sterile packet, rolled up like a flattened nipple. It must be unrolled so that it completely covers the erect penis *before* the penis is inserted into the vagina. To be effective, the penis must remain in the condom until *after* the ejaculation of semen.

The condom acts as a contraceptive by preventing sperm from reaching the female tubes, where an egg could be waiting for fertilization. Its effectiveness is increased if some spermicidal cream is placed in the vagina before intercourse. The condom containing ejaculated sperm must be discarded in a sanitary way.

3 The diaphragm or cap is the female's counterpart of the condom. When inserted, it fits closely over the cervix. The female must first be examined internally by a doctor, so that the size of diaphragm that fits her can be prescribed. Before sexual intercourse, a spermicidal cream is applied to both sides of the diaphragm which is then placed in the vagina. The cream kills sperm which reach it, while the diaphragm acts as a barrier, preventing sperm from going into the female tubes. Fertilization is thus prevented.

4 The coil, loop, or IUD (intra-uterine device), is a small piece of metal or plastic which must be inserted in the woman's uterus by a doctor. It is left in place constantly and must *not* be taken out either before, during or after sexual intercourse. The string attached to it protrudes into the vagina to indicate that the coil is still in place.

The material of which the coil is made irritates the wall of the uterus so that, even if an egg is fertilized, it will not become implanted. This effectively prevents pregnancy. Those coils made from copper also act as a spermicide since sperm are killed when they come into contact with the metal.

5 The pill prevents ovulation, since the hormones it contains upset the delicate balance of hormones produced by the body. No fertilization can therefore occur. To be effective, *all the pills must be taken* over a three week period without interruption. If one pill is forgotten ovulation may occur and a pregnancy may start. Hormones similar to those found in the pill are sometimes given by injection every three months; this injection prevents conception in the same way as the pill.

6 Sterilization in males involves a surgical operation called **vasectomy** in which each vas deferens is cut. Sperm cannot then reach the penis to be ejaculated. In women, the Fallopian tubes are tied to prevent eggs from reaching the tubes where fertilization takes place. Sterilization is a permanent method of contraception, since it is very unlikely that the operation can be reversed. This is not a popular method of birth control among men, many of whom do not see that they too have a responsibility to help to control the rapid increase of the population. For example, in Kingston (Jamaica) in 1982, 4000 women had their tubes tied, compared with only 2 men!

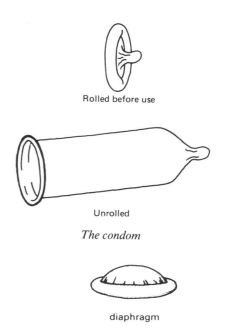

Rolled before use

Unrolled

The condom

diaphragm

The diaphragm (above) and (below) side view showing position once inserted in the vagina

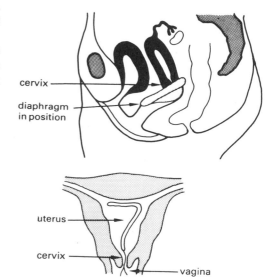

cervix

diaphragm in position

uterus

cervix

vagina

A T-shaped coil in place in the uterus

Questions

1 What is meant by:
  (a) census;
  (b) crude birth rate;
  (c) crude death rate.
2 How can knowledge of the crude birth and death rates be used to predict population growth?
3 In what ways has the death rate been lowered by:
  (a) improved pre- and post-natal care?
  (b) use of vaccines?
  (c) increased scientific knowledge?
4 What is meant by the 'population explosion'? Describe some of its adverse effects which you can observe in your country.

10

Sexually transmitted diseases

Unlike most other mammals, humans use sexual intercourse to derive pleasure as well as to reproduce the species. Because of the pleasurable sensations experienced, especially during the increased sexual awareness of adolescence, frequent sexual relationships are a common occurrence. Also, the use of drugs such as alcohol and ganga, peer-group pressure, and the influence of pornographic books, movies and songs, often pressurize young people into frequent and illicit sexual relationships.

The dire effects of such sexual relationships are:

(a) teenage pregnancies, which markedly increase the birth rate of a population, with the ensuing problems of over-population;
(b) an upsurge in the incidence of sexually transmitted, and sexually related, diseases.

Venereal diseases

Diseases that are transmitted by sexual contact are called **venereal diseases**; they are common where there is **promiscuity** (i.e. frequent sexual intercourse with different partners). The two most common are gonorrhoea and syphilis.

Gonorrhoea is caused by a bacterium. It attacks the reproductive organs, causing intense itching, especially in the vagina. The passing of urine is accompanied by a burning sensation. If untreated the disease may later cause sterility, affect the heart valves, may lead to blindness and could also cause death. The disease can also be transmitted from an infected woman to her child at birth, who could therefore become blind. Only expert medical attention in its early stages, coupled with restraint from promiscuous sexual activities, can cure this disease.

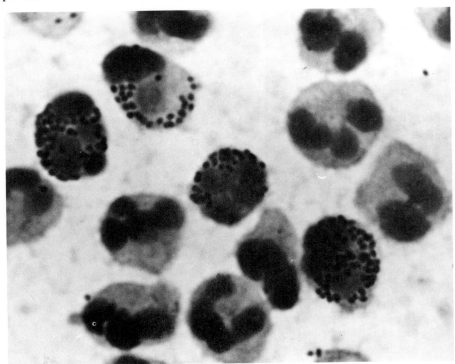

Gonorrhoea bacteria × 1500

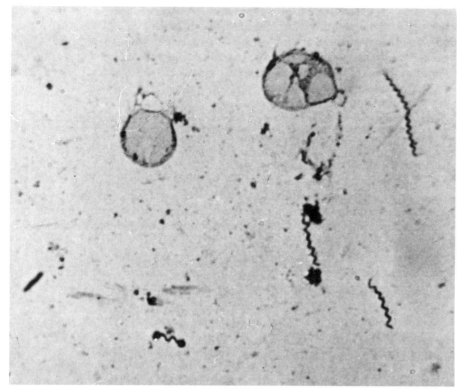

Syphilis bacteria (corkscrew shapes)

Syphilis first appears as sores in the genital area, followed by a sore throat, and then rashes appear all over the body. This disease, which is also caused by a bacterium, is more dangerous than gonorrhoea, because the external symptoms may disappear for several years. The infected individual, believing himself cured, usually continues to have several sexual partners, each of whom will also become infected. Meanwhile, the bacterium rapidly reproduces and continues to attack various body tissues. In the later stages of the disease the tissues of the spinal cord and the brain become infected, with resultant insanity and eventual death.

Genital herpes has recently become prevalent, particularly in Caribbean islands. The disease, caused by a virus (similar to that causing cold sores and 'night fever' on the lips), first appears as blisters on the penis or the vulva. The blisters later erupt into painful, itching sores. To date, there is no known cure for herpes; treatment is aimed at trying to ease the discomfort. The sores disappear periodically, so the sufferer might show no signs of the disease, but can still transmit it.

Cancer is a general term that covers a wide range of diseases. Although it is not transmitted by intercourse, it may be related to its frequency and the number of sexual partners. In the reproductive system, it attacks the scrotum, testes and prostate in males. In females, cancer commonly occurs in the cervix, the uterus and the breasts. Its incidence has been related to starting to have sexual intercourse at an early age, and to promiscuity. Cancer of the cervix and uterus can be detected in its early stages by a **Pap smear test** which is performed by a doctor during a regular check-up, following a monthly period. Cells are gently scraped from around the cervix in a painless procedure. The cells are placed on a slide, stained and examined by a Medical Technologist using a high-powered microscope. Any potential cancer-causing cells usually show up much larger, and react differently to the stain.

Women who have frequent sexual contacts must have Pap smears done at regular six-month intervals. Cancer destroys all the tissues of the body, and spreads rapidly from its point of origin to other areas. Its presence is often undetected until too late—when it has already destroyed massive amounts of tissue.

Nutrition in man

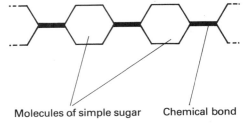

Representation of a complex starch molecule

Molecules of simple sugar   Chemical bond

Composition of our food

Carbohydrates, proteins and fats, the products of photosynthesis, are complex molecules which have been built up from relatively simple molecules of carbon dioxide and water. Starch, an example of a carbohydrate food, is made up from simple sugars which are linked to each other in long chains by chemical bonds.

Proteins are also made of simpler units called **amino acids** which are linked together by chemical bonds. Similarly, fats and oils are made up of units called **fatty acids** and **glycerol**.

Digestion

Higher animals can only use simple sugars, amino acids, glycerol and fatty acids in their bodily activities. They can neither absorb into their cells, nor make use of complex carbohydrates, proteins or fats. In order to make these simple units available for use by their body, higher animals, including man, must break down these complex food molecules into their component units ready for their **assimilation**.

Digestion is the process in which enzymes are used to break down complex carbohydrates, proteins and fats, into their simplest components.

Enzymes are organic chemical substances, produced by living cells. They can speed up the rate of chemical reactions that take place in an animal, e.g. the breaking of the chemical bonds which link simple molecules to each other. Only a small amount of enzyme is normally needed, and each enzyme acts only on a specific type of substance or substrate. For example, **lipases** are enzymes which speed up the breakdown of complex fats into soluble fatty acids and glycerol. **Proteases** are enzymes which speed up the breakdown of complex proteins into simple amino acids, while **amylases** or **carbohydrases** speed up the breakdown of carbohydrates into simple sugars.

Enzymes will only act at a certain 'optimum' temperature, and are inactivated by extremes of cold or heat. They also work best in either an acid or an alkaline surrounding, according to the particular enzyme.

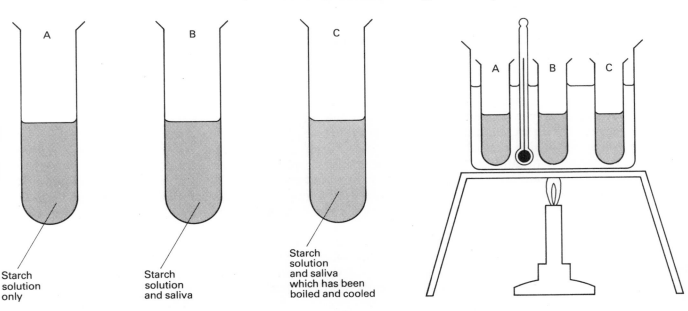

Starch
solution
only

Starch
solution
and saliva

Starch
solution
and saliva
which has been
boiled and cooled

Process of digestion

There are two phases in digestion:

1 **Mechanical digestion** involves the cutting, grinding and churning actions of the tongue and teeth, and the muscles of the alimentary tract.
2 **Chemical digestion** or **hydrolysis** involves the reaction of food with water; this reaction is speeded up by specific enzymes.

Experiment A: To demonstrate the action of the enzyme in saliva

What you need

Beaker, 6 test tubes, thermometer, bunsen burner, starch, iodine solution.

What you do

1 Prepare a starch solution by boiling a small amount of starch powder in water.
2 Cool the solution by placing the test tube under running water. Pour off a small quantity of the solution into another test tube and test it for the presence of starch by adding a few drops of iodine solution. Observe that the clear starch turns blue-black, confirming that starch is present.
3 Divide the remaining starch solution equally between three test tubes, A, B and C. Collect a sample of your own saliva in a beaker and divide it into two. Boil and then cool one sample of the saliva.
4 Now prepare test tubes A, B and C as shown in the diagram (on page 32).
5 Put all three test tubes into a water bath and keep its temperature at 37 °C.
6 After 10 minutes, take a small sample from each of the three test tubes; put each in a different tube. Then test them for starch using iodine solution as before. Record and explain the results of the iodine test in each case.
7 Test the remaining contents of each test tube for simple sugars, using Benedict's Solution.
  (a) In which do you expect to get a brick-red precipitate, indicating the presence of simple sugars? Why?
  (b) How do your actual results relate to your expectations?
  (c) Explain why the water bath was maintained at 37 °C.
  (d) What is the purpose of test tube A in this experiment?
  (e) What action does the salivary enzyme have upon starch?

Experiment B: To demonstrate the effect of acidity and alkalinity on the enzyme in saliva

What you do

1 Repeat steps 1 and 2 of the previous experiment.
2 Mix a small amount of dilute sodium carbonate solution with the starch solution in one test tube; mix a small amount of hydrochloric acid with the other. Leave both test tubes in the heated water bath.
3 After 10 minutes pour off a sample from each test tube and test them for presence of starch using iodine solution.
  (a) In which test tube is starch still present?
  (b) Does the salivary enzyme work best in an acid or alkaline medium? Explain your answer.
  (c) Starch is a carbohydrate food; what type of enzyme do you conclude is present in your saliva?
  (d) How do these two experiments help you to explain the chemical process of digestion?

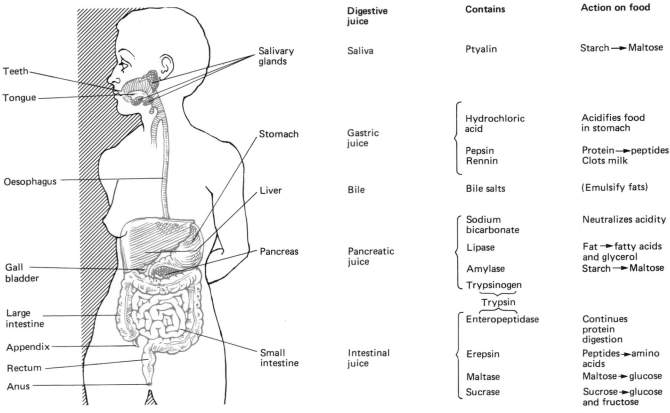

	Digestive juice	Contains	Action on food
	Saliva	Ptyalin	Starch → Maltose
	Gastric juice	Hydrochloric acid	Acidifies food in stomach
		Pepsin	Protein → peptides
		Rennin	Clots milk
	Bile	Bile salts	(Emulsify fats)
	Pancreatic juice	Sodium bicarbonate	Neutralizes acidity
		Lipase	Fat → fatty acids and glycerol
		Amylase	Starch → Maltose
		Trypsinogen → Trypsin	
	Intestinal juice	Enteropeptidase	Continues protein digestion
		Erepsin	Peptides → amino acids
		Maltase	Maltose → glucose
		Sucrase	Sucrose → glucose and fructose

Diagram labels (human digestive system): Teeth, Tongue, Oesophagus, Gall bladder, Large intestine, Appendix, Rectum, Anus, Salivary glands, Stomach, Liver, Pancreas, Small intestine

The human digestive system and action of the digestive juices (above)

The alimentary canal of the rat (left)

Cross section of a villus (below left)

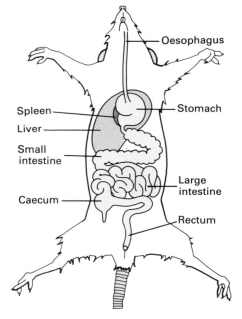

Rat alimentary canal labels: Oesophagus, Spleen, Liver, Small intestine, Caecum, Stomach, Large intestine, Rectum

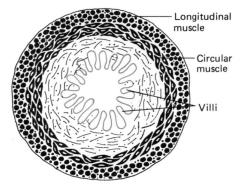

Villus cross section labels: Longitudinal muscle, Circular muscle, Villi

The alimentary canal in man

To accomplish the processes of mechanical and chemical digestion, various structures, each specially modified to perform a particular function, are found grouped together to form the digestive or alimentary canal.

The alimentary canal or **gut** is a muscular tube which runs from the mouth to the anus. Specific functions are performed by specific parts. Associated organs and glands open into this muscular tube, e.g. the liver, gall bladder, salivary glands, and the pancreas, which play vital roles in the chemical digestive process.

The main structures concerned in mechanical digestion are the teeth and the layers of smooth muscle which compose the wall of the digestive tube. As food passes through the alimentary canal, it gradually undergoes mechanical and chemical digestion. A **bolus** or ball of food is pushed along the alimentary canal by waves of muscular contraction known as **peristalsis**. When the food is in a suitably digested state it leaves the alimentary canal and is absorbed into the blood stream. Undigested foods leave the body through the anus, as **faeces**.

Food takes from three to six hours to pass through the alimentary canal, and it remains longest in the stomach. Of course, the time taken varies for different types of foods: carbohydrates pass quickly out of the stomach, proteins remain there longer, while fats take longest of all. The sequence of stages in digestion is shown on the next page.

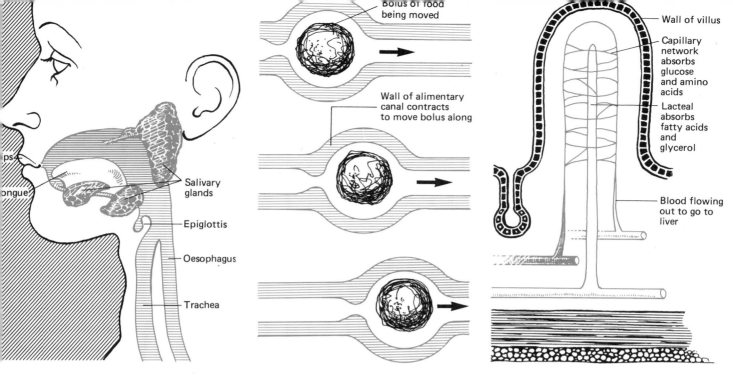

Labels on diagram:

Salivary glands
Epiglottis
Oesophagus
Trachea
Bolus of food being moved
Wall of alimentary canal contracts to move bolus along
Wall of villus
Capillary network absorbs glucose and amino acids
Lacteal absorbs fatty acids and glycerol
Blood flowing out to go to liver

The position of the salivary glands (left)
peristalsis (centre)
vertical section of a villus (right)

Ingestion   The intake of food, aided by the lips, teeth and tongue, occurs in the mouth.

↓

Digestion   (a) Mechanical breakdown is performed by teeth and tongue and aided by the muscular action of the stomach. (b) Chemical breakdown is performed by enzymes; it occurs in the mouth, stomach and small intestines. Simple sugars, amino acids, glycerol and fatty acids are produced as a result of the chemical breakdown.

↓

Absorption   In the small intestine, simple soluble foods, e.g. amino acids, glucose and other simple sugars, pass out of the alimentary canal into the blood capillaries within the villi. They are taken from the intestine to the liver in the blood. Fatty acids and glycerol pass into the lacteals of the villi, and so leave the alimentary canal. Vitamins, minerals and water are also absorbed here.

↓

Assimilation   Absorbed foods are recombined in specific ways to form the cellular proteins and other body chemicals and structures; some are used in respiration, and excess is stored in fat cells. Harmful nitrogen from amino acids is removed in the liver, and passed in the blood to the kidneys for excretion.

↓

Egestion   Undigested matter is passed out through the anus, as faeces.

Summary

Digestion is necessary because the pieces of food we eat are too large, and too complex in structure, to pass into our body cells. So food is mechanically broken up into pieces small enough to allow enzymes to break apart the chemical bonds in the large molecules. The simple molecules that are produced as a result of the enzyme action are absorbed into the blood and carried, dissolved in the blood, around the body. The simple food molecules eventually leave the blood and enter cells where they are used (assimilated) in various ways. The undigested portions of food are passed out of the digestive canal as faeces.

Activities

1   Draw an annotated diagram of the mammalian digestive system.
2   Describe the digestion of Geoffrey's lunch (see p. 43).

12

Types of food

There are six classes of food; each type has different functions.

Carbohydrates

Carbohydrates supply the body with energy: when they are oxidized during cellular respiration the chemical energy 'locked' into each molecule during photosynthesis is released for use by the animal's cells. Rich sources of carbohydrates include sugary foods like jams, honey, sugar cane and many fruits, as well as starchy foods such as bread, cereals, and storage organs like potatoes and yams.

Proteins

Proteins are needed to build the protoplasm of cells without which body tissues do not form. In Section 6 you looked at the growth curve for children of various ages, and noticed the sharp incline in the graph as rapid growth occurred from birth to age five years old. Children are especially susceptible to a disease called **kwashiorkor** which they get when there is insufficient protein in their diet. In addition, since protein is used to repair damaged tissues, cuts and sores fail to heal quickly if an inadequate amount is consumed.

Proteins are found in many plants, and in animal products. Proteins derived from the meat of fish and cattle, as well as animal products such as milk, are **first class proteins**. They are called **complete proteins** because they contain the full range of amino acids (the building blocks of proteins) needed by the body. Plant proteins, found in soya beans, peas, peanuts (groundnuts) etc., are **second class proteins**; these do not supply the full range of amino acids, but are nevertheless good sources of proteins. Of course, the protein requirement varies according to the sex, age and therefore the stage of growth of the person. Individuals actively producing new muscle tissues during growth periods require large amounts of first class proteins. Pregnant mothers should also have a good supply of proteins to ensure the health of their babies. The individuals' requirements must be borne in mind when planning their meals.

Fats and oils

Fats and oils are similar in chemical composition, but 'fats' is the name given to those substances which are solid at normal room temperature, while oils are liquid at that temperature. When broken down, they give the simple molecules of glycerol and fatty acids. Fats and oils also release energy from their chemical bonds when they are oxidized and though less easily digested than carbohydrates they have more than double the energy value. Rich sources of fats are castor oil, sunflower and coconut seeds, as well as butter and margarine, soya beans, peanuts and some meats like pork. Excess fat is stored in the human body in a special tissue just beneath the skin which also acts as an insulating layer.

Child with kwashiorkor. Note his swollen stomach and the unhealed skin sores

Finding out more

The presence of each of the three main classes of foods can be detected by their reactions with specific chemicals. Do the following tests on various foods and fruits, to determine the chief type of food reserve in each.

Test for starch

Add a few drops of iodine solution to the cut surface of food. A blue-black colour indicates the presence of starch.

Test for simple sugars

You need some Benedict's solution (or equal amounts of Fehling's Solutions 1 & 2 mixed together just before doing this test).

1   Squeeze about 1 cm³ juice from the food into a test tube. Add the same amount of Benedict's solution, and mix them thoroughly.
2   Heat the contents of the tube to boiling, and note the colour change while heating. The final formation of a fine, brick-red sediment or precipitate indicates the presence of simple sugars.

Test for fats

1   Rub the cut surface of the solid fat, or place a drop of oil, onto a clean piece of paper. The appearance of a translucent mark, which does not dry out as water does, indicates the presence of fat.
2   You can also shake up some fat or oil with the dye Sudan III. Note that only fatty droplets are stained red.

Test for proteins—the Biuret Test

1   Pour about 2 cm³ milk into a test tube.
2   Add 1 cm³ sodium hydroxide solution, and mix well.
3   Using a dropping pipette, add about 3 drops of 1% copper sulphate solution to the mixture. A pale violet colour is a positive test for presence of protein.

Note   You can use the above tests to find out which of the three main classes of foods are present in cheese, bread, egg white, egg yolk, uncooked peas, chicken meat, potato, and any other foods that are available. You may need to grate foods like potato, and extract the juice when testing for proteins and sugars.

Mineral salts

Mineral salts are essential for the growth of animals as well as plants. Among the minerals essential to man are the following:

Iron   Needed for the formation of haemoglobin in red blood cells. Lack of iron causes anaemia. Good sources are liver, yeast, kidney and green vegetables.

Copper   In small traces helps in the formation of haemoglobin. Sources are liver, peas and beans.

Calcium   Needed for clotting of blood and the correct formation of bones and teeth. (Calcium will not be used properly if the diet is lacking Vitamin D.) Pregnant mothers and babies need a good supply to help build teeth and bones. If there is insufficient calcium in the diet during pregnancy, the developing foetus will draw on its mother's bone calcium, thus weakening her bones, and causing tooth decay. Sources are milk and dairy products and green vegetables.

Phosphorus   Also needed to build bones and teeth. Rickets results if this mineral, and calcium, are absent from the diet. It is also part of a high-energy molecule, called ATP, from which energy is released during respiration. Sources are fish, meat, eggs and cheese.

Sodium   Required in small traces to form part of the blood plasma, and to contribute to the electrical charge found across cell membranes. Sources are green vegetables and table salt.

Potassium   Necessary in small traces; aids transmission of nerve impulses. Sources are vegetables, meat and coffee.

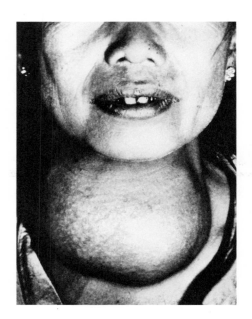

A goitre or enlargement of the thyroid gland caused by lack of iodine in the diet

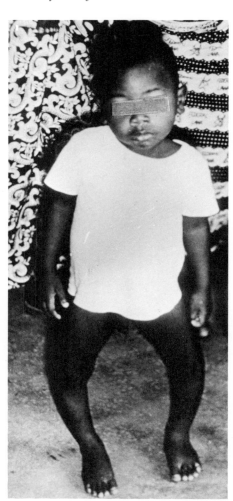

Rickets

Iodine	Aids formation of the hormone thyroxin. When iodine is absent from the diet the thyroid gland enlarges, forming a **goitre**. Sources are sea foods and iodized table salt.
Fluorine	Increasingly recognized as necessary to prevent tooth decay. It is usually added in small amounts to toothpaste and to drinking water.
Zinc	Needed in traces only to prevent skin diseases and falling hair. Sources are meat, cheese and cocoa.

Vitamins

Vitamins are organic substances needed in minute amounts to promote healthy growth and development. For convenience, they are identified by letters and are grouped according to whether they will dissolve in fats or in water. Foods containing **water-soluble vitamins** B complex and C, *should never be boiled*, as the vitamins will go into solution and be lost from the food.

Vitamins must be eaten in the diet as they cannot be manufactured by a human's own body cells. Most can be obtained easily if fresh fruits, liver, milk and green vegetables are eaten in adequate amounts, and on a regular basis.

Margarine, fish-liver oils and egg yolk contain vitamins A and D. The body stores both these vitamins, so excessive intake can be harmful. Vitamin D helps the body to incorporate calcium and phosphorus into bones, so its absence (in the young) can result in **rickets**. The symptoms of this disease are weak bones which bend under the weight of the body. Exposure to sunlight causes the formation of vitamin D in the skin. Vitamin A keeps the skin and eye membranes healthy and also assists in the formation of visual purple in the eye, preventing **night blindness**.

Red meats provide the body with vitamins B_1 (thiamine), B_{12} and P (nicotinic acid). Liver is a good source of vitamins B_1, B_2 and B_{12}, while yeast provides vitamins B_1, B_2 and B_6. Vitamin B_1 prevents **beri-beri**, whose symptoms are muscular weakness and nervous disorders. B_2 prevents **dermatitis**, especially of the eyes and mouth. Vitamins B_6 and nicotinic acid prevent the disease called **pellagra** in which the nervous system is damaged and madness may result. B_{12} controls the development of red blood cells, and so helps prevent **anaemia**.

Fresh citrus fruits and cherries should be present in the human diet as they are excellent sources of vitamin C. This vitamin is water-soluble, so can be found in fresh citrus juice and cherry juice. Boiling destroys this vitamin, so these juices should not be prepared with boiling water. Absence of vitamin C results in internal bleeding under the skin, and swollen, bleeding gums, a condition known as **scurvy**.

Green, leafy vegetables supply vitamins E and K. Vitamin E affects the reproductive processes while vitamin K helps promote blood clotting as it flows through the blood vessels of the body.

Water

Water is the main constituent of the human body. Although it provides no nutrients, it is an essential part of the diet. Much of the body's water comes from fruit and vegetables; the rest comes from various drinks. We constantly lose water through sweating, breathing and excretion, so it must be replaced daily by eating the appropriate foods and by drinking various liquids. The average daily requirement to maintain a healthy body is about 5 glasses of water.

Roughage must also be present in the diet. Although it provides no nutrients, since the human alimentary canal is unable to digest it, it is nevertheless useful since it stimulates peristalsis and helps the intestines to function normally. Roughage is obtained from cellulose and other fibrous materials found in fruits and vegetables. Cereals such as All-bran, and the skin of vegetables such as Irish potatoes or cucumbers are excellent sources of roughage.

Which foods provide essential nutrients?

| FOOD (100g) | Protein (g) | Fat (g) | Carbo-hydrate (g) | Energy value (kJ) | MINERALS | | VITAMINS | | | | | |
					Calcium (mg)	Iron (mg)	A (µg)	Thiamine B1 (mg)	Riboflavin (B2) (mg)	Nicotinic acid (mg)	Ascorbic acid C (mg)	Calciferol D (µg)
Apple, sweet	0·3	0·4	15	244	6	0·3	–	0·04	0·02	0·2	30	–
Banana, ripe	1·2	–	23	420	8	0·6	12·0	0·09	0·06	0·6	10	–
Orange	0·9	0·2	11	190	33	0·4	8·0	0·08	0·03	0·2	49	–
Cabbage	1·6	0·1	6	105	43	0·6	50·0	0·06	0·05	0·2	60	–
Tomatoes	1·0		4	88	15	0·4	3·0	0·05	0·04	0·7	25	–
Potato (Irish)	2·0	–	19	353	11	0·7	1·0	0·10	0·05	1·0	15	–
Peanuts (roasted)	30·0	46·0	18	2350	74	1·9	–	0·30	0·15	21·0	–	–
Bread, wholewheat	9·3	2·6	49	1010	96	2·2	–	0·30	0·13	3·0	–	–
Cornmeal	9·5	4·0	68	1462	18	3·0	3·0	0·35	0·10	0·10	–	–
Rice (cooked)	2·2	0·1	23	420	8	0·2	–	0·01	0·01	0·4	–	–
Chocolate, milk	6·0	33·5	54	2275	216	4·0	6·6	0·10	0·04	0·8	–	–
Butter	0·6	81·0	0·4	3007	16	0·2	995·0	–	–	0·1	–	1·26
Cheddar cheese	25·0	32·0	2·0	1670	680	0·9	420·0	–	0·83	1·6	–	0·35
Milk (pasteurized)	3·3	4·0	4·9	270	125	0·1	44·0	0·04	0·15	0·9	1·8	0·05
Egg, whole (raw)	12·8	11·5	0·7	660	54	2·7	140·0	0·12	0·34	0·1	–	3·4
Bacon, medium fat	25·0	55·0	1·0	2550	25	3·3	–	0·48	0·31	4·8	–	–
Liver, beef (raw)	20·0	4·0	3·6	570	8	12·6	6000	0·27	2·80	16·0	31	0·75
Chicken	18·2	10·2	–	170	14	1·5	20	0·08	0·16	9·0	–	–
Sea fish (snapper)	19·8	0·6	–	90	12	0·8	–	0·05	0·05	1·7	–	–
Green banana	1·4	0·2	28·7	110	8	0·9	95	0·04	0·02	0·6	31	–
Yam	2·4	0·2	24·1	105	22	0·8	–	0·09	0·03	0·5	10	–

Activities

1 (a) What are **food additives**? Explain why they are used.
   (b) What is the likely effect of food additives on health?
2 Examine the labels shown below, reading each one carefully and completely.
   (a) For each label list the food additives and say what purpose(s) they serve.
   (b) Which of the labels, in your opinion, provide the most comprehensive information. Explain your choice.
3 (a) Obtain a label from a can of soup produced in your country. Compare the information with that on the label taken from the European soup can.
   (b) Assume that both tins of soup are on your supermarket shelf and cost the same amount for the same volume. State which brand of soup you would buy and give reasons to justify your choice.
4 Examine a variety of packaged foods to find out their nutritive content.

MILKO
FORTIFIED FOOD DRINK

A chocolate flavoured dried milk food product containing not less than 8·5% milk fat. It is prepared from malt extract, milk constituents, sugar, cocoa, lecithin, artificial flavours, spices and contains added vitamins and minerals.

Each ounce of MILKO contains not less than 500 International Units Vitamin A, 0.15 mg Vitamin B₁, 100 International Units Vitamin D₃

MINERAL SALTS
Phosphorous P_2O_5 .... 325 mg
Calcium CaO .... 180 mg
Magnesium as MgO .... 70 mg
Iron as Fe_2O_3 .... 6 mg

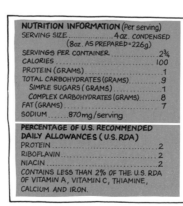

NUTRITION INFORMATION (Per serving)
SERVING SIZE .... 4oz. CONDENSED
         (8oz. AS PREPARED=226g)
SERVINGS PER CONTAINER 2¾
CALORIES 100
PROTEIN (GRAMS) 1
TOTAL CARBOHYDRATES (GRAMS) 9
   SIMPLE SUGARS (GRAMS) 1
   COMPLEX CARBOHYDRATES (GRAMS) 8
FAT (GRAMS) 7
SODIUM .... 870 mg/serving

PERCENTAGE OF U.S. RECOMMENDED DAILY ALLOWANCES (U.S. RDA)
PROTEIN 2
RIBOFLAVIN 2
NIACIN 2
CONTAINS LESS THAN 2% OF THE U.S. RDA OF VITAMIN A, VITAMIN C, THIAMINE, CALCIUM AND IRON.

INGREDIENTS: WATER, MUSHROOMS, PARTIALLY HYDROGENATED VEGETABLE OILS (SOYBEAN OIL; PALM OR COTTONSEED OIL), WHEAT FLOUR, CREAM, SALT, CORN STARCH, DRIED DAIRY BLEND (WHEY, CALCIUM CASEINATE), MODIFIED FOOD STARCH, WHEY, MONOSODIUM GLUTAMATE, SOY PROTEIN ISOLATE, MARGARINE (BUTTEROIL, PARTIALLY HYDROGENATED SOYBEAN OIL, WATER, NATURAL FLAVORING, VITAMIN A PALMITATE), NATURAL FLAVORING, YEAST EXTRACT AND DEHYDRATED GARLIC.

TASTY SOUP INC.

Oceans five chunk light tuna
IN VEGETABLE OIL
NET WEIGHT 6½ oz. 184g.

INGREDIENTS
TUNA IN SOYBEAN OIL, SEASONED WITH VEGETABLE BROTH, SALT ADDED.

PACKED FOR UNITED FISH CO. LTD TRINIDAD, TOBAGO

A balanced diet

An individual may eat large amounts of food daily, and yet starve! This happens when there is a large intake of starches, with no protein at all. Such a person would be starved of certain essential nutrients. In developing and underdeveloped countries many people suffer from **malnutrition**, in which the quantity of food eaten is adequate, but the diet is not balanced.

A **balanced diet** is one which contains the right kinds of foods in the proportions necessary for the body to carry out all its functions. To prevent malnutrition, and to enable the body to function properly, there must be the correct balance between each of the six classes of foods (see Section 12). A diet containing about 65% carbohydrates, 15% protein and 10% fat, with about 10% water and fibre obtained from fruits and vegetables included daily provides a good balance. However, the relative proportions of carbohydrates, proteins and fats will vary according to the body's energy requirements.

The amount of energy required daily depends on the person's age and stage of development, their sex and the type of physical activity they undertake, as well as the climate of the country in which they live.

A balanced diet

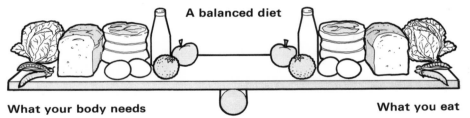

What your body needs   **What you eat**

Experiment: To compare the energy values of foods

In this experiment you will use the knowledge that when 1 g of food is burned, the heat produced can be used to cause a change in the temperature ($T\,°C$) of a known volume of water. From the observed rise in the temperature of the water you can calculate the number of calories given out when the food burned.

Use the following information to calculate energy values.

To raise the temperature of 1 g of water by 1 °C needs 4·2 J

∴ To raise the temperature of 100 g of water by 1 °C needs 420 J

∴ To raise the temperature of 100 g of water by $T\,°C$ needs $420 \times T$ J

But 100 g of water has a volume of 100 cm³ and to change J to kJ, we must divide by 1000.

∴ To raise the temperature of 100 cm³ of water by $T\,°C$ needs $\dfrac{420 \times T}{1000}$ kJ

i.e. **To raise the temperature of 100 cm³ of water by $T\,°C$ needs $(0{\cdot}42 \times T)$ kJ**

e.g. If burning 1 g of (dry) bread raises the temperature of 100 cm³ of water by 20 °C, then the approximate energy value of bread would be $0{\cdot}42 \times 20 = 8{\cdot}4\,kJ/g$

Note This method ignores the heat lost to the surroundings and to the metal can holding the water as it is heated, so your answer is likely to be a little less than the one given above.

What you need

Empty metal can, thermometer showing °C, thick pin, plasticine, peanut, peas, corn, cheese, measuring cylinder, stirrer.

What you do

1. Read through the experiment *completely* before starting to do anything. Assemble all the things you will need.
2. Weigh out 1 g of peanuts (without their shells) and stick them onto one or two large pins, set into plasticine as shown.
3. Fill your calorimeter (the metal can) with 100 cm³ cold water and clamp it in place so that the peanuts are 2–3 cm beneath.
4. Measure and record the water temperature. Leave the thermometer in the water.
5. Very carefully light the peanuts. Make sure that, as they burn, the flames are in contact with the base of the metal can. Stir the water gently while it is being heated.
6. When the peanuts have completely burned away, immediately note and record the temperature of the water.
7. Use the *rise* in temperature (T °C) to calculate the number of kJ given out by the burning peanuts.
8. Using fresh cold water each time, repeat the experiment using peas, corn, cheese, etc.

Questions

(a) Which food sample released most energy during burning?
(b) Do you think this food will also provide more energy when you eat it?
(c) What are some of the possible sources of error in this experiment, and how could they be overcome?

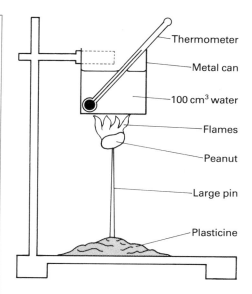

Amount of energy (kJ) needed daily by different people

AGE (years)	SEX	ACTIVITY	ENERGY (kJ)
Baby			
0–1	Boy or girl		3760
1–2			5040
2–3			5880
Child			
5–7	Boy or girl	Going to school	7560
7–9			8820
Adolescent			
12–15	Boy		11760
12–15	Girl	Going to school	9660
15–18	Boy	and playing sports	12600
15–18	Girl		9660
Adult			
Over 20	Male	Active work or playing sports	15120
		Sedentary job; no exercise	10920
	Female	Active work or playing sports	10500
		Breast-feeding a baby	11340
		Pregnant	10080
Old person			
Over 60	Male or female	Retired from work	8600

If active people with high energy needs do not eat enough high energy foods, their diet will not be a balanced one

As you see from the table on page 41, a footballer, cricketer or a cane-cutter needs more high-energy foods in his diet than a man of the same age who works as a clerk in an office and leads a quiet life with little physical activity. (This is the reason that athletes' diets are carefully monitored by their trainers to ensure that they eat the right amounts of energy-giving foods, protein, minerals and vitamins.) While the physically active man may eat enough food to prevent hunger, he may not get enough high-energy foods to meet his daily energy requirements. When this occurs his diet is not a balanced one.

Some people eat more foods than their body can actually use up. If the diet contains too much sugar, starches and fats which are not 'burned up' by physical activity, the extra high-energy foods are soon stored as fat. Excess fat is usually deposited under the skin and around the internal organs. Fat people have a condition called **obesity**. Some effects of obesity are likely to be:

(a) difficulties in breathing;
(b) high blood pressure and greater muscle strain, especially on the heart;
(c) greater strain on the joints, especially the hip joints, since the skeleton has more weight to support and carry around;
(d) frequent feelings of tiredness, and difficulty in doing physical activity;
(e) flabby muscles.

The diet of obese people is not balanced.

Obese people eat too many sugary foods, starches and fats

Very often the food a person eats is determined by their **appetite**, and thus does not provide a balanced diet. The term 'appetite' refers to the desire for food, which is not always related to the body's needs. Appetite is often caused by eating habits, the smell, or the appearance of the food.

If you select enough of the right kinds of each type of food, using your knowledge of their importance to help you choose, then your body will work well as it was meant to!

Activities

1 Write down everything you eat during the course of today, including the amounts of each food. State whether you have had a balanced diet today, and justify your answer.
2 Use the information given in the table on p. 41 to construct a graph showing the daily energy requirements of different people.

Questions

1 Two 16-year-old boys, both members of their school's football team have $3.00 for lunch. This is how they spend it.

George

1 bottle of 'sweet' drink	= $0·90
1 slice of chocolate cake	= $1·10
1 sugar bun	= $0·30
1 pack chewing-gum	= $0·50

Total = $2·80
Bal. $0·20

Geoffrey

1 pack fresh milk	= $0·60
1 meat patty	= $1·00
1 bun and cheese	= $1·00
1 orange	= $0·30
2 icy mint sweets	= $0·10

Total = $3·00

Which of the two boys do you consider has obtained a balanced lunch for his money? Justify your answer.

2 Explain why a healthy 8-year-old boy needs more energy than a retired 65-year-old man.

3 9·8 joules are required to lift a mass of 1 kilogram through a vertical distance of 1 metre.
   (a) How many kilojoules will an 80 kg boy use to climb up a stair 5 m vertical height?
   (b) Calculate how many kilojoules you will need
      (i) to climb up any flight of stairs in your school;
      (ii) to carry a 10 kg bag up the same stairs.

14

Teeth

A child's first teeth appear when he is about six months old. By the end of the third year there are twenty teeth in all. This first set of teeth are the **milk** teeth. From about the sixth year they are gradually replaced by the **permanent** teeth: There are thirty-two permanent teeth in a complete set.

Kinds of teeth

The permanent set is made up of three kinds of teeth. Each kind is easily recognized by its shape, which is related to the special function that tooth performs. They are illustrated in the diagram on the left.

There are two types of molars in the permanent set of teeth, **premolars** and **true molars**. Premolars are absent from the set of milk teeth.

Dentition

The number of each kind of teeth, and their arrangement in the skull of an animal is called the **dentition**. The diagram below shows half of the teeth in the lower jaw of man (i.e. 2 incisors, 1 canine, 2 premolars and 3 molars) in the order that they are in the mouth.

Inside a tooth

Each tooth is inserted in a **socket** or hole in the jawbone of the skull. The jawbone is covered by the gum. The **root** of the tooth cannot be seen, since it is buried in the jawbone.

The part of the tooth above the gum is called the **crown**. The various kinds of teeth all have the same parts inside. **Enamel** covers the outside of the crown and **cement** covers the root. Underneath the enamel is **dentine**, which contains living cells. In the centre of the dentine is a hole, or **pulp cavity** in which are found the blood vessels and nerves. The blood vessels bring nutrients and oxygen to the living cells of the dentine, and take away waste products. The nerves register heat, cold or pain and send messages to the brain about circumstances which may affect the teeth.

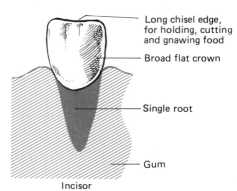

Long chisel edge, for holding, cutting and gnawing food
Broad flat crown
Single root
Gum

Incisor

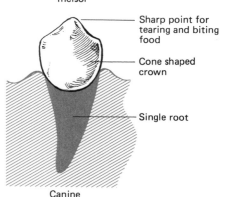

Sharp point for tearing and biting food
Cone shaped crown
Single root

Canine

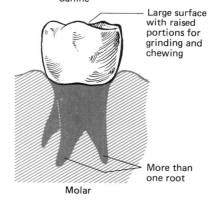

Large surface with raised portions for grinding and chewing
More than one root

Molar

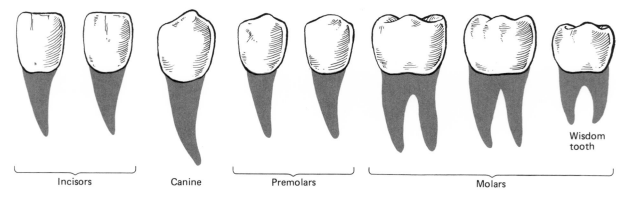

Incisors   Canine   Premolars   Molars   Wisdom tooth

Types of teeth in the lower jaw

Care of teeth

Maintaining the cleanliness of the teeth is an important part of personal hygiene. Teeth should be cleaned after meals, to prevent food particles from settling around them. When food settles around teeth it creates an ideal breeding place for the bacteria which are normally present in the mouth. Bacteria change sugars into lactic acid, which dissolves the tooth enamel and creates a **cavity**. The living dentine is very soon exposed, causing intense pain, and increased sensitivity to hot and cold substances. Bacterial infection of one tooth often leads to infection of nearby teeth and abscesses of the gum. The bacterial activity also produces the unpleasant odours which are known as 'bad breath'.

Sometimes, too, when food particles accumulate, a hard layer called 'plaque' slowly builds up, especially on the inner surfaces of the teeth. Plaque can later cause gum disease.

Rinsing the mouth with water, brushing your teeth after meals, using a toothpick or dental floss, and paying regular visits to the dentist help to prevent tooth decay. Remember, too, that including calcium, vitamin D and fresh fibrous foods in the diet, and limiting sugary foods, will also help to keep the teeth in good condition.

Fluoridation and teeth

Scientists have observed that people who drink water from rivers and springs containing fluoride salts tend to develop fewer dental cavities. Not all water supplies contain naturally occurring fluoride. So, in some countries, small concentrations of fluoride have been added to the drinking water. Many manufacturers also include fluoride in toothpastes.

But the research findings have not been conclusive and some countries now believe that in highly industrialized areas, there is already enough fluoride in foods. They believe that the addition of even small amounts to drinking water could present a health risk. Many countries have more recently decided against adding fluoride to public water supplies. The effectiveness of fluoride in the prevention of tooth decay should therefore be interpreted with caution.

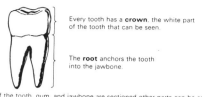

Every tooth has a **crown**, the white part of the tooth that can be seen.

The **root** anchors the tooth into the jawbone.

If the tooth, gum, and jawbone are sectioned other parts can be seen:

enamel the outer coating of the crown, this is the hardest substance made by the body

pulp cavity a space containing nerves and blood vessels

gum protects the jawbone and roots

cement and **peridontal fibres** — anchors the root to the jawbone

dentine, a living layer, more like bone, which makes the enamel

jawbone

nerves and **blood vessels**

Structure of a tooth

Questions

1   (a) Why do you think the temporary teeth are generally referred to as 'milk teeth'?
    (b) Which of the 'milk teeth' usually appear first in a baby's mouth?

2   (a) Using the information in the diagram on page 44 write out the complete **permanent dentition** of man.
    (b) What are the differences between premolars and molars?
    (c) Are 'wisdom teeth' found in the milk set or the permanent set of teeth?

3   (a) Man is described as an '**omnivore**', Explain what this means, making reference to his dentition.
    (b) Explain the terms '**herbivore**' and '**carnivore**'; giving one example of each.

Activity

1   (a) Use a mirror to examine the teeth in your mouth; identify all the teeth according to the diagrams opposite.
    (b) Draw up a table as shown below, and complete it.

TYPES OF TEETH	NUMBER IN EACH JAW	FUNCTIONS
(a) Incisors		
(b) Canines		
(c)		
(d)		

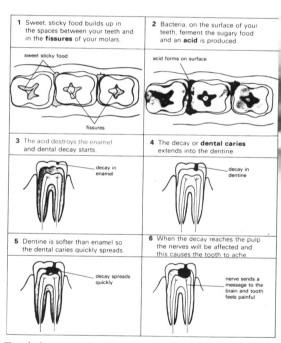

1 Sweet, sticky food builds up in the spaces between your teeth and in the **fissures** of your molars.

sweet sticky food

fissures

2 Bacteria, on the surface of your teeth, ferment the sugary food and an **acid** is produced.

acid forms on surface

3 The acid destroys the enamel and dental decay starts.

decay in enamel

4 The decay or **dental caries** extends into the dentine.

decay in dentine

5 Dentine is softer than enamel so the dental caries quickly spreads.

decay spreads quickly

6 When the decay reaches the pulp the nerves will be affected and this causes the tooth to ache.

nerve sends a message to the brain and tooth feels painful

Tooth decay results from food particles building up around your teeth

Nutrition in green plants

The feeding process of living organisms is known as **nutrition**. It varies greatly among plants and animals. Plants are capable of making organic foods within their body cells from simple inorganic compounds using light energy. This process is called **photosynthesis**. Animals must typically obtain their food from sources outside their own body cells.

What do plants need to make food?

In Section 2 you learned about organs of vegetative propagation, and the way in which plants reproduce asexually by means of these organs. Vegetative organs such as tubers of the Irish and sweet potato, the onion bulb or ginger rhizome have rich stores of food in their cells—the products of photosynthesis which were not immediately needed by the plant.

What do plants need to make food? One important requirement is the presence of a green pigment, **chlorophyll**, which is normally found in all green plant parts, such as the leaves and some stems. Chlorophyll, contained in sacs called **chloroplasts**, is able to absorb certain types of light (blue and red rays in the visible spectrum of light). Light is a form of **energy**. Energy is the ability to do work, and to bring about change. It can exist in many forms—as light, sound, heat, chemical or mechanical energy—and one form of energy can be changed into other forms. Light energy can split apart a water molecule so that hydrogen and oxygen are formed. For plants to make food, chlorophyll must be present, and light energy must be available. Two other things are required: there must be a supply of **water** (written H_2O), and of **carbon dioxide** (written CO_2).

Experiments have shown that certain minerals, although not directly involved in photosynthesis, are nevertheless important for the process to occur. Magnesium forms part of the chlorophyll molecule and phosphorus is needed to build up some proteins and the high-energy compound ATP (adenosine triphosphate). Nitrogen is an essential element in every protein molecule, while sulphur is often present in certain proteins. Without these mineral elements, food-making is incomplete and the plant's growth is stunted. The plant also fails to flower and fruit at the usual times.

The chemical reactions of photosynthesis

Photosynthesis occurs in two distinct stages, each having specific requirements.

Stage 1 requires light, and is called the **light reaction** of photosynthesis. During this stage energy, usually from sunlight, splits water molecules. Hydrogen and oxygen are produced when the water molecule splits apart.

Scientists use symbols to show what happens during this light reaction; they write what is called an **equation**.

$$2H_2O + \text{light energy} \longrightarrow 2H_2 + O_2$$

two molecules of water	and	light energy	$\xrightarrow{\text{produce}}$	two molecules of hydrogen	and	oxygen gas

Stage 2 does *not* require the presence of light and uses the hydrogen formed in Stage 1 to 'reduce' carbon dioxide. The outcome of this reduction of carbon dioxide is the formation of a **simple sugar** and **water**. This stage can also be represented by equation.

$$6CO_2 \quad + \quad 6 \times 2H_2 \longrightarrow C_6H_{12}O_6 \quad + \quad 6H_2O$$

| six molecules of carbon dioxide | and | twelve molecules of hydrogen | react to form | one molecule of simple sugar | and | six molecules of water |

For simplicity, the two stages are combined in one equation, which is conveniently written:

$$6CO_2 + 6H_2O \xrightarrow[\text{of chlorophyll produces}]{\text{sunlight energy in the presence}} C_6H_{12}O_6 + 6O_2$$

During these reactions the light energy is changed to chemical energy and is trapped and stored in sugar molecules. By exposing plants to radio-active carbon, called 'labelled C_{14}', scientists have been able to prove that carbon from carbon dioxide forms part of the simple sugars produced during photosynthesis.

Events following photosynthesis

The sugar molecules formed during photosynthesis are then linked to each other by chemical bonds to form more complex substances such as starch. The starch molecules accumulate, and form starch grains inside the cells which are continuing to photosynthesize. Their presence in such cells can be confirmed by specific tests using iodine.

Activity

To observe the products of photosynthesis

What you need
Green leaf from plant growing in sunlight, alcohol, iodine, water bath, white tile.

What you do
1 Boil the green leaf in alcohol to decolorize it.
2 Dip it in hot water to soften it again.
3 Spread the leaf flat on a white tile. Add some iodine solution.

A blue-black colour indicates the presence of starch.

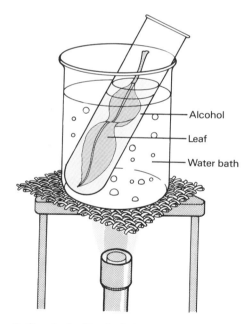

Boiling the leaf in alcohol

The plant uses some of this manufactured starch for its own metabolic activities. Most plants, however, cannot use all the starch they make, so during the dark hours of night, the excess starch which has been produced and which is *insoluble*, is changed back into *soluble* simple sugars. These simple sugars, dissolved in water, are now easily transported by the plant to storage areas such as underground stem tubers. In the plant cells in these storage areas, the simple sugars are then converted back into starch which, because of its large molecules, cannot escape from the cells by diffusion. The whole process is known as **translocation**.

Some of the simple carbohydrates made in photosynthesis link up with other elements (e.g. nitrogen) to form **proteins**, or else become modified to form **fats** and **oils**. These may be used by the plant, or stored in organs of vegetative propagation, in seeds, or in fruits. The cellulose and lignin which strengthen plant cell walls are also formed from the products of photosynthesis.

Why are foods stored?

In Section 5 you learned that seeds such as peas and beans, sunflower and castor oil seeds, as well as fruits like the mango and orange, store various kinds of food substances. Vegetative organs also store large amounts of foods.

These food reserves ensure that the plant can survive periods of unfavourable or hostile habitat conditions. Because seeds have food reserves, they can be dried out, packaged for sale, or kept for long periods.

When they absorb water later, and begin to germinate, the stored food keeps the young seedling going until it can start to make its own food. The seedling's chances of survival are increased by the presence of the food reserves on which it 'feeds'. Vegetatively propagating organs are usually found in plants whose aerial parts die at the end of one growing season. When the buds on these storage organs become active at the start of the next growing season, the stored food ensures their survival and growth, since the new aerial shoots are established at the expense of the stored foods.

Experiment A: What happens to food in storage organs?

What you need
Irish potato, onion bulb, potting soil, two flower pots.

What you do
1   Place potting soil in each flower pot and water both of them.
2   Place an onion bulb and an Irish potato in each pot after carefully noting the shape, size and general appearance of each one. Leave the pots undisturbed for about two weeks, but water them every other day.
3   Notice when the first aerial shoots just begin to push through the surface. Carefully dig out the potato and the onion. How does the size of each compare now with its original size?
4   Replant each, and leave them until they have grown into well-established plants with green leaves. Carefully dig out each storage organ. Record your observations, and explain the differences you observed.

The site of photosynthesis

Each body part of a living organism is structured to suit it for the specific functions it must perform. A site suitable for photosynthesis must satisfy the following requirements.

1   It must be located where most of its surface area is exposed to sunlight.
2   Its cells must contain chlorophyll, and must be close enough to the surface to be able to 'trap' light energy.
3   It must contain conducting tissues which link it to the rest of the plant, so that water and mineral salts can be transported to the cells for photosynthesis, and the products of photosynthesis can be translocated to other plant parts.
4   The chlorophyll-containing cells must have access to the surrounding atmosphere to allow entry of carbon dioxide and exit of oxygen.

The following diagram shows how the structure of the leaf fulfils these requirements, making it ideally suited for photosynthesis.

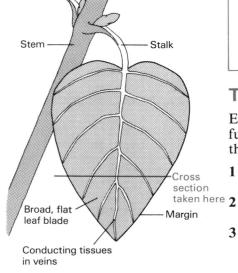

Parts of a dicot leaf

Summary

The products of photosynthesis are starches and other carbohydrates, proteins and fats. These complex organic molecules are built up within green cells from simple inorganic substances, i.e. water and carbon dioxide, using light energy to 'power' the process. As soon as they are formed they are quickly translocated from the leaves via the phloem, so that they can be used in other metabolic activities, or stored.

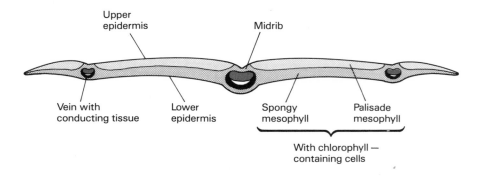

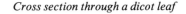

Cross section through a dicot leaf

48

Experiment B: Can a plant make starch if carbon dioxide is absent?

What you need

Two healthy plants of the same species and same approximate age, soda lime, plastic bags, alcohol, iodine, water bath, test tubes, sodium hydrogen carbonate solution, watch glass, beaker.

What you do

Water the plants and keep them in complete darkness for at least 48 hours before you do the experiment.

1 Label the pots and the test tubes A and B.
2 Remove a leaf from each plant and immediately test for presence of starch as described on p. 47. (If any leaf gives a blue-black colour, showing that starch is present, the plants cannot be used and must be kept in darkness for a further 24–48 hours before starting this experiment again.)
3 Place 20 g soda lime in a small watch-glass. Soda lime absorbs carbon dioxide, turning cloudy as it does so. Place 10 cm³ sodium hydrogen carbonate solution in a small beaker. This solution slowly decomposes, releasing carbon dioxide.
4 Place the container with soda lime on the soil in pot A, and that with sodium hydrogen carbonate solution on the soil in pot B.
5 Water each plant, then cover it with a transparent plastic bag as shown in the diagram.
6 Place the pots side by side where they can obtain equal amounts of sunlight for several hours.
7 Remove one leaf from each and place it in its appropriate test tube. Test each leaf separately for the presence of starch.

Questions

(a) Why was it necessary to leave the plants in darkness before doing the experiment?
(b) Why did you have to test a leaf at the start of the experiment?
(c) Was there any evidence that CO_2 was removed from the air in pot A?
(d) Was there a 'control' in this experiment? If so, did it fail or succeed in showing that CO_2 is needed in making starch?

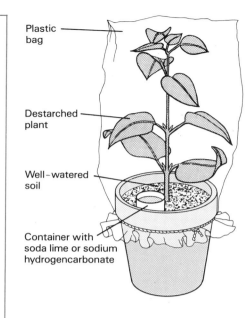

Plastic bag

Destarched plant

Well-watered soil

Container with soda lime or sodium hydrogencarbonate

Experiment C: Will starch be formed in the absence of chlorophyll?

1 Look around for plants with variegated leaves, such as the hibiscus.
2 Predict where in the leaves starch will be found, then design controlled experiments to verify your predictions. Make sure you write down exactly what you do, and what you observe.

Experiment D: Is light needed for photosynthesis?

1 Design controlled experiments to show how excluding light from leaves affects starch formation.
2 What is the difference between a **destarched** plant and an **etiolated** plant?

16

Diffusion and osmosis

Smells and odours

You usually know when a meal is prepared since the smell of food alerts you long before you see it or are told about it. Similarly, if there is a dead and rotting animal in the neighbourhood, you are also alerted by the smell and so avoid getting too close.

You are able to smell odours because tiny particles leave objects and spread out through the surrounding particles of air. These particles cannot usually be seen as they move away from the source. Quite often, too, if there is no odour, you will be unaware that particles are moving about.

You can do some simple experiments to show that the particles of different substances move away from their source and spread out between other particles. Many liquids will easily change into vapour (gas), which gives off a strong odour, or else can be seen.

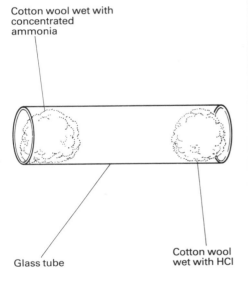

Cotton wool wet with concentrated ammonia

Glass tube

Cotton wool wet with HCl

Activity

Looking at diffusion
1 Get a piece of wide glass tube, or a boiling tube. Use forceps or tongs to hold a piece of cotton wool while you moisten it with concentrated ammonia solution, then moisten another piece with hydrochloric acid in the same way.
2 Carefully place one piece of cotton wool in one end of the tube, and the other piece in the opposite end. Make sure that they do not touch each other.
3 Lay the tube horizontally on the desk as shown in the diagram. Leave it for about 10 minutes while you watch what happens.
   (a) What do you see happening inside the tube?
   (b) Draw the tube in your book. Write down what you observe.

Diffusion

Here is an explanation of what you saw happening. Tiny particles of ammonia are escaping from the cotton wool soaked in ammonia. But you cannot see them. Tiny particles of hydrochloric acid are also moving away from the other piece of cotton wool. Since these particles are enclosed within the tube, they can only travel in that space. So they spread out along the tube and eventually come in contact with particles from the other piece of cotton wool. When this happens, the two types of particles react together and form a new substance called **ammonium chloride**. The particles of ammonium chloride are larger and white, and you can see them form a white, powdery deposit inside the tube.

This spreading out of particles occurs rapidly in gases but more slowly in liquids and solids. The specific movement of particles of one substance among particles of another substance is called **diffusion**.

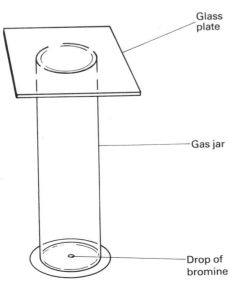

Glass plate

Gas jar

Drop of bromine

Activities

Diffusion of a gas
Your teacher will demonstrate this because *bromine gas is poisonous*!
1 One drop of liquid bromine is placed, using a syringe, at the bottom of a gas jar in which there is only air.
2 A flat glass plate is quickly placed over the gas jar.
3 Draw the gas jar. Use arrows to show what happens within the jar after 10 minutes. Describe what you saw happening. Explain what has happened.

Diffusion of a solid
You can carry out this activity yourself.
1 Write your name and the date on the outside of a gas jar. Fill it with clean water.
2 Carefully drop about four small crystals of blue copper sulphate into the water. Leave it undisturbed.
3 Record and explain what has happened by the end of the class; after 24 hours; and after one week.

Diffusion of liquids
Try this activity at home.
1 Fill a clean glass with water. Tip a few drops of coloured syrup into the water. Do not stir it.
2 Leave it undisturbed for 24 hours.
3 Write down and explain what you see happening.

Movement through membranes

If two solutions are separated by a semi-permeable membrane, water will diffuse across the membrane, travelling from the solution of lower concentration (which has a higher proportion of water molecules) to the more concentrated solution (which has fewer water molecules). This process is called **osmosis**. It is a special kind of diffusion.

In the cells of living organisms there are many substances necessary for various functions. In order to get where they are needed, these substances must often pass across a cell membrane, travelling from an area of high concentration to one of low concentration.

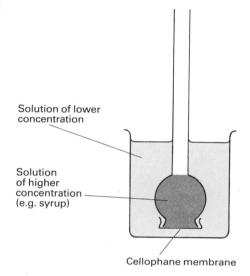

Solution of lower concentration

Solution of higher concentration (e.g. syrup)

Cellophane membrane

Experiment A : Observing osmosis

1 Set up the apparatus shown in the top diagram. Put water in the beaker and a syrup solution in the thistle funnel. Make the membrane out of cellophane.
2 Suspend the thistle funnel in the water with a clamp stand.
3 After about 24 hours draw what has happened.

Questions
(a) How do you account for what you observed?
(b) How has the concentration of the syrup changed?
(c) What is meant by a **semi-permeable membrane**?
(d) Of what value is diffusion and osmosis to living cells?
(e) Name two organs in the human body in which diffusion occurs, and state what substances diffuse in or out of them.

Experiment B : A semi-permeable membrane

Artificial, non-living material such as Visking tubing and some compounds of cellulose are semi-permeable to molecules of certain sizes.

1 Obtain a sample of a mixed solution containing 5% sodium chloride, 5% glucose and 5% soluble starch.
2 Test small samples of the solution for the presence of glucose, starch and chloride (add a drop of silver nitrate—the formation of a white precipitate means a chloride is present).
3 Cut about 20 cm Visking tubing and knot one end to form a bag. Soak the bag in distilled water.
4 Pour in the salt, sugar and starch solution and set up the bag as shown in the diagram. Make sure that you wash the outside of the Visking bag thoroughly with distilled water. Leave the apparatus for 1 hour.
5 Test samples of the distilled water surrounding the bag for the presence of glucose, starch and chloride.

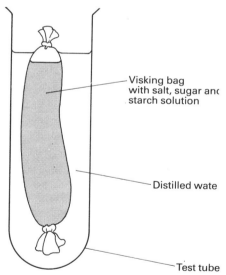

Visking bag with salt, sugar and starch solution

Distilled water

Test tube

Questions
(a) Which substance is present in the distilled water at the end of the hour?
(b) Use your knowledge of diffusion to explain the presence of that substance.
(c) Why do you think some substance(s) remained inside the Visking bag?
(d) What is meant by **dialysis**?

17

Transport in plants

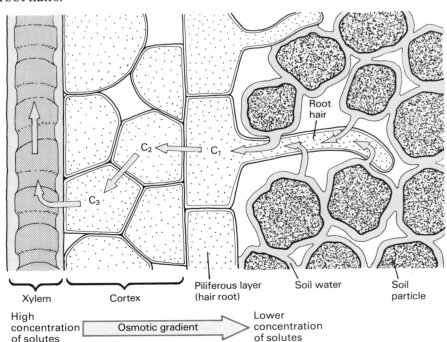

Water from the soil (a low concentrate solution) is absorbed into the cell sap of the root hair (a higher concentrate solution) by osmosis

How does water enter plants?

Plants, unlike most animals, have no 'mouths', yet they need nutrients in order to manufacture their food and nourish themselves.

Plants take in most of their food through the **roots**. These roots, which are usually firmly buried in the soil, help the plant to absorb nutrients in a process known as **absorption**. The tiny thread-like **root hairs** are the main areas of absorption. Roots are always widely dispersed in the soil to reach the greatest area for this absorption.

Water is absorbed from the soil by the process of **osmosis**. Think for a moment about the roots and the soil water in between the soil particles.

The cell sap in the root hairs contains many dissolved substances, and so has a concentration relatively higher than the soil water. Water therefore passes from the soil water to the cell sap of the root hair through the semi-permeable membrane surrounding the root. From there the water is passed to the xylem along the **osmotic gradient**, as explained in the diagram below.

Some researchers also believe that water enters the plant by **diffusion** and **capillary action**. These movements could be due to the large inter-molecular spaces which are present in the cell wall.

How do mineral salts enter the plant?

Soil water contains varying amounts of dissolved mineral salts. These salts, e.g. potassium, sodium, nitrate and phosphate, are present as ions in the dilute solution. These ions move into the root hairs against the likely concentration gradient, that is from a low to a higher concentration. Their movement is thus not passive, as is the movement of water, but is active. This movement requires energy to pull against the concentration gradient. This energy is supplied by **aerobic respiration** in the root hairs.

Transport of water from the root hair to the xylem. A layer of water surrounds each soil particle (right). Root hairs in contact with this water absorb it into their cell sap by osmosis (C_1). Cell sap in C_1 therefore becomes a less concentrated solution than that in its neighbour C_2 which has not yet taken in water. So C_2 absorbs some water from C_1 by osmosis and so on, until the water reaches the xylem for transport to the leaves. Remember in osmosis, the water always moves from lower concentration solutions to higher concentration solutions.

Transport of nutrients from the root to the leaves

Water and mineral salts must travel from the root to the leaves where they are required in the manufacture of food. Several theories have been put forward to explain how they make this journey along the stem. Experiments have shown most definitely, however, that the water and mineral salts travel up through the xylem elements. The xylem is a complex tissue made up of vessels, tracheids, fibres and parenchyma.

There are three main explanations of how materials travel through the xylem and up to the leaves. These explanations are root pressure, capillarity and transpiration pull (the transpiration cohesion–tension theory).

Root pressure

Pressure forces water several centimetres up the stem. It is believed to be caused by a combination of active absorption and turgor pressure in the cells of the cortex. This pressure can only explain the rise of water up to a certain level, and it is difficult to see how it could explain the movement of water up tall trees, since the pressure required would be so much greater.

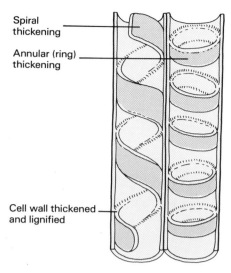

Vertical section of xylem tissue

Experiment: How far does water travel under root pressure?

1 Cut through the stem of a well-watered hibiscus or croton plant at 10–20 cm above the ground.
2 Place a piece of rubber tubing over the cut surface and insert a piece of glass tubing in the free end of the rubber tubing.
3 Measure the height of the water that collects in the glass tube.

Questions
(a) What happens to the cut end of the plant?
(b) How far does the liquid move up the glass tube?
(c) Does the level of water change when a different plant is used?
(d) If so, how do you explain this?

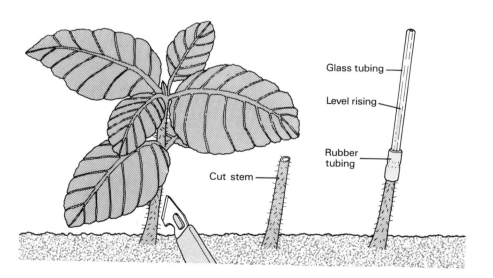

Capillarity inside the narrow glass tube means that water can be drawn up inside it against the pull of gravity

Capillarity

Capillarity is another factor that may help the movement of water and mineral salts up the stem.

When a tube of narrow bore is dipped into water, the water rises automatically up the tube as shown in the figure (*left*). This occurs because the glass above the water level attracts water molecules upwards, while the cohesive forces between the water molecules themselves draw more water into the tube.

Like root pressure, capillarity alone cannot explain the upward movement of water in very tall trees.

Transpiration pull

Perhaps the most generally accepted theory of how water moves up the stem is the one called the transpiration pull, proposed by Dixon and Joly in 1894. This theory suggests that the motive power for the ascent of water is the result of the evaporation of water from the leaves in transpiration. Water is therefore pulled upwards through the continuous column which stretches from the root xylem, through the stem, all the way along the veins of the leaf and into the mesophyll cells. In effect, loss of water molecules from the leaf surface sets up a 'chain reaction' pull which results in molecules of water being taken in at the root.

Water molecules behave in this way because of the strong attraction they have for each other. This attraction between molecules is called **cohesion**.

Transpiration as a cooling system

Transpiration is the process by which a plant loses water vapour, through the stomata of the leaves, by evaporation. It has already been shown that transpiration sets up a pulling force which could explain the uptake of water and mineral salts in the plant.

Transpiration also acts as a means of temperature control in the plant. The evaporation of water from the leaf requires heat (latent heat of vaporization), which is provided by the cells of the leaf. In this way the temperature of cells is lowered, so that the internal areas of the leaf become cooler than the external atmosphere. Such a cooling mechanism is similar to the way in which mammals use sweat (and its evaporation) to control their body temperature.

Summary of intake

Most plants absorb water from the soil through their roots. The bulk of this water enters the plant by the process of **osmosis**. The intake of mineral salts is against the diffusion gradient, and is therefore considered to be an active process requiring energy from metabolic activities.

Water and mineral salts travel from the roots to the leaves along the xylem elements by using a combination of forces such as root pressure, capillarity and the transpiration pull. When they reach the leaves they are manufactured into food which is then distributed throughout the plant.

Translocation of food

Food materials manufactured in the leaves during photosynthesis are transported in soluble form to other parts of the plant. During the dark hours of the night, the excess starch which has been produced and which is **insoluble**, is changed back into **soluble** simple sugars. These simple sugars, dissolved in water, are now easily transported by the plant to storage areas such as underground stem tubers. In the plant cells in these storage areas, the simple sugars are then converted back into starch which, because of its large molecules, cannot escape from the cells by diffusion. The whole process is known as **translocation**, and it takes place in the **phloem** cells.

The phloem consists of different types of specialized cells. The main cells are tubular **sieve elements** joined end to end to give long sieve tubes. Each sieve element is separated from its immediate neighbours above and below by **sieve plates**, which are perforated by numerous small holes (pores). These sieve pores allow the passage of materials.

Closely linked to the side of each sieve element are one or more **companion cells**. Each contains a nucleus, endoplasmic reticulum, ribosomes and mitochondria, all of which are largely absent from the sieve element.

Experiments have been carried out to show conclusively that the phloem tissue is the site of food transport. Two of these are the ringing or barking experiment and an experiment using radioactive tracers ($^{14}_{6}C$). In the ringing experiment, when the bark is removed from the trunk of a tree it is found that sugar continues to move from the leaves to the remainder of the plant. In the tracer experiment the plant is exposed to $^{14}_{6}C$ which becomes incorporated in photosynthetic products. These products can then be detected in the phloem by cutting sections of the stem and placing them on photographic film. It has been shown that the areas where radioactivity is found correspond exactly to the phloem elements.

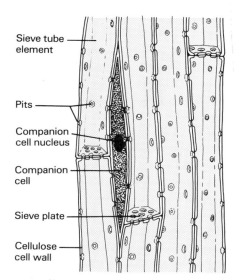

Specialized cells of the phloem

The mechanism of translocation

At present there is no complete picture of the movement of materials in the phloem. Several outstanding researchers have hypothesized about this translocation.

One of the main suggestions is that of **mass flow**, sometimes called the Munch mechanism after the scientist who initially suggested it. This mechanism suggests that because of a high turgor pressure in the leaves, caused by the high concentration of sugar, there is high osmotic pressure in the leaf cells. In the roots, on the other hand, the osmotic pressure is relatively low. These two conditions result in a pressure gradient along which materials flow.

Another suggestion which has found some following is that the movement of materials is caused by electro-osmosis. Experiments with some plants have shown that there is a potential difference across the sieve plates. It is argued that this electrical potential, small though it is, could act as a pump which pushes materials through the sieve plates.

Another well-established suggestion relates to the fine protein filaments which are evident in sieve tubes. The argument is that materials move by **cytoplasmic streaming**, the necessary energy coming from the sieve tubes or the companion cells.

There is speculation as to how these various mechanisms and phenomena actually work. Maybe the answer lies in the combination of several factors.

Questions

1 What do you think are the main objections to the mass flow hypothesis of translocation?
2 How would you attempt to find out how materials move in the phloem?

18

Circulation and the blood

Lower organisms transport body fluids in very simple ways. In unicellular organisms, fluids move in and out by simple diffusion. In small multicellular organisms, there is a simple 'pump' which is used for intake, circulation and for getting rid of unused or waste materials. Because higher organisms usually have larger bodies, they cannot rely on such inefficient ways of getting materials into the body and moving these materials from one point of the body to another. Such complex bodies need a **circulatory system** which distributes nutrients and oxygen and eliminates waste products.

The fluid that carries all body substances in humans is called **blood**. The average adult has about six litres of blood.

Composition of blood

Blood is made up of solid parts and a liquid part. The liquid is called **plasma**; and the three solid components are **red blood cells** (erythrocytes), **white blood cells** (leucocytes) and **platelets** (thrombocytes).

Plasma

Plasma is a straw-coloured fluid which is about 90% water. Plasma is important for clotting, providing immunity to various diseases, and carrying digested food and nitrogenous wastes.

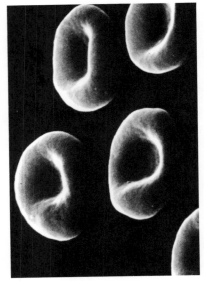

Red blood cells

Red blood cells

Red blood cells are tiny bi-concave discs containing a red pigment called **haemoglobin**. They do not have a nucleus. Oxygen is carried to the tissues and carbon dioxide is carried back from the tissues in the haemoglobin.

$$Hb + 4O_2 \rightleftharpoons HbO_8$$

Carbon dioxide is also carried by the red blood cells as carbonic acid or in combination with amino (2) groups in the haemoglobin molecule. Red blood cells are very numerous; a normal person has about 5 000 000 in 1 mm³ (cubic mm) blood. These red cells are produced in red marrow of the bones and have a life span of about 120 days. Red blood cells which no longer function are removed by the liver or the spleen.

White blood cells

Unlike red blood cells, white blood cells have a nucleus and are colourless. Some of them exhibit amoeboid movement. They are also much larger than red blood cells and there are fewer in a given volume of blood. Their main function is to defend the body against infection. White blood cells are always there when microbes invade the body, ingesting and destroying them before they cause much damage. Sometimes **pus** can be at an infected cut or scratch; this is made of the bacteria, white corpuscles and some entrapped tissue fluid.

Platelets

These floating fragments are colourless and have no definite shape. They are important mainly in the clotting of blood.

Activity

Making a blood smear

What you do

1 Using a sterile needle or pin, lightly pierce the top of your finger.
2 Allow a drop of blood to collect on a clean glass slide. Slide a second clean glass slide across the surface of the slide with the drop of blood on it. This will help to spread the blood and make it easier to examine under a microscope.
3 View the slide under the low and high powers of a microscope.
4 Draw the various types of solid components that you see, and identify them.

If you require a more permanent smear, warm the blood (after spreading it) over a flame. To stain the blood add a few drops of Wright's Stain and then rinse away any excess.

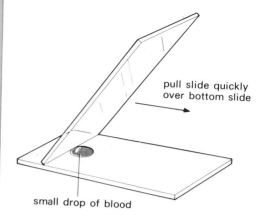

pull slide quickly over bottom slide

small drop of blood

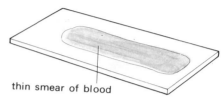

thin smear of blood

Preparing a blood smear

Circulation in the human body

In humans there are two distinct parts to the circulation—from the heart to the lungs and back to the heart (pulmonary circulation); and from the heart to the rest of the body and back to the heart (systemic circulation). This **double circulation** prevents oxygenated blood mixing with de-oxygenated blood. Organisms such as fish have **single circulation**.

The heart

The heart is a large pump which keeps the blood flowing round the body. During a normal life span the heart may beat more than $2 \cdot 0 \times 10^9$ times. With each beat blood is pumped to the various parts of the body.

The heart is made up of four 'chambers'. It is divided into two halves, left, for oxygenated blood and right, for de-oxygenated blood. Each half has an upper auricle (or atrium) and a lower ventricle. The four chambers are therefore the left auricle, the left ventricle, the right auricle and the right ventricle. Large valves are present at the partition between the right auricle and right ventricle (tricuspid valve) and the left auricle and left ventricle (bicuspid valve). The valves prevent back flow of blood, which could be dangerous.

The diagram shows how blood flows through the heart. Blood which carries little oxygen and contains a relatively high concentration of carbon dioxide enters the right auricle from the head and body via the vena cava. This de-oxygenated blood is pumped through the tricuspid valve

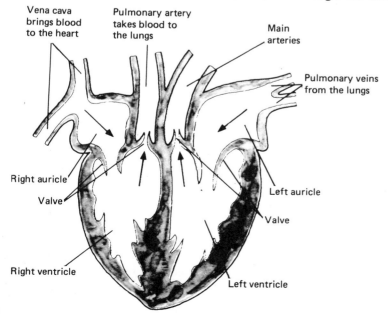

Vena cava brings blood to the heart

Pulmonary artery takes blood to the lungs

Main arteries

Pulmonary veins from the lungs

Right auricle

Valve

Right ventricle

Left auricle

Valve

Left ventricle

to the right ventricle. From the right ventricle the blood is pumped into the pulmonary artery for its journey to the lungs. In the lungs it gives up its carbon dioxide and takes a new supply of oxygen, returning to the left auricle via the pulmonary vein. The blood is then pumped through the bicuspid valve to the left ventricle and from there to the remainder of the body.

Each heart beat has two phases. During the **systole** the ventricles contract and force blood into the arteries; in the **diastole** the ventricles relax to draw in blood from the auricles.

Arteries, veins, capillaries

Arteries

Arteries, and their branches—arterioles—are the blood vessels which carry blood away from the heart to the organs of the body. They have muscular, elastic walls which are exposed to great pressure as the heart pumps blood into them. The **pulse** which you can feel at your wrist is caused by the pressure in an artery.

Veins

These have much thinner and less muscular walls than arteries because the blood is under less pressure. Veins also contain one-way valves which prevent black flow of blood as it travels from the parts of the body back to the heart.

Capillaries

Capillaries are tiny, thin-walled vessels which penetrate the tissues of the body. Materials pass through the walls to and from the tissues. The diameter of a capillary is just wide enough for one red blood cell to pass through. Whereas arteries and veins are important for *circulation* of blood, it is in the thin-walled capillaries that transfer and exchange of materials really take place.

The circulatory system

Pulmonary (lung) circulation

De-oxygenated blood is pumped from the heart to the lungs where it takes up oxygen and expels carbon dioxide. The oxygenated blood then returns to the heart so that it can be distributed to the other parts of the body.

Systemic (body) circulation

The oxygenated blood leaves the heart along the **aorta**, a large artery in the arterial system. The aorta branches and gives rise to the carotid artery (to the head), the hepatic artery (to the liver), the mesenteric artery (to the gut), the renal arteries (to the kidneys), and other arteries which carry blood to the legs and lower body.

Veins with similar names (e.g. the hepatic vein from the liver) carry de-oxygenated blood away from the various organs, eventually emptying into the **vena cava**, which carries the blood back to the heart.

Lymph and the lymphatic system

As the blood passes round the circulatory system the pressure of the blood forces fluid through the thin capillary walls to become what is called tissue fluid or **lymph**. Some of this tissue fluid does not return to the circulating blood but instead is collected into the lymph vessels. Lymph is thus blood without its solid components and fragments.

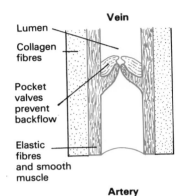

Vein

Lumen
Collagen fibres
Pocket valves prevent backflow
Elastic fibres and smooth muscle

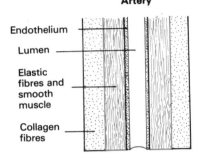

Artery

Endothelium
Lumen
Elastic fibres and smooth muscle
Collagen fibres

Section of vein and artery

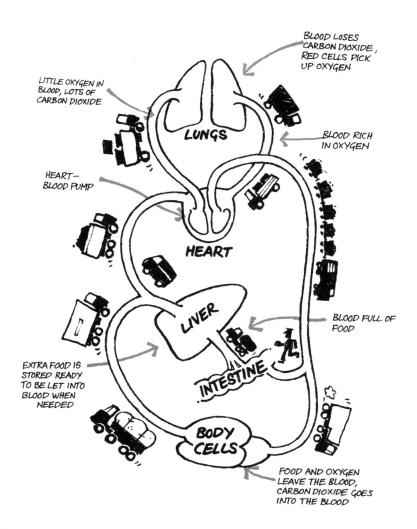

BLOOD LOSES CARBON DIOXIDE, RED CELLS PICK UP OXYGEN

LITTLE OXYGEN IN BLOOD, LOTS OF CARBON DIOXIDE

LUNGS

BLOOD RICH IN OXYGEN

HEART — BLOOD PUMP

HEART

LIVER

BLOOD FULL OF FOOD

EXTRA FOOD IS STORED READY TO BE LET INTO BLOOD WHEN NEEDED

INTESTINE

BODY CELLS

FOOD AND OXYGEN LEAVE THE BLOOD, CARBON DIOXIDE GOES INTO THE BLOOD

The circulation of blood transports oxygen, carbon dioxide and food around the body

The **lymphatic system** has tubes similar to the circulatory system. **Lymph capillaries** are small in diameter, and their walls are permeable to large molecules and microbes. These lymph capillaries empty into the larger **lymph vessels** and these in turn empty into relatively larger channels known as **lymph ducts**. Along the lymphatic system, at such points as the groin, armpit and neck, there are swellings known as **lymph nodes**. These help to produce the **lymphocytes** which help to defend the body. In times of infection the lymph nodes may swell, for example when the tonsils are swollen, or when the node in the groin enlarges. This occurs because the node is removing great numbers of the infecting organisms.

Eventually all the lymph is carried into the **thoracic duct** and the **right lymphatic duct**. The thoracic duct empties the lymph into the venous system at the junction of subclavian and jugular veins; the right lymphatic duct empties into the corresponding position on the right side.

Blood groups

From early times many attempts were made to put the blood from one individual into another. In many cases there was rapid deterioration leading to death. In 1901 Karl Lansteiner, a German, showed conclusively that the failure of this transfer of blood was due to the **antigen**–antibody reaction which takes place when different blood types are mixed. This reaction makes cells clump together, which can lead to kidney blockage.

It is now known that whether blood from two individuals can be mixed depends on antigens which are present on the surface of some red blood cells, and to antibodies present in the plasma.

As a result of antigen–antibody reaction, blood is divided into groups according to the antigens present on the red cell surface. The four main groups are called A, B, AB, and O. Group A has antigen A, group B has antigen B, group AB has antigens A and B, and group O has no antigen.

The table summarizes antigens and antibodies in each blood group.

BLOOD GROUP	ANTIGEN PRESENT	ANTIBODY PRESENT
A	A	anti-B
B	B	anti-A
AB	A and B	none
O	none	anti-A and -B

Antibody anti-A reacts with Antigen A. Antibody anti-B reacts similarly with antigen B. These reactions form clumps of cells, which in turn can lead to kidney blockage.

For blood transfer (a **transfusion**) to be a success, the donor's blood must not contain the antigen which reacts with an antibody present in the recipient's plasma.

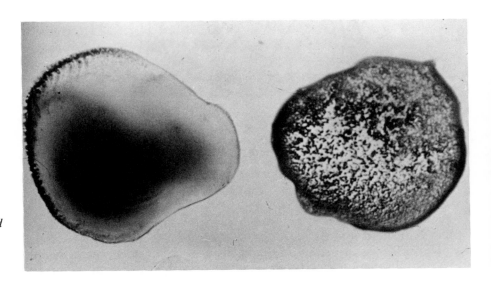

Two samples of mixed blood types examined under a microscope show good blending (compatibility) on the left and clumping (incompatibility) on the right

The Rhesus factor

As well as ABO grouping, blood is also grouped according to its reaction with the blood of the Rhesus monkey. A Rhesus positive person has antigens called Rhesus bodies on the surface of their red blood cells. A Rhesus negative person has anti-Rhesus antibodies in their plasma. Thus a complete blood type should give the group A, B, AB, or O along with whether the person is Rhesus negative ($-$) or positive ($+$). Only about 15% of most populations are Rhesus negative, however.

The Rhesus factor is also important during pregnancy since there could be complications in the pregnancy of a Rhesus negative (Rh$^-$) mother who is carrying a Rhesus positive (Rh$^+$) foetus.

During a first pregnancy the Rh$^-$ mother could become sensitized by Rhesus bodies when her Rh$^+$ baby's blood mixes with hers, across the placenta. Subsequent pregnancies with Rh$^+$ foetuses could have complications because the mother's blood 'declares war' on the blood of the foetus. When this happens the baby may be jaundiced and anaemic, and survival depends on giving a completely new set of blood by transfusion.

Death due to Rhesus incompatibility of mother and foetus was common in the not too distant past. However, modern technology has developed some ways of overcoming the problem. One is the method of complete transfusion mentioned above. Alternatively, the mother could be given an injection of antibody against the Rhesus antigen at the birth of the first Rh$^+$ baby. These antibodies would effectively destroy the antigen and subsequent foetuses would thus be free from attack.

Blood transfusions and the spread of disease

Some people regularly give some of their blood so that it may be used in transfusions. Great care needs to be taken to screen blood donors to make sure they are healthy, since disease can be passed on in the blood. Recently this caution has become even more critical as a rare and incurable disease called AIDS (Acquired Immunity Deficiency Syndrome) has been discovered. In this illness the immune system which fights microbes does not work properly, and the patient soon dies. Researchers suggest that one means of the spread of AIDS is linked to blood transfusions.

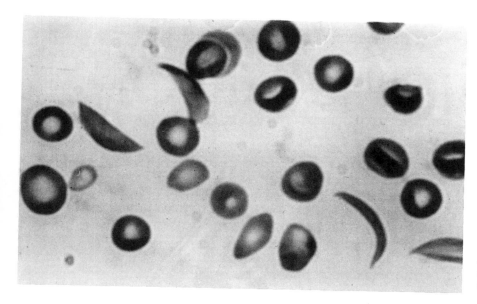

Sickle cell anaemia is an inherited disorder of the blood. Note the characteristic sickle-shaped red blood cells, the result of an abnormal type of haemoglobin which reduces their efficiency in carrying oxygen

Questions

1 In what ways is the structure of (a) arteries; (b) veins; (c) capillaries related to their blood-carrying functions?
2 Briefly outline how the structure of the mammalian heart is related to its function in double circulation.
3 Why is the left ventricle so much more muscular than the right ventricle?
4 Why do you think that the right side of the heart has a three-flapped valve, while the valve on the left side has only two flaps?
5 How would you demonstrate that blood only flows one way in blood vessels?
6 What are varicose veins? Do some research into how they are caused and how they can be treated.
7 Use the information given above to determine which blood groups are (a) universal donors; (b) universal acceptors. Give reasoned arguments for your choice.
8 What would happen if blood groups were incorrectly matched?

19

Respiration

Respiration is the process in which organic compounds are broken down to release energy. The organic compounds are usually carbohydrate but they may be protein or fat. All organisms—plants and animals—require energy to perform natural vital activities. Respiration is therefore essential.

Respiration may be of two types: **external** and **internal**. External respiration or **breathing** is the physical process in which gases are exchanged in organisms which breathe air, exchanging gases between the organs of respiration (lungs, gills) and the external environment. **Internal respiration** or cell respiration refers to the biochemical process which takes place inside living cells.

Internal respiration

Internal respiration may proceed in two ways: in the presence of air (**aerobic**) or in the absence of air (**anaerobic**). The main respiratory substance is glucose ($C_6H_{12}O_6$). The two types of internal respiration may be represented by the following equations:

Aerobic

$$\underset{\text{glucose}}{C_6H_{12}O_6} + \underset{\text{oxygen}}{6O_2} \rightarrow \underset{\substack{\text{carbon} \\ \text{dioxide}}}{6CO_2} + \underset{\text{water}}{6H_2O} + \underset{\text{energy}}{2830 \text{ kJ}}$$

Anaerobic
(in plants)

$$\underset{\text{glucose}}{C_6H_{12}O_6} \rightarrow \underset{\text{ethanol}}{2C_2H_5OH} + \underset{\substack{\text{carbon} \\ \text{dioxide}}}{2CO_2} + \underset{\text{energy}}{210 \text{ kJ}}$$

Anaerobic
(in animal muscles)

$$\underset{\text{glucose}}{C_6H_{12}O_6} \rightarrow \underset{\text{lactic acid}}{2CH_3CHOHCOOH} + \underset{\text{energy}}{150 \text{ kJ}}$$

These equations over-simplify the process of respiration since there are several enzyme–controlled reactions involved in the formation of the products. The equations, however, help to focus on the essentials of the process.

Most animals and plants perform aerobic respiration. However, some organisms, e.g. certain bacteria, parasites (tapeworms) and plants (yeast) can carry out anaerobic respiration alone.

Energy and respiration

It has been found that about 60% of the energy released in respiration is in the form of heat (see Experiment A below). The other 40% is chemical energy in the form of a compound rich in high energy bonds. This compound is called adenosine triphosphate (ATP). ATP can be moved around the body, releasing its energy for various body activities.

ATP consists of an organic molecule, adenosine, attached to three phosphate groups:

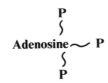

The breaking of one of the energy-rich bonds results in the release of approximately 34 kJ energy. The resultant compound, adenosine diphosphate, and the phosphate can again be synthesized into ATP but this requires energy.

$$ATP \rightleftharpoons ADP + P + energy$$

This reaction also takes place during photosynthesis in green plants.

ATP is the chemical compound in which energy is stored in the body for subsequent use. It is derived from the oxidation (burning) of food substances. Different food substances have different energy values. Various experiments have shown that one gram of carbohydrate yields 16 kJ energy; 1 g fat yields 37 kJ and 1 g protein yields 17 kJ. It is interesting to note that alcohol yields about 29·5 kJ energy for each gram burnt in respiration. (See Section 13.)

Experiment A: To show that respiration produces heat

What you need
2 vacuum flasks, some peas, cotton wool, 2 thermometers, 10% formalin.

What you do
1 Divide the peas into two sets. Soak set A in water for 24 hours; boil set B for about 7 or 8 minutes and then soak them in 10% formalin.
2 Place one set of seeds in each vacuum flask and insert the thermometers in the mouths of the flasks, as shown. Use the cotton wool to plug the mouth of the flask.
3 Observe what happens and report and explain your findings.

Questions

(a) Why was it necessary to (i) boil some of the seeds; (ii) soak them in 10% formalin?
(b) What was the purpose of the cotton wool?

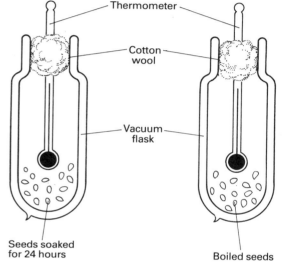

Experiment A

Experiment B: To show anaerobic respiration in yeast

What you need
10% glucose solution, cotton wool, flask, lime water, 2 g yeast, glass tube.

What you do
1 Put the yeast into the glucose solution in the flask. Insert the glass tube through the cotton wool stopper, as shown in the diagram.
2 Dip the free end of the glass tube into the lime water.
3 Observe and record what happens and explain your findings.

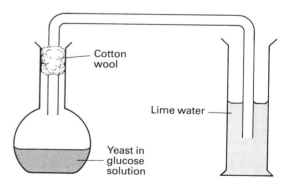

Experiment B

Questions

1 In the light of the evidence given which food would you consider the best for storage in a body?
2 Would you suggest alcohol as a main source of energy?
3 Compare and contrast respiration and photosynthesis.

20

Air and breathing

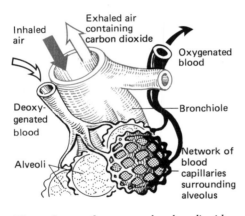

Parts of the human respiratory system

The labels on the diagram read:
- Nasal cavity
- Epiglottis
- Larynx
- Trachea
- Right bronchus
- Bronchioles
- Heart
- Rib
- Intercostal muscle
- Diaphragm

The exchange of oxygen and carbon dioxide takes places between the air in the alveoli and the blood in the surrounding capillaries

The labels on the diagram read:
- Inhaled air
- Exhaled air containing carbon dioxide
- Oxygenated blood
- Deoxygenated blood
- Bronchiole
- Network of blood capillaries surrounding alveolus
- Alveoli

The mechanism of breathing

In Section 19 you discovered that the exchange of gases that takes place during breathing (or ventilation) is known as external respiration.

In mammals, air is taken in through the nose, which consists of two nostrils. From the nostrils the air travels along the nasal passages, through the pharynx and down the windpipe or **trachea**. The trachea is covered at the upper end by a cartilaginous flap called the **epiglottis**. When swallowing is taking place this flap closes to prevent food from going into the lungs, or as is commonly expressed, 'food going the wrong way'. The voice box (larynx) and vocal cords are situated at the upper end of the trachea.

At its lower end the trachea divides into two, forming the **bronchi** (sing. bronchus). One bronchus enters each lung, branching profusely to form **bronchial tubes**, and eventually even finer tubes called **bronchioles**. At the end of the bronchioles are the tiny air sacs called **alveoli** (sing. alveolus). Alveoli have very thin walls to facilitate the passage of gases to and from the capillaries which surround them.

Breathing is controlled by the respiratory control centre at the base of the brain. When air is inhaled (inhalation) the chest bulges because (a) the muscles between the ribs (the intercostal muscles) contract; (b) the muscular diaphragm contracts and moves down; (c) abdominal muscles relax. These movements result in the chest cavity becoming larger. Since the air pressure in the chest cavity then becomes lower than that of the atmosphere outside, air rushes in. In expiration (exhalation) of air the three movements listed above are reversed, i.e. the rib muscles relax, the diaphragm also relaxes and the muscles of the abdomen contract. As a result the size of the chest cavity decreases, and air is squeezed out from the lungs. Look at the diagrams on the opposite page.

Inhalation and exhalation may be demonstrated by using the apparatus in the diagram below. The apparatus is simple: you need a bell jar, two balloons, a forked piece of glass tubing, and a rubber sheet. As you pull the rubber sheet downwards the pressure inside the bell jar decreases, and air rushes in to inflate the balloons.

This simple model demonstrates the respiratory movements. Perhaps you could study carefully what happens when you inhale and exhale and note the various changes in the size of the chest cavity.

Inhaled and exhaled air

When air is inhaled the proportions of various gases present is the same as that in the external atmosphere from which it came. Exhaled air, however, has altered proportions of oxygen, carbon dioxide and water vapour.

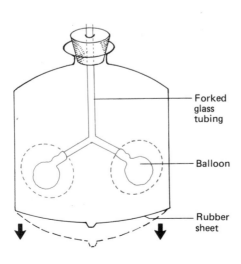

A simple apparatus to demonstrate the mechanism of breathing

The labels on the diagram read:
- Forked glass tubing
- Balloon
- Rubber sheet

Proportions of gases in inhaled air		Proportions of gases in exhaled air	
Oxygen	20%	Oxygen	16%
Nitrogen	79%	Nitrogen	79%
Carbon dioxide	0·03%	Carbon dioxide	4·03% (approx.)
Other gases (inert)	0·97%	Other gases (inert)	0·97%
Water vapour	variable	Water vapour	saturated

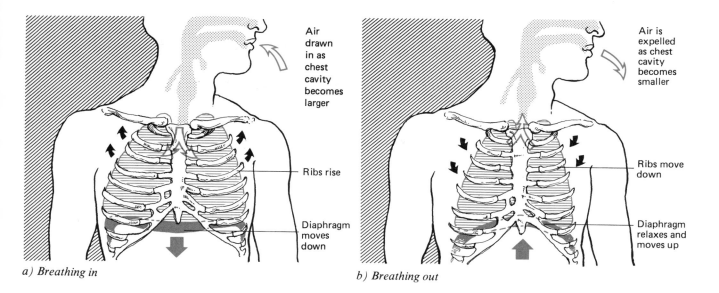

a) Breathing in   b) Breathing out

It is interesting to note that not all the oxygen in a given volume of air is extracted by the body.

Experiment: To show that green plants give off carbon dioxide in respiration

What you need
Bell jar, black cloth, lime water, potted plant, 2 conical flasks, filter pump, vaseline, glass tubes.

What you do
1 Set up the apparatus as shown in the diagram below and leave it for a few hours.
2 Observe what happens in the lime water in flask 2.
3 Report and explain your findings.

Questions

(a) What is the function of (i) the vaseline; (ii) the lime water in flask 1?
(b) Why is a black cloth used to cover the potted plant in the bell jar?
(c) Is there any way in which you could modify or add to the apparatus shown to make your observations more conclusive?

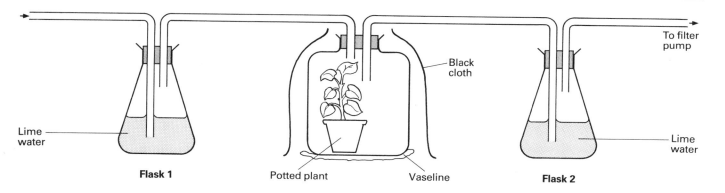

Lime water — Flask 1 — Potted plant — Vaseline — Black cloth — Flask 2 — To filter pump — Lime water

Questions

1 What do you think are some of the factors which can alter the percentage of oxygen and carbon dioxide in the atmosphere?
2 Why do mountain climbers require special air tanks?
3 Under what conditions would nitrogen dissolve in human blood? What would be the effects of this on the body?
4 Design an experiment to show that carbon dioxide is given off in respiration in a small mammal.

21

Excretion

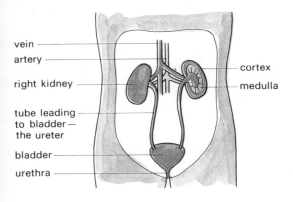

vein
artery
right kidney
tube leading to bladder — the ureter
bladder
urethra
cortex
medulla

The kidneys and associated organs of excretion

Excretion is the process by which organisms get rid of metabolic wastes from their bodies. Some of the wastes come from protein metabolism and are called **nitrogenous wastes**. If these wastes were allowed to remain in the body they could lead to a malfunction of the animal's metabolism, and eventually to death.

Sometimes the term 'excretion' is used interchangeably with **elimination** or **egestion**. However, the two processes are very different and should not be confused.

In heterotrophic animals (animals which cannot synthesize organic materials from inorganic compounds, e.g. man), nutrition consists of several processes (see Section 11). First of all, complex food must be taken in through the mouth; a process called **ingestion**. This is followed by **digestion**, in which the complex food is broken down into simpler, soluble forms. The digested food is then absorbed into the body (**absorption**) where it undergoes **assimilation**—the nutrients are used by the body—or it is expelled as waste material. The expulsion of this waste material is properly called **excretion**.

Sometimes food that is ingested cannot be digested. Such indigestible material is eliminated in the process of **egestion**. The removal of faeces from the body is egestion or elimination, while the main excretory product in man is a nitrogenous substance called urea (urine).

Organs of excretion in mammals

The kidneys

These two bean-shaped organs, situated in the lower back on either side of the spine, are usually the size of a clenched fist.

Each kidney is made up of an outer layer called the **cortex**. The inner layer, called the **medulla**, is filled with projections known as pyramids. These pyramids point into the cavity of the kidney, which is known as the **pelvis**. The pelvis leads into a long, narrow channel or tube called the **ureter**, which itself empties into the **urinary bladder**.

Waste materials are filtered out of the blood as it passes through the kidneys. Filtration of the blood occurs in minute structures called **nephrons**. Each nephron consists of a funnel-shaped top, called the **Bowman's capsule** with a narrow tube leading from it. Inside the cup of the Bowman's capsule is a knot of capillaries—the **glomerulus**.

Blood is forced through the capillary walls of the glomerulus into the Bowman's capsule. The walls through which it passes are selectively permeable, allowing only molecules below a certain size to pass through. The filtrate in the Bowman's capsule usually contains useful materials which are selectively re-absorbed by the cells lining the tubule. Water is also re-absorbed into the blood vessels coiled around the nephrons, so that the body does not become dehydrated due to excessive water loss. Research has shown that about 99% of the fluid that passes through the nephron system is re-absorbed. The remainder passes eventually into the pelvis of the kidney and is removed as **urine**. Urine passes into the bladder via the **ureter**. It may be stored there until it passes through the **urethra** to the outside.

The kidney is known as an **osmoregulatory organ** because it controls the amount of water present in the body.

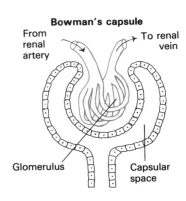

Nephron

Bowman's capsule
Collecting duct
Capillary
Loop of Henlé

Bowman's capsule
From renal artery
To renal vein
Glomerulus
Capsular space

The skin

The skin excretes water, salts, and in some cases urea. The watery solution exuded from the skin is called **sweat** or **perspiration**. Apart from its excretory function, sweating is also the main means of keeping the body temperature constant. A similar temperature regulating role has already been identified in the case of transpiration in the leaves of plants (p. 54).

The skin is composed of two distinct regions: the outer **epidermis** and the inner **dermis**. The epidermis is itself made up of three layers: the **horny layer** on the outside, the **middle layer**, and the **Malpighian layer**. The horny layer is very thick on the soles and the palms. The innermost Malpighian layer consists of actively dividing cells and is the layer in which the pigment **melanin**, which gives the skin its colour, is found. The **dermis** has several structures embedded in it. These include sebaceous glands, sweat glands, hair follicles, blood and lymph vessels, nerve endings and muscles.

Sebaceous glands secrete a fatty substance called *sebum* which acts as a lubricant and germicide. Each gland is closely associated with a **hair follicle**. The **hair papilla** at the base of the follicle provides growth and pigment. The muscular attachment (**erector muscle**) between the papilla and the epidermis can cause a hair to 'stand upright', giving rise to 'goose pimples', especially in times of extreme cold or intense fear.

The **sweat glands** are ducts which produce sweat when stimulated. Each gland is richly supplied with blood capillaries. When the body is hot the blood vessels in the skin dilate, bringing more blood to the surface where it can lose heat. The sweat glands produce watery sweat (99% water) which exudes onto the surface of the skin. As the fluid evaporates it takes heat from the skin and hence lowers the body temperature.

The skin also has the following functions: it provides protection from the external environment; permits storage of fats (in this layer vitamin D is synthesized in the presence of sunlight).

Questions

1 What happens to the blood vessels in the skin when the body is exposed to cold conditions?
2 How does the exudation of sweat help to lower body temperature?
3 What is the function of melanin in the skin?

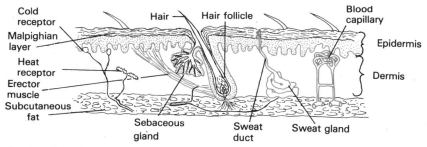

Section of the skin

The lungs

When looking at respiration (p. 64) it was established that the lungs get rid of carbon dioxide and water. In this respect the lungs are organs of excretion because they rid the body of products of metabolism.

Flowering plants and their methods of excretion

For a variety of reasons, excretion in green plants does not pose as many problems as excretion in animals.

In the first instance the metabolic processes in plants which produce wastes are slower than those in animals. Besides, many of the waste products are used in anabolic processes (building up processes). Water and carbon dioxide produced by respiration can be used during photosynthesis. Nitrogenous compounds can be used in the production of proteins. In addition the metabolic by-products of plants are not as poisonous as those in animals. They may be stored in the plant without much deleterious effect. Certain plants store their wastes as gums, as resins, e.g. *Acacia spp.* (gum-arabic), or as dyes in various cells of the plant, e.g. logwood.

22

Heat transfer

Heat transfer takes place in all three states of matter: gases, liquids and solids. Heat is transferred from the material where molecules are vibrating more rapidly to that where molecules are relatively slower in movement. Effective heat transfer is very important in the proper functioning of organisms. Heat may be transferred by one or more of the following methods.

Conduction

In the process of conduction energy is passed from more rapidly moving molecules to relatively slower moving ones by **collision**. This mode of transference is more important in the solid state than in the other two states.

> ### Activity
> **To demonstrate the conduction of heat**
>
> Dip pieces of different metals, e.g. copper and iron, into a saucepan containing boiling water, while holding the other end in your hand. Which piece of metal feels hotter? Why?

While all materials transmit some heat by conduction, some are better conductors than others. Those which conduct little heat are called **insulators**, e.g. cotton wool, woollens, and are used for clothing in cold climates. These insulators function by reducing the flow of heat from the body to the air outside. The hairs on the skin may also function as heat insulators.

Some examples of common insulators: cotton wool, sheep's wool and animal fur

Convection

When fluids are heated the molecules gain energy. As they gain energy they spread out and take up more space, so the fluid becomes less dense. This makes the hot fluid rise above the colder fluid, which moves in to take its place. Thus a **convection current** is set up. Convection cannot occur in solids. The control of mammalian body temperature by contraction and dilation of blood vessels in the skin uses the process of convection. A properly ventilated room has windows open at both top and bottom. This allows hot air to escape above and cooler air to rush in at the bottom.

Radiation

Radiation is the transfer of heat by an electromagnetic wave. This type of transfer does not require molecules as in the cases of conduction and convection. Radiation can travel through a vacuum (at the same speed as light); it causes a heating effect when it is absorbed; and it is reflected by shiny surfaces. Radiation plays a very important role in the efficient functioning of solar energy water heaters, ovens, driers, etc. The Sun heats the Earth's atmosphere by radiation.

Evaporation

Evaporation is the change of a liquid into vapour at the surface of the liquid. Unlike boiling, it takes place at any temperature. As already men-

Evaporation of sweat from the skin produces a cooling effect

tioned in relation to the effect of sweating in mammals (Section 21), evaporation causes cooling.

In order to bring about the change of state from liquid to vapour, the molecules in the liquid require extra energy. They obtain this from the heat of their surroundings. The result is that the surroundings become cooler.

Experiment: To investigate the effect of evaporation

1 Put some methylated spirits on the back of your hand. What happens?
2 Put some water on the back of your hand. Is there any difference between this effect and the effect of methylated spirits?

Question
Briefly explain the difference, if any, between the effect of water and the effect of methylated spirits on the back of the hand.

Heat regulation in animals

Animals may be classified into two groups according to how they regulate heat transfer in their bodies. Many animals have no constant body temperature. Instead they take the temperature of the environment. Such animals are called **poikilothermic** or cold-blooded, e.g. fish, reptiles, amphibians. Birds and mammals, however, maintain a constant body temperature even when environmental changes occur. These animals are called **homoiothermic** or warm-blooded.

Large mammals have a very small surface area/volume ratio, while small ones have a relatively high surface/volume ratio. Therefore the heat loss and heat conservation, respectively, are major considerations. The small mammals (and birds) use their metabolic rates to produce heat and so balance its loss. Large mammals use their blood supply, sweat glands, and ability to reduce hair cover to facilitate heat loss. The main structure involved in heat regulation is the skin.

Activity

To discover the nature of the sun's rays
1 Hold a magnifying glass or hand lens in the sunlight so that the Sun's rays are focused to a fine point on a piece of tissue paper.
2 Observe what happens and report your findings.

Question
How could mirrors and lenses be used to harness solar energy?

The vacuum flask

The vacuum flask is a common container used to keep things either cold or hot. Heat transmission to and from the contents of the flask is minimized so that little heat is lost or gained. The heat transmission is reduced in three ways.

(a) The flask consists of a double-walled bottle inside a protective case. A vacuum is created between the glass walls, thus preventing conduction and convection of heat.
(b) The inner walls of the vacuum bottle are silvered to prevent heat transmission by radiation.
(c) The top of the flask is fitted with a stopper of insulating material, e.g. cork or plastic.

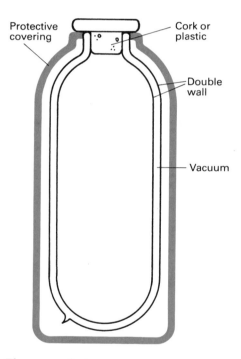

The vacuum flask

Questions

1 Why do you think conduction is more important in solids?
2 What role does convection play in rainfall in your territory?
3 Briefly explain why cricket is usually played in light-coloured clothes. What would be the effect if everyone on the field wore black?

23 Nervous and endocrine systems

Nervous systems

The nervous system coordinates the movement of our bodies, and informs us about the environment. The two main parts of the nervous system—the central nervous system and the peripheral nervous system—are discussed in Section 70. This section introduces a third part of the system—the **autonomic nervous system**—which regulates the body's involuntary activities. This system is entirely automatic.

The autonomic nervous system is composed of two portions—the **sympathetic** and the **para-sympathetic** systems. In both of these, nerve fibres emerge from the brain or spinal cord and pass to the appropriate organs. In the sympathetic system cords are found on either side of the spinal column. On each cord cell bodies of neurons called **ganglia** lie close to the vertebrae. The main ganglion just below the diaphragm is the **solar plexus**. Branches radiate from the ganglia to areas such as the heart, neck, and lower abdomen. The sympathetic nervous system controls the action of the heart, the smooth muscles of the stomach and intestines and the secretion of endocrine glands.

The para-sympathetic nervous system serves to oppose the action of the sympathetic. Its main nerve is the **vagus nerve** which extends from the base of the brain down to the chest and abdomen via the neck. The ganglia of this system are close to the organ concerned. The para-sympathetic system slows heart beat, dilates arteries, causes flow of saliva, stimulates production of tears. Each of these actions opposes an action of the sympathetic nervous system.

Endocrine system

Endocrine glands have no ducts, i.e. they *pour their secretions directly into the blood stream*. The network of such glands in the human body facilitates chemical coordination. There is a great deal of interaction among all the glands which together form the **endocrine system**.

The secretions of the ductless glands are called **hormones**, and they regulate the body processes. Some of the hormones produced in the body are **thyroxine** (in the thyroid gland); **parathyroid hormone** (in the parathyroid glands); **adrenalin** (in the adrenal glands); **insulin** (in the pancreas); **progesterone** and **oestrogen** (in the ovaries); and **testosterone** (in the testes).

The thyroid gland is situated in the region of the neck. It consists of two lobes, one on each side of the trachea. The thyroxine it produces has a high concentration of iodine, and regulates metabolic activities related to growth and oxidation. The thyroid gland may be overactive (hyperthyroidism), which causes an increased heart rate, nervousness and irritable behaviour. There is usually a symptomatic bulging of the eyes. The main treatment of this condition is surgery, in which a part of the gland is removed. However, drugs and doses of radioactive iodine have been recently used.

The gland may also be underactive (hypothyroidism), in which case the symptoms are reduced heart rate and arrested physical and mental development. Malfunction of the thyroid gland from infancy leads to stunted growth and physical and mental retardation, a condition known as **cretinism**.

If iodine is deficient in the diet the thyroid gland enlarges to form a **goitre**. This condition could be alleviated simply by administering iodine. However, if a person consumes sufficient iodine in their diet (mainly from sea foods) they are not likely to develop a goitre.

The four **parathyroid glands** are embedded in the back of the thyroid gland. They secrete parathyroid hormone which controls the use of calcium in the body.

The **pituitary gland** is located at the base of the brain. The secretions of the gland affect the activity of many other glands in the body, and the gland itself seems to be affected by some of them. The so-called 'master gland' consists of anterior and posterior lobes, each having distinct secretions. The table that follows lists the various secretions of the pituitary gland and their functions.

Secretions of the pituitary gland

LOBE	HORMONE	FUNCTION
Anterior	Somatotropic hormone	Controls growth of skeleton
	Gonadotropic hormone	Controls development of reproductive organs
	Lactogenic hormone	Stimulates mammary glands to produce milk
	Thyrotropic hormone	Stimulates thyroid gland
	Adrenocorticotropic hormone	Stimulates adrenal cortex
Posterior	Oxytocin	Regulates blood pressure and stimulates smooth muscles
	Vasopressin or antidiuretic hormone	Controls water reabsorption in kidney. Deficiency causes *diabetes insipidus*

A malfunctioning pituitary gland could lead to several conditions. If the gland secretes too much growth hormone (somatotropic hormone) the person grows too fast and becomes a giant. If the growth hormone is undersecreted then the person may become a dwarf. The dwarf differs from the cretin in that, although growth is retarded, the body and head are well proportioned, and the brain functions normally.

The **adrenal glands** are situated on top of each kidney. The glands consist of an outer layer (the **cortex**) and an inner layer (the **medulla**). the cortex secretes complex hormones called **corticoids** which regulate the phases of carbohydrate, fat and protein metabolism. Damage to the cortex could lead to Addison's disease, the symptoms of which are feelings of tiredness and nausea and weight loss. Addison's disease may be treated with cortisone. The medulla secretes **adrenaline** or epinephrine, the so-called 'fright and flight' hormone. In times of fright adrenaline (a) affects the blood circulation—the heart beat and blood flow are increased, and the blood vessels dilated; (b) increases the conversion of glycogen stored in the liver to blood sugar. The result is that the person can run faster, jump higher and further, and generally achieve feats impossible under normal conditions.

The **pancreas** contains a special group of cells called **islets of Langerhans** which secrete the hormone **insulin**. Insulin is important because it stimulates the conversion of glucose into glycogen, which is then stored in the liver. Insulin deficiency can be detected by the presence of glucose in the urine, a condition known as **diabetes mellitus**. Although incurable at present, it may be controlled by daily injections of insulin. If too much insulin is produced by the pancreas the person suffers a low blood sugar level—a condition called **hypoglycemia** which is characterized by tiredness and 'black-outs'.

The **reproductive organs** (ovaries in the female and testes in the male) are important producers of hormones. The ovary produces **oestrogen** and **progesterone**. Oestrogen controls the development of the pubic hair, the mammary glands (breasts), the menstrual cycle and the secondary sexual characteristics such as the typical soft voice and body.

Testosterone, produced by the testes, controls the development of secondary sexual features, facial hair, pubic hair, and the typical deep male voice. It is also responsible for normal sex drives in males.

There are a few other important ductless secretions besides those listed above: in the stomach the hormone **gastrin** stimulates the secretion of gastric juice; in the intestine the hormone **secretin** stimulates the production of pancreatic juice; and in the duodenum **cholecystokinin** stimulates the production of bile.

Other hormones, acting through the autonomic nervous system, cause various behaviour changes. Female reproductive hormones are believed to be responsible for pre-menstrual tension, depression and general lassitude. Mental alertness may be decreased and there may be less interest in work. Individuals have even been known to commit crimes of petty larceny, or to beat their children seriously during such periods of emotional stress, which are thought to result from the sharp decrease in the level of both progesterone and oestrogens just before menstruation. Cases of 'post-partum blues', in which women become severely depressed immediately following the birth of a child, are also believed to result from the increased levels of reproductive hormones circulating in the body.

A simple reflex action

A reflex action is a fixed response to a stimulus. If a particular stimulus causes the same response over and over again, the action eventually becomes automatic. Examples of reflex actions are the secretion of saliva when food is eaten; the appearance of goose pimples when the body is exposed to cold conditions; the knee jerk. Reflexes may also be **conditioned** (as shown by the work of Ivan Pavlov).

Question
Why is adrenaline called the fright, flight, or fight hormone?

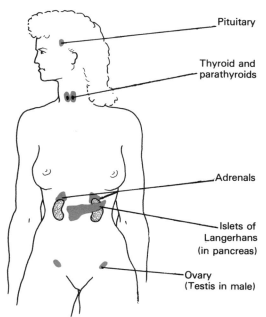

Pituitary

Thyroid and parathyroids

Adrenals

Islets of Langerhans (in pancreas)

Ovary (Testis in male)

The position of the endocrine glands in humans

24

Parasitic diseases

A **parasite** is an organism that lives and feeds on another living organism. The **host** organism usually suffers from the infestation. Parasites may live on the surface of the host (**ectoparasites**) or they may live inside the host (**endoparasites**). An example of an ectoparasite of man is the louse (head and pubic); an endoparasite is the tapeworm.

Parasites are also classified as **obligate** or **facultative**. An obligate parasite cannot exist without living hosts, i.e. when the host dies they also cease to function. Facultative parasites, on the whole can and do exist on their own, but when conditions are favourable they parasitize.

Lice

There are three varieties of lice that are parasitic on man: head lice, body lice, and pubic lice (crabs).

The head louse lays a set of 8–12 eggs a day on the hair of a person. These eggs are very firmly attached to the hair so that removal is difficult. After 6–8 days the eggs hatch into young nymphs. These young lice resemble the adults but are not yet sexually mature. (Lice exhibit **incomplete metamorphosis**.) After about 20 days, in which they moult three times, the lice are full-grown adults. The female then lays eggs and the cycle is repeated. Adult lice use the claw and hook on their legs to attach themselves to a hair. In this position they suck blood from the host, causing an itching irritation at the point where their mouthparts pierce the scalp.

Lice breed very fast, preferring clean conditions. Infestations begin on contact with an infected person, e.g. wearing their clothes, using their comb, or simply by touching heads.

Lice are also vectors of diseases such as epidemic typhus and relapsing fever. Infection occurs at the point at which the lice bite the skin, since the microbes are carried from person to person on the parasite's mouthparts.

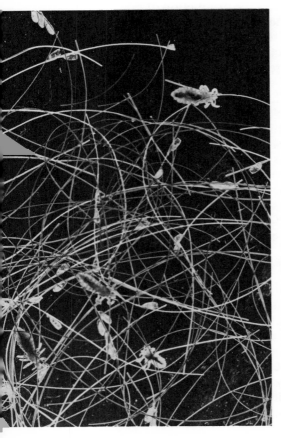
Head lice and eggs on human hair snippings

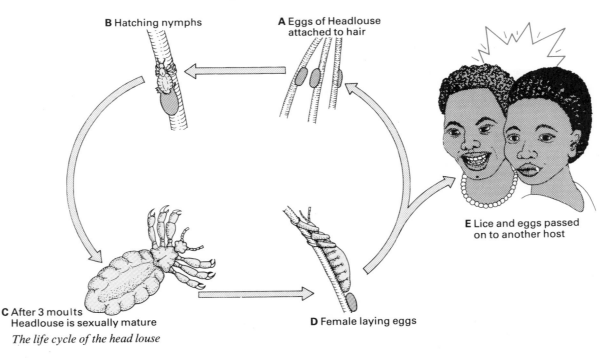

B Hatching nymphs
A Eggs of Headlouse attached to hair
E Lice and eggs passed on to another host
C After 3 moults Headlouse is sexually mature
D Female laying eggs

The life cycle of the head louse

Egg case deposited
on ground in
faeces

The life cycle of the tapeworm

Pig eats egg case.
Eggs hatch into
embryos which form
cysts in the pig's
muscle cells

Cysts in undercooked
meat eaten by person.
Young tapeworm
attaches its head to
the intestine

Tapeworms (*Taenia sp.*)

The tape-like body of a tapeworm is made up of flat, long segments, known as **proglottides** (sing. proglottis), joined end to end. Each tapeworm may be composed of hundreds of segments.

The pork tapeworm (*Taenia solium*) requires two hosts (man and pig) to complete its life cycle. The adult tapeworm grows in the intestine of humans. Each segment of the parasite is hermaphrodite (having male and female organs), and each absorbs nourishment from the intestine. New proglottides are added at the neck of the worm, a region situated behind the 'head'. Hooks and suckers on the 'head' attach the animal to the inside of the intestine.

The mature segments at the 'tail' end contain fertilized eggs which develop into embryos. These segments become detached and are passed out in faeces. Feeding pigs may ingest the segment, dissolving the shell with its digestive juices. The embryo then burrows into the intestine of the pig, passes into the blood stream, and is transported by the blood to the muscles where it forms a cyst. The parasite may be passed to man if infected pork is eaten raw or not properly cooked. The worm attaches itself to the human's intestine and the cycle continues.

Question

What precautions would you take to avoid infestations by ecto- and endoparasites?

Activity

Do some research into
(a) other types of tapeworms;
(b) ways in which tapeworm infection could be treated.

Prevention and cure of tapeworm

(a) Examine pork and beef before consumption.
(b) Cook pork and beef thoroughly to kill cysts.
(c) Improve sanitation when rearing pigs and cattle
(d) Medicines, made from ferns, are available. They expel the head from the gut.

Prevention and cure of lice

(a) Practise good personal hygiene.
(b) Keep brushes and combs clean.
(c) Soak hair in medicated solutions if affected.
(d) Comb out nits.

25

Pests and pesticides

Cockroaches, flies, rats and mosquitoes are household pests that present great problems to man. Generally speaking they are encouraged if houses are kept dirty, and food scraps are left lying about (this is especially true for cockroaches and rats). Flies thrive best near warm decaying organic matter like garbage heaps and manure piles. Mosquitoes breed in stagnant water, especially old cups, car tyres, tins and vases which lie outside for long periods and collect water.

By far the best method of controlling these pests is to prevent them from breeding. The eradication of their breeding places should be an individual and community responsibility, since we all suffer eventually from the ravages of these pests. If we fail to control the pests by removing their breeding places then other methods of control must be employed.

Rats

The rat can be controlled by using poisons which are either mixed with food or closely resemble the foods they like. Traps may also be used. Recently some governments have been exploring the possibility of controlling them with owls, and cats may also be used. This practice, in which one organism is used to control another, is called **biological control**. Great care needs to be exercised in studying and choosing the organisms which are to control others lest they themselves become pests.

If the rat is allowed to multiply unimpeded it will cause great damage to human life. The rat carries the causative organisms of such dreaded diseases as the plague, leptospirosis, tick typhus, and rat-bite fever. Care should always be taken that rat faeces and urine never come into contact with humans' food and drinking water. The faeces may contain the organisms responsible for some of the above diseases, which would then infect whoever consumed the food.

Houseflies

The housefly breeds in faeces or on rotting organic matter. The adult female lays batches of about 150 eggs which hatch in 7–14 days, depending on environmental factors such as temperature. In hotter climates hatching is more rapid. The whitish, wriggling, rapid-feeding larva which emerges from the egg is usually called a maggot. These larvae always seem to move away from light so they may not easily be detected while they continue to grow and develop. After about 8 days the larva forms a pupa, enclosed in a brown case, which is the resting stage of the housefly. In about 5–6 days the pupa has developed into a fully-formed adult fly. During the 4-week life span the female lays and hatches her eggs. The fly thus reproduces rapidly, but the spread of flies may be curtailed or eradicated by either destroying their breeding places, or by using insecticides.

Although no pathogen seems to use the housefly as host for a phase of its life cycle, the fly is a mechanical vector of diseases such as cholera, typhoid, dysentery and tuberculosis. Flies spread disease due to their indiscriminate feeding habits. When the fly feeds on faeces and refuse heaps, particles of this matter may be attached to the insect's hairy legs and body. If by chance the fly then visits our food the portions of faeces and decaying matter may be deposited there. They also tend to 'vomit' liquid onto their food in order to make it fluid, and hence easier to take in. They may thus mix particles of their last meal with their next.

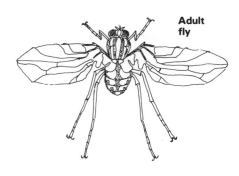

Egg

Maggot

Pupa

Adult fly

Stages in the life cycle of the housefly

Mosquitoes

Mosquitoes may be of two types: culicine (*Culex* and *Aedes*) or anopheline (*Anopheles*).

Like the housefly, the mosquito has a complete metamorphosis (i.e. it passes through the four stages of egg, larva, pupa and adult). The eggs, which are laid in stagnant water, hatch into wriggling larvae after 6–7 days. The larvae can be seen 'hanging' at the surface of the water, breathing through their respiratory tubes. During this stage they feed voraciously on microscopic organisms in the water. After a few moults, the larvae grow into pupae. The pupal stage is a relatively quiet period from which the adult emerges after a few days.

The feeding habits of the female mosquito are responsible for spreading disease. The females suck blood using their piercing mouth parts. To prevent the blood clotting they inject a fluid into their victim's bloodstream, thus facilitating the flow. In this way germs may be passed from an infected person to those as yet unaffected, and so spread the infection.

The *Aedes* mosquito spreads yellow fever and dengue; *Culex* spreads filiarsis and encephalitis; *Anopheles* spreads malaria. All these diseases are very dangerous to man since even when they do not kill they are capable of doing lasting damage to the body.

Cockroaches

The cockroach is a pest which does great damage to books and clothing. Its mouth parts, which are well adapted for biting and chewing, make it extremely destructive. The insect has incomplete metamorphosis. The eggs are laid in shiny brown cases in covered, dark areas. These brown cases eventually break open to release a nymph, which grows into an adult without the pupal stage.

Cockroaches are usually encouraged by untidy, overcrowded surroundings where scraps of food and paper are abundant. Although there is no known pathogen to which the cockroach is primary or secondary host, it is strongly felt that the insect is a mechanical vector of disease, carrying bacteria and germs on its legs and body.

The best method of controlling the cockroach involves preventing its breeding by destroying favourable conditions. It may also be controlled by spraying insecticides into the cracks and crevices, and under the ledges where the animal hides and lays its eggs.

Pesticides

Pesticides are widely used in the control of insect pests. However, they are also harmful to other animals because they can upset the ecosystem. Not only do they destroy the pests, they remove the food supply from the animals which prey on the pests, and they may also cause harm to humans. Some pests build up a resistance to the most widely used pesticides, and evolve strains that are unaffected by their use.

Pesticides may also interfere with the nitrogen and carbon cycles (see Section 77), so that the valuable means of recycling these elements are destroyed. Herbicides may also cause great harm to the ecosystem.

In the Caribbean area far too many very poisonous pesticides are still being used. In developed countries it was found that the disappearance and extinction of some birds and other wildlife coincided with the heavy use of certain insecticides, e.g. DDT. Although many of these dangerous chemicals have been removed from the consumer market, several still remain, and many banned pesticides are 'dumped' in the Caribbean.

The danger posed by pesticides has triggered a search for safer yet equally effective ways of controlling the pests.

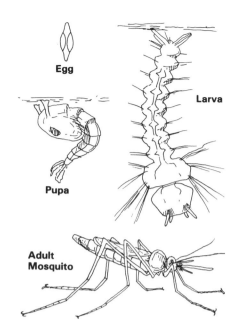

Stages in the life cycle of the mosquito

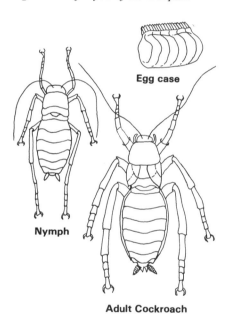

Stages in the life cycle of the cockroach

Questions

1 Bearing in mind the life cycle of the mosquito, where it lives and how it feeds, can you suggest methods that are likely to control it?

2 How effective do you think a programme of biological control against mosquitoes would be? What are some of the precautions that you need to take before implementing such a programme?

3 How effective in controlling mosquitoes are the 'coils' and 'mats' which we burn in our homes?

26

Microorganisms

*Unicellular algae (**Volvox**) × 100*

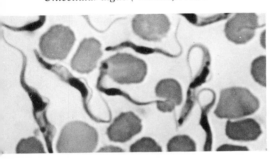

Protozoa in blood (sleeping sickness) × 1750

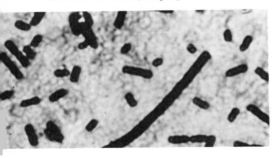

Bacteria (typhoid) × 2000

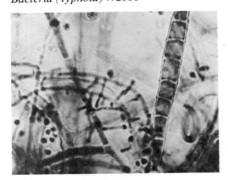

*Fungus (**Tinea**) × 1000*
Virus (hepatitis) × 130,000

'Microorganisms' is the term used to describe the minute, relatively simple organisms which cannot usually be seen with the naked eye. The following are included in this group: unicellular algae (e.g. *Chlamydomonas*); protozoa (e.g. *Amoeba*); bacteria (e.g. *Streptococcus*); fungi (e.g. Tinea); and viruses (e.g. Herpes).

Scientists classify some of these microorganisms as plants and some as animals, depending on the features that are most prominent. Some microorganisms defy such classification and are placed in a third kingdom, the **Protista**. Most microorganisms have common characteristics:

(a) they grow rapidly due to their small size and relatively simple structure;
(b) when conditions are favourable they multiply asexually, so rapidly that their colonies could completely take over a host;
(c) under unfavourable conditions many produce protective coverings to form spores or cysts, which tide them over such conditions;
(d) many can be cultured on artificial media and used for biological studies, e.g. genetic engineering, enzyme production and antibiotic research.

Microorganisms are found in the soil, water, the atmosphere, animals and plants. In these habitats they show various modes of nutrition and association: **parasitic**, **saprophytic**, **commensal** and **symbiotic**.

The majority of microorganisms are beneficial to man. They are responsible for decay and putrefaction, and are important in the nitrogen and carbon cycles, as well as in other cycles in nature. Some microorganisms, however, cause disease and are of negative economic importance. These are called **pathogens** (some have already been mentioned in relation to parasitic diseases, pests and the diseases they carry in Sections 24 and 25). In this section we will focus on the effect of microorganisms on food, and the ways in which this could be minimized.

Microorganisms and food

Infections in humans are spread mainly through food and water. Microorganisms that are spread in this way usually infect the intestine.

Some of the microorganisms carried in food and water are *Escherichia* (e.g. *E. coli*) *Aerobacter*, *Klebsiella*, *Proteus*, *Salmonella*, *Shigella*.

Because of the importance of typhoid fever in the historical past of the Caribbean region, it would be useful to look in depth at the *Salmonella* bacterium.

The genus *Salmonella* are rod-shaped, non-spore forming, and motile due to presence of flagella. They are facultative parasites and can be cultured in the laboratory. Among the diseases caused by *Salmonella* are typhoid and paratyphoid fever. They also cause gastro-enteritis in chickens and pigs.

Food poisoning

One of the most dangerous causes of food poisoning is the bacterium *Clostridium botulinum*. When it attacks a cooked medium a foul smell and bubbles of gas are produced. Tins that are 'blown out' at the sides are probably infected with this bacterium, and should *not* be consumed.

The microorganism forms spores which are extremely heat-resistant and germinate if food is not processed at a high enough temperature.

They are destroyed by heating the food at 80 °C for 45 minutes, or by boiling for 15 minutes.

The potency of the toxins produced by botulinus is extreme. They attack the nerves, usually causing paralysis of vital parts such as the diaphragm. The incubation period is rather short (2–48 hours), and the symptoms include headache, weakness, respiratory difficulty, and pains in the gastro-intestinal tract. The most effective method of prevention and control of botulism is to employ efficient and proper canning and preservation techniques.

Other forms of food poisoning may be caused by *Salmonella spp.*, *Staphylococcus aureus*, and *Bacillus cereus*.

Food preservation

As societies expand, an effective method of preserving surplus food must be found. Spoilage has to be cut to a minimum and certain types of food must be made available all the year round. Many elaborate methods of food preservation have been developed. These involve the use of heat, low temperatures, dehydration, smoking, chemicals, osmotic pressure, and sterile conditions for handling.

Heat is used in boiling, pressurized steam treatment, and pasteurization to destroy organisms in food products. Usually the substance is heated for a certain specified time under strictly measured conditions of temperature (and sometimes pressure). Pasteurization does not kill all microorganisms so pasteurized milk and juices still have to be stored at low temperatures to further avoid spoilage. Some of these foodstuffs, e.g. packs of milk, have a definite shelf life that is printed on the package.

Low temperatures have been used as a method of preservation for a long time. Freezing or refrigeration does not destroy the organisms in the food, instead it retards their metabolic activities. The product is sometimes steamed before freezing, so that preservation is more effective.

In **dehydration** the foods are dried by sun or air. Here again the microorganisms are not necessarily killed, but their growth is curtailed by the reduced moisture content. Dried fruits and fish are well known products in the Caribbean.

Some foods such as ham and bacon are **smoked** as a means of preserving them.

Chemicals may be added to food in order to preserve it. Some nitrates and nitrites which pass the tests of the various food and drug agencies are used as effective preservers. Foods may be pickled in acetic acid (vinegar). Research has shown that some antibiotics, e.g. tetracycline, may retard microbial activity in foods, and these may be used for preservation under strict supervision.

Osmotic pressure relations are also used to preserve food. Salt or sugar may be added to the food, plasmolysing it, and so curtailing the microorganism's metabolism. Preserves such as jellies and jams, and the use of brine for curing meats are instances of the use of increased osmotic pressure for food preservation.

Different types of preserved foods

Questions

1 Briefly distinguish between symbiosis and commensalism.
2 In what ways are parasitic microorganisms suited for their mode of life?

27 Water for life

Although water provides no nutrients, it is so important that we would live for only a few days without drinking any.

More than 60% of the human body is composed of water; most higher plants contain over 80% water. Each living cell is made of protoplasm. Protoplasm is composed of proteins, fats, carbohydrates and 80–90% water. When these cells lose water they soon become **dehydrated**. Extreme dehydration results in death, because all cell activities, such as respiration and excretion, cease in the absence of water.

Why is water necessary?

All the functional activities that take place in cells involve chemical reactions of one sort or another. Water, present in the cells, is the medium in which all these chemical reactions occur. Processes such as photosynthesis, germination and growth cannot occur in its absence.

Water also serves as a solvent in which other cellular substances are dissolved. So it also acts as an excellent transport medium in plants and animals.

Animal killed by drought in Africa

An aquatic habitat (Tobago)

Water is the only habitat for many plants and animals, and is also necessary to the reproduction of aquatic and some land animals. Some fruits and seeds are dispersed by water.

Water is also necessary for the removal of the waste products of metabolism, which leave the body in a watery solution called urine. In addition, sweat is largely water and wastes, excreted through pores in the skin. But water not only aids excretion; the cooling effect it creates when sweat evaporates on the skin surface is used in controlling the body temperature.

Most of you have seen how stems and leaves droop, and the whole plant wilts on hot, windy days. When herbaceous plants absorb water, their cells become turgid and the plant is held erect. But as transpiration occurs, the cells progressively lose water and become flaccid. If water cannot be taken in to replace the lost water the plant will be unable to remain erect and will droop under its own weight. Water, therefore, acts as a supporting skeleton in such herbaceous plants.

Water also acts as a **hydrostatic** skeleton in many lower animals which have no bony tissue. The body cavity of a worm, for example, is filled with watery fluid. The pressure exerted by the water against the body muscles gives the animal some rigidity, while allowing it to be flexible enough to bend and move.

Questions

1 Why is water called a 'transport medium' in plants and animals?
2 Give examples of a land plant and a land animal to which water is essential for sexual reproduction.

28

Using water in the home

The Caroni Arena dam and reservoir, Trinidad

Supplying water to the home

One major influence in the settling of man in towns and villages has been the availability of water. The water is necessary for industrial purposes, for transporting goods and people from place to place, for growing crops, for rearing animals and for domestic purposes.

A good supply of clean water for drinking, cooking, personal hygiene and washing is essential for healthy living. Well-sited, large towns seldom have a water shortage since they are supplied by a government water authority. The water is usually stored behind dams and in reservoirs and is then purified and piped into houses.

Supplying water to the public involves the following stages.

(a) **collection** in dams and reservoirs;
(b) **sedimentation**, in which aluminium sulphate is added to assist the process, causing heavier particles to settle out;
(c) **filtration** first over fine sand and then over gravel, to remove suspended matter; then
(d) chemical treatment by **chlorination** to kill harmful bacteria.

The result is odourless, colourless, germ-free, **potable** (drinkable) water.

Many developed countries now also add minute amounts of fluoride to their piped water, to help reduce the incidence of tooth decay in the population.

In many rural areas and small settlements each individual is responsible for collecting, storing and purifying his domestic water supply. Quite often, rainwater is collected from the roof and stored in tanks. Many impurities are naturally present in rainwater, and more are added as the water flows over the rat or bird droppings, and other debris present on roofs.

Rainwater for domestic purposes, especially for drinking, can be effectively purified in the home as follows:

(a) Collect the water in a tank or other large container and allow any sediment to settle.
(b) Remove any large pieces of floating debris; filter the water to remove the smaller suspended particles.
(c) Heat the water to boiling, and boil it thoroughly for about 10 minutes.
(d) Cool it in a closed container.
(e) Strain the water through a clean, white cloth.
(f) Store it in closed containers.

In towns and cities where there are water problems, and the piped water is locked off from time to time, householders are strongly advised to use home purification methods for their drinking water.

The domestic water supplies in country districts are often taken from lakes, rivers and streams. Water from such sources must also be purified in the home before drinking, as it could be contaminated. If the water is taken from the stream near its source it will be relatively free from germs since it has been exposed to sunlight, has not yet settled, and has had little chance to collect the usual contaminants. Water from very deep, natural wells is also fairly free of germs, since most would have been filtered off as the water passed through rock and soil to collect underground. But there could be chemicals, e.g. lime, dissolved from the rock and soil, which have to be removed. Care must also be taken to ensure that sewage does not seep into underground water reserves. Contamination of the water supply by faeces could cause intestinal diseases such as typhoid, cholera, dysentery and gastro-enteritis. These are characterized by vomiting, fever and diarrhoea, with the risk of dehydration and death, especially if the victims are children.

Conservation of water in the home

Water is one of our most precious resources, and is necessary to support life. But a constant supply of potable water can only be achieved by good management. In many countries, National Water Authorities have well established programmes for the management of watersheds, rivers and other natural water sources. But their efforts will only be successful if they are backed up by careful water use and if each individual or household makes conscious efforts at **conservation**.

The measures that can be taken include:

(a) fixing faulty household plumbing to prevent the daily loss of several litres of water;
(b) recycling bath, kitchen and laundry water for use in gardens;
(c) using smaller volumes of water when cooking, e.g. boiling just enough water 'for a cup of tea' instead of a whole kettleful;
(d) taking showers instead of baths.

Research projects

(a) Visit a water purification plant. Write a report on your visit.
(b) Write a report on the sources of domestic water in your area.
(c) Find out what type of material is used to pipe water into homes and schools. Explain the advantages and disadvantages of each type of piping.

W.A.S.A
YOU NEVER MISS THE WATER
'TIL THE TAP RUNS DRY!

Question

'You can conserve water by using detergents when laundering clothes.' Justify this statement.

29

Hard and soft water

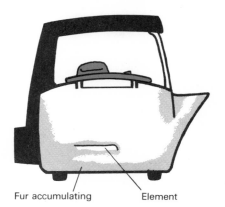

Fur accumulating   Element

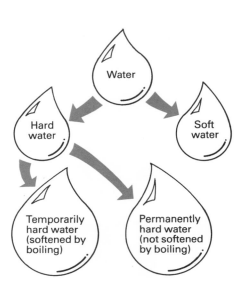

Water

Hard water

Soft water

Temporarily hard water (softened by boiling)

Permanently hard water (not softened by boiling)

All the water you use, even water which is considered safe for drinking, contains varying amounts of dissolved substances. Some of these substances make it difficult for soap to lather in the water. Water that does not readily form a lather with soap is called **hard water**. Water that does not contain these substances, and so easily forms a lather with soap, is called **soft water**.

Hard water which can be softened by boiling is known as **temporarily hard water**. Hard water which is not affected by boiling is known as **permanently hard water**.

The hardness of a water sample is usually expressed in terms of the proportion of calcium ions it contain. The unit of hardness is parts per million (ppm) of calcium.

How does water become hard?

Rain leaves the clouds as chemically pure water, but as it falls to the ground it mixes with and dissolves carbon dioxide and other acidic gases.

carbon dioxide + water → carbonic acid

Rain water thus contains carbonic acid and, especially in highly industrialized areas, nitric and sulphuric acids.

When the rain water falls on magnesium-bearing or calcium-bearing rocks (e.g. chalk, limestone, gypsum, dolomite and magnesite), calcium and magnesium go into solution as 'free ions'. They combine with the dissolved gases in the water, making what is known as 'hard water'.

Which salts make water hard?

When water containing calcium (or magnesium) hydrogencarbonate is boiled the hydrogencarbonate is decomposed to the corresponding carbonate. Since this is not soluble in water it is deposited as a 'scale' or 'fur' in the container.

$$\textbf{calcium hydrogencarbonate} \xrightarrow{\textbf{boiling}} \textbf{calcium carbonate}$$
(soluble in water)   (insoluble in water)

Since the dissolved calcium hydrogencarbonate is removed by boiling the water is known as temporarily hard water. The deposited scale can be removed from the container with a solution of ethanoic acid (vinegar).

Water containing dissolved calcium (or magnesium) sulphate or chloride is not softened on boiling and is therefore permanently hard.

Soap and hard water

When soap is added to water it first acts on the dissolved chemicals (e.g. calcium hydrogencarbonate and calcium sulphate) to form a precipitate which appears as a scum on the surface of the water. The scum or precipitate is the insoluble salt calcium stearate. Soap is essentially the sodium salt of a fatty acid.

sodium stearate   +   **calcium salt**   →   calcium stearate   +   sodium salt
(soap)   (in water)   (scum)

In this way the soap removes any dissolved calcium salts. The cleaning or detergent action of the soap begins only when all the calcium or magnesium ions have been precipitated. You thus use more soap in hard water areas than in soft water areas.

Methods of softening water

Soft water is preferred to hard water

(a) in laundering, when soaps are used as the detergent;
(b) in boilers, so that scale does not develop.

Unfortunately, most of our water sources, whether from private wells, boreholes or from the tap give hard water which needs to be softened before it is used for these purposes.

The common methods of softening water include:

(a) boiling;
(b) addition of calcium hydroxide (lime water);
(c) addition of sodium carbonate;
(d) use of ion exchange resins.

A substance which is added to hard water to make soap lather more easily is called a **water softener**.

Hard water is sometimes preferred, however. The dissolved calcium salts are essential for the building of healthy teeth and bones, so it is better to drink hard water than soft water. Hard water is also preferred to soft water in the brewing industry.

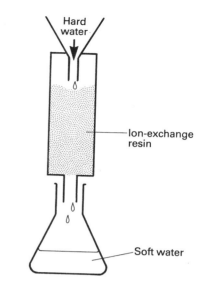

One method of turning hard water into soft is to pass it through an ion-exchange resin

---

Experiment: To compare the hardness of different samples of water

The hardness of different samples of water can be compared by noting the number of drops of a 1% soap solution needed to produce permanent lathers with equal volumes of each sample.

What you need
Samples of (A) distilled water; (B) rain water; (C) temporarily hard water made by adding 10 cm³ lime water to 90 cm³ distilled water and blowing exhaled air through it until there is no further change; (D) permanently hard water, e.g. water saturated with calcium sulphate; (E) tap water; (F) river water; (G) pond water; (H) some 1% soap solution.

What you do
To 10 cm³ of each sample add, drop by drop from the burette, the 1% soap solution. Shake the sample after the addition of each drop. When a permanent lather forms stop adding the soap solution. Record your results in table form.

Questions
1 Which sample contains the greatest amount of dissolved calcium ions?
2 Which sample(s) do you consider to be soft water?
3 What experiments can you carry out to divide the samples of hard water into those which are permanently hard and those which are not?
4 Compare the effects of washing articles of clothing, using soap, in sea water or salt water and rain water.

Questions
1 Use any reference material to find out the meaning of the terms:
   (a) potable water;
   (b) ground water;
   (c) disinfection of water.
2 Would you expect ground water to be hard or soft? Give a reason for your answer.
3 Why is soft water preferred to hard water for laundry purposes?

Summary

1 Dissolved calcium (or magnesium) hydrogencarbonate causes temporary hardness in water. Temporary hardness can be removed by boiling or the use of ion-exchange resins and water softeners.
2 Dissolved calcium (or magnesium) sulphate causes permanent hardness in water. Permanent hardness can be removed by water softeners and ion-exchange resins, but not by boiling.

30

Water pollution

The importance of water as a resource has already been stressed. In this section we will look in greater detail at the various ways in which water can be polluted, and some possible means of prevention.

Pollution

Pollution is the process in which a substance or form of energy is released into the environment in a sufficient quantity to disrupt the delicate ecological balance. This disruption may affect the health of the population, or change resources so that they are no longer useful. In some cases the pollutant is not in itself harmful under normal conditions, indeed sometimes it is beneficial. However, its presence in excessive quantities in the wrong place at the wrong time constitutes the pollution. It must be noted that a pollutant need not be a waste product. A good example of pollution in which a waste product is not involved is the washing into a lake of excess nitrates and phosphates, applied as fertilizers. These substances are required by living organisms for healthy growth, and they form the basis of the practice of increasing soil fertility with fertilizers. However, when in the lake they promote algal growth, disrupting the ecosystem and causing other organisms to suffer.

Sewage and garbage disposal

Sewage and garbage disposal is a major problem in pollution control. As settlements spring up in various countries, and with the great development of tourism, more and more waste materials need to be got rid of. In many cases the bulk of the sewage is emptied untreated into the sea and rivers. This has been common practice throughout the Caribbean.

The disposal of garbage, although collected fairly regularly, poses a major problem. Garbage may be used to fill swampy areas and so form a firm base for the land's subsequent use. However, great care needs to be taken in choosing the dump sites because the garbage may emit foul smells which upset nearby residents, or poisonous substances may seep from it into water supplies.

Wastes from agro-based industries also add organic materials to waterways. This results in imbalance and damage to the natural ecology.

Industrial wastes

Industrial wastes, other than from agro-based industries, present great problems as pollutants of the water. Many of these wastes are not **biodegradable**, that is, they cannot be decomposed by microorganisms. They are therefore much more difficult to dispose of than, for example, agrobased wastes. Some sources of this type of pollution are power plants, oil refineries and steel mills. There are examples of all these in the Caribbean region.

Pollution by **oil** is an ever-present danger in the Caribbean. Since the region lies in the main shipping lanes, the possibility of spillage from the supertankers which carry both crude and refined petroleum products is very great. The recent collision of two supertankers off the coast of Tobago amply illustrates this fact. Oil spills can destroy marine wildlife—fish and birds—directly and indirectly. In a direct effect the oil soaks the feathers of birds, making flight impossible and causing them to die of exposure. Indirectly, the oil destroys the algae and plankton upon

Garbage pollution

which these animals feed. The oil slicks which such spillages produce may be washed ashore, fouling the beaches and doing untold damage to tourism.

Pollution may also be caused by the addition of **heat** to waterways. Some industries use water to cool their machinery, and this warmed water may be channelled into rivers and streams, where it destroys organisms which are needed, and encourages the growth of those which are not.

Detergents

Detergents are also water pollutants. Some detergents are high in phosphates and, as mentioned above, an over-abundance of these compounds can cause excessive algal growth, and hence disrupt the ecosystem.

The condition which develops in a reservoir or lake as a result of excessive amounts of nutrients causing algal bloom is called **eutrophication**. Eutrophication may be prevented by using coagulants to reduce the phosphorus concentration; by the proper positioning of water sources and reservoirs; by the judicious use of nitrate and phosphate fertilizers.

Questions

1 List five ways in which you would try to prevent pollution of water in your country.
2 Your government is about to build a huge oil refinery on a beautiful beach. Outline some of the pros and cons of such a development.

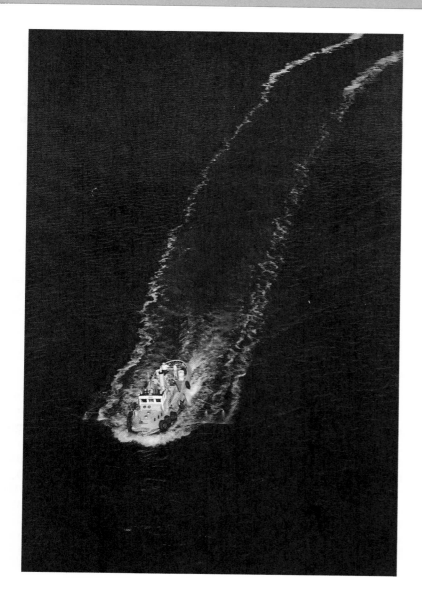

Combatting oil pollution. Spraying the slick with chemicals to make it sink

31

When is electricity dangerous?

Which of the following do you consider safe to handle: a 1·5 volt dry cell; a 9 volt dry battery; a 12 volt car battery; the 110 volt mains; the 240 volt mains? You may be in for some surprises as you consider the following three dangers that can arise when dealing with electricity.

Shock

It is unlikely that anyone has ever died from an electric shock from a 1·5 volt dry cell or even from a 12 volt car battery (however, a 12 volt car battery connected to the ignition 'coil' of a car *can* produce a deadly shock). The lowest voltage recorded as having caused death is 60 volts. Death has often been caused by both 110 and 240 mains voltages. Children are often warned not to fly kites near electric power lines as these wires sometimes carry voltages as high as 169 000 volts which can produce fatal shocks. Shock is the best known danger associated with electricity.

What is an electric shock?

Most of the functions of the human body are regulated by tiny **electric impulses** that travel along the nerves within the body. Suppose you wish to close your hand. Some tiny electric currents will be sent from your brain along nerves to the muscles of your hand. This electrical stimulation will cause the muscles to contract. Similarly, if your body is in contact with an electric wire and some current from the wire reaches the nerves of the hand, the muscles may again contract. You will not be able to open your hand while the current flows. The electric current has affected the physiology (functioning) of the body. Thus an electric current produces a **physiological** effect. The sudden change the electricity produces in the functioning of the body is what is called shock.

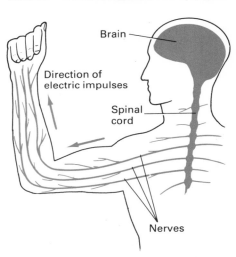

Closing a hand involves the brain sending electric impulses along the nerves to the muscles of the hand

Burns

Another dangerous effect of electricity is a burn. An electric current often heats the object that it passes through. Wires can get so hot that the plastic around them melts (house fires start this way). A large current passing through a part of the body can produce a severe burn. Some electric insect killers make use of this effect. When an insect touches the current-carrying wires a large current flows through the insect and roasts it to death.

Arcs

Arcs are another kind of danger that can be encountered when using electricity. Motor mechanics sometimes connect one end of a 12 volt battery to a wire and use the other end of the wire to touch the other terminal of the battery. This produces arcing. The practice is dangerous for two reasons. First, a tremendous current flows whenever battery terminals are **shorted**, which heats up the battery. This can spoil the battery or cause it to explode. Secondly, if there is gasolene vapour around (as there often is in a garage), a spark is all that is needed to ignite the vapour and start a fire. Arcs are usually produced whenever an electric circuit is opened or closed. Thus arcing may occur at switches or contact breakers.

In situations where combustible material is likely to be around, arcing may be prevented by placing a suitable **capacitor** across the arcing gap. The electrical energy flows safely through the capacitor instead of jumping across the gap. However, it is always good practice to remove any combustible material and to wear clothing that does not burn easily whenever working with electricity.

Using electricity

Although there are dangers connected with electricity, it is used widely. Its use is sometimes even based on the dangers mentioned above. Electric shocks are used to treat mental patients and those suffering from certain types of heart disease. Arcs are used in cinema projector lamps because a very bright beam is produced; they are also used in arc welding. The heating effect of the electric current is put to work in the electric iron and the electric stove.

What we must do is learn how to use electricity safely. The next few sections should help you to do so.

Arc welding

Motor car distributor. Can you locate the capacitor which prevents arcing at the points?

Rotor Arm

Capacitor

Contact break points

Questions

1 Which is less dangerous—to be shocked by a wire touching the palm of the hand or one touching the back of the hand? Give a reason for your answer.
2 Certain household plastic switches are translucent. Why is it that you see a flash of light when these switches are switched off? Should these switches be used near gasolene pumps? Give a reason for your answer.
3 A wire from one terminal of a battery is made to touch the thigh nerve of a suspended frog's leg. When the other terminal of the battery is made to touch the foot, the frog's leg jumps. What does this tell us about nerves?

32

Materials that conduct electricity

Many people who received an electric shock did not come into direct contact with the battery or other source of electricity. Some people have bought appliances (e.g. freezers) which worked well at the store but which worked poorly or not at all when plugged into their home circuit even though it has the same voltage as the store. How do these things happen? A knowledge of how well materials *conduct* electricity is needed to understand both these occurrences.

Making a conductivity tester

A simple conductivity tester can be made by connecting a dry cell in series with a low voltage lamp as shown in the top diagram (the apparatus can be mounted in a hollow tube or box to make it easy to handle). If the lamp lights when a material is placed across ends A and B of the wires, it means that current is flowing through the material. In this case the material is a **good conductor** of electricity. If the lamp does not light we cannot say for sure that no current is flowing through the material. This is because a certain amount of current must flow before the lamp can light. All we can say this time is that the material is a **poor conductor** of electricity.

By looking at the brightness of the lamp we can tell whether the material that is being tested is a good conductor, a poor conductor, or somewhere in between. An alternative design of conductivity tester uses a milliammeter, protected by a resistor, in place of the lamp. In a third design, a light-emitting diode (LED) protected by a resistor replaces the lamp.

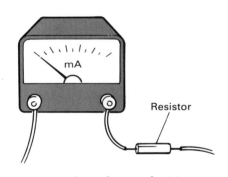

A simple conductivity tester

An alternative design for a conductivity tester using a milliammeter

A light-emitting diode

Activities

How well do solids conduct electricity?
You can use the conductivity tester to answer this question. Here are some tests for you to try. (But remember to try and control variables.)

1 Collect a set of objects made from different materials. Test the materials to find out which types are the good conductors, which are the poor conductors, and which are in between.
2 Find out if a fat wire conducts electricity better than a fine wire. Nichrome wires can be used.
3 Find out if a long wire conducts electricity better than a short wire. Again, nichrome wires can be used.

Do liquids and gases conduct electricity?
The ends A and B of your conductivity tester can be attached to a **conductivity cell** for testing liquids (see *opposite*). Each liquid to be tested is placed in the vessel up to a certain mark. Test various liquids to find out if they are good, poor, or in-between in their conduction properties (some suggestions: rain water, distilled water, tap water, trench water, sea water, water to which salt is added, water to which dirt is added, vinegar, milk, coconut oil). You should *not* use your tester on highly flammable liquids because if arcing takes place they may catch fire.

Most gases are very poor conductors of electricity. But if they are **ionized** (if the gas molecules gain or lose electrons) they can become good conductors. For example, in a fluorescent tube ions of mercury vapour help to conduct the electric current. Air is normally a very poor conductor of electricity. But when there is a high voltage, i.e. in excess of 10 000 volts per cm between clouds and the earth, the air becomes ionized. The movement of the ions constitutes the huge electric arc which we call lightning. The motion of the ions results in visible light being given off, and the heat produced causes a rapid expansion of the surrounding air which we hear as thunder.

The importance of good and poor conductors of electricity

We need good conductors of electricity to transport electrical energy from the power stations to our homes and to our appliances. Metals such as copper and aluminium are widely used for this purpose. But we also need to be careful not to let these good conductors touch us when they are connected to a voltage supply. We must never touch bare live wires, and we should avoid doing electrical work in damp areas. Electrical fires should never be put out with water because water can be a good conductor, as your experiments have shown.

Rubber, cotton, plastic, and glass are examples of very poor conductors (**insulators**). They are commonly used to insulate the conducting parts of appliances so that we cannot get shocked. However, if there is a very high voltage, some of these 'insulators' may conduct enough electricity to kill a person in contact with them.

Although metals are usually very good conductors, very long or very fine wires tend to behave like poor conductors. That is why fat wires are used when connecting heavy-duty equipment to the voltage supply. If the connecting wires are too fine, the appliance (e.g. a freezer) might not be able to get the current it needs, and will not work.

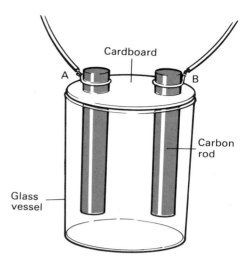
A conductivity cell. The liquid for testing is poured into the vessel

Questions

1 Are wires that conduct electricity best usually (a) long and stout; (b) long and thin; (c) short and stout; or (d) short and thin?
2 Name one material that is found in homes and that is:
   (a) a good conducting solid;
   (b) a good conducting liquid;
   (c) a poor conducting solid;
   (d) a poor conducting liquid.
3 Name two parts of the electric iron which are poor conductors and two which are good conductors.

Lightning is an arc of electricity conducted by ionized air between clouds and the earth

33

Measuring electricity

Reading a household electricity meter

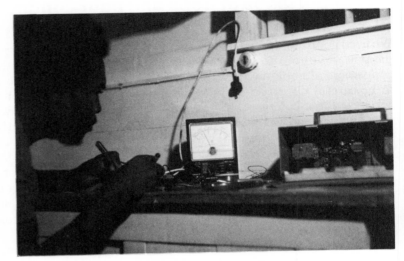

Radio technician at work

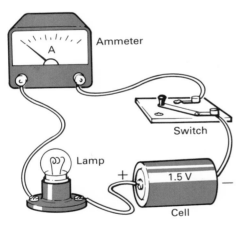

Using an ammeter to measure current through a lamp

The persons in the pictures are measuring electricity. But they are not both measuring the same thing. The meter reader is measuring electrical **energy**. The radio technician is measuring electrical **voltage**. If you look closely, you will see that they are using different instruments. In this section you will learn how to measure voltage and current, like the radio technician. In Section 35 you will learn how to read the household electricity meters.

Current

The instrument used for measuring electric current is called an **ammeter**. The diagram shows the correct way of connecting this instrument. Which terminal of the ammeter is connected towards the + side of the cell? Which terminal of the ammeter is connected towards the − terminal of the cell?

The reading on an ammeter tells how much current is flowing through the meter. This will be the same as the amount of current flowing through the lamp. Electric current involves a flow of charged particles (usually electrons) around a circuit. The number of electrons that pass through the ammeter every second will therefore pass through the lamp every second. Current is measured in **amperes**. A flow of $1 \cdot 6 \times 10^{18}$ electrons past a point every second is called **one ampere** of current.

Series and parallel circuits

There are two basic methods of connecting components into a circuit. In a **series** arrangement the current can take only one path round the circuit. The same current therefore flows through each device in the circuit. The ammeter is connected **in series with** the devices to measure the current that flows in the circuit.

In the **parallel** circuit the current divides when entering the lamps. After leaving the lamps, these smaller currents recombine. The diagram (top of page 91) shows where the ammeter must be placed to measure the current flowing through lamp L_5. The ammeter is placed **in series with** L_5. Where should the ammeter be placed to measure the current flowing through L_4; L_6; all three lamps?

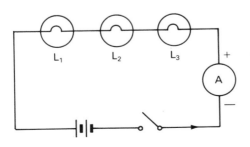

Series circuit – the same current flows through each device in the circuit

Voltage

Voltages can be produced by batteries or by generators. But what is **voltage**? Voltage is a kind of electrical pressure. The greater the voltage of a battery, the greater the electrical pressure which causes the electrons to go around the circuit.

The voltage of a battery is measured by placing a **voltmeter across** (or **in parallel with**) it. The + side of the voltmeter is connected to the + side of the battery and vice-versa.

In the series circuit in the diagram below the voltmeter is wired to read the voltage across lamp L_3. Although lamps do not produce voltages, there is a voltage drop across them when a current is flowing through them. If we add the voltage drops across lamps L_1, L_2 and L_3 we can discover the total voltage of the battery. You can verify this by experiment.

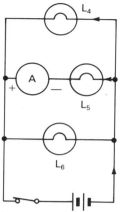

Parallel circuit – the current divides up

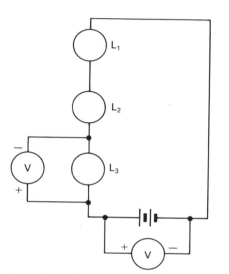

Measuring voltage in a series circuit

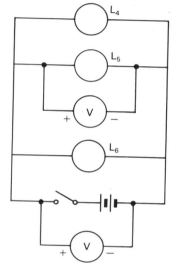

Measuring voltage in a parallel circuit

A careful look at the parallel arrangement will show that each lamp experiences the *same* voltage drop, which is also the voltage of the battery. This is because in a parallel arrangement the two wires from each lamp are *directly* connected to the battery. A voltmeter will therefore give the same reading whether it is placed across L_5, L_4, L_6, or the battery. You can verify this by experiment too.

Household circuits are usually parallel circuits because most mains appliances need the full mains voltage in order to operate properly. That is why there are sometimes many cables leading from a fuse panel but only one entering. Each of the cables leaving is connected in parallel with the cable entering the fuse box. One great advantage of the parallel arrangement is that if one circuit fails, the others are not affected. Can you work out why?

Some types of 'fairy lights' are wired in series, and if one of the lights 'blows', the entire string of lights goes out because the circuit is broken.

Questions

1 Explain the meaning of the terms **current** and **voltage**.
2 'We have 220 volt current in our house', says Tom. Explain what is wrong with Tom's statement.
3 Draw a circuit diagram to show each of the following:
   (a) Three 1·5 V torchlight cells connected to light a 4·5 V lamp.
   (b) One 1·5 V torchlight cell connected to light three 1·5 V lamps.
   (c) One 9 V battery connected to light two 4·5 V lamps.
4 Draw a diagram to show where an ammeter must be placed to measure the current in one of the lamps in part (b) of question 3.

Activities

1 Measure the voltages of new and used batteries of various voltages.
2 Design and carry out experiments to show that when lamps are connected in series
   (a) the sum of the voltage drops across the lamps is equal to the voltage of the battery;
   (b) the current flowing through each lamp is the same.
3 Design and carry out experiments to show that when two lamps are connected in parallel
   (a) the voltage across each lamp is equal to the voltage of the battery;
   (b) the current flowing from the battery is equal to the sum of the currents flowing in each lamp.

34

Resistance and power

Protective resistor

mA Milliammeter

Resistance wire placed across this gap

Fixed resistors

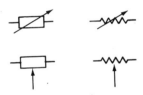

Variable resistors

Symbols used for different types of resistor

Inside a transistor radio. Can you see the resistors?

Voltage and current are related in two very important ways, which you will learn about in this section.

Resistance

A short length of wire conducts electricity better than a long length of the same type of wire. We say that the long wire has more **resistance** than the short one. The diagram on the top left shows a circuit that can be used to demonstrate this effect. Nichrome or constantan wire can be used. How can you use the circuit to find out whether a fat wire conducts electricity better than a fine one?

If we measure the voltage V across a fixed piece of wire and the current I passing through it, we find that, at constant temperature, the voltage is directly proportional to the current. This means that if the voltage doubles, the current also doubles, and if the current becomes 7 times as big, the voltage would also have become 7 times as big, and so on. This finding is called **Ohm's law**.

A large voltage across the wire produces a large current through it. This can be expressed mathematically as

$$V \propto I \quad \text{or} \quad \frac{V}{I} = \text{constant}$$

The constant is called the resistance of the wire at that temperature. The unit of resistance is the **ohm** (symbol Ω). Thus the resistance R is given by the equations

$$\frac{V}{I} = R \quad \text{or} \quad V = IR$$

Commercial resistors may be made of lengths of wire or compressed carbon. Resistors can be found in radios, electric irons, and electric stoves. Even the incandescent lamp has a filament which is a resistor.

To measure the resistance of a device, the current through it and the voltage across it must be measured. Then the equation $R = V/I$ is used. Alternatively, an **ohmmeter** can be used. The multimeter that technicians use becomes an ohmmeter at the flick of a switch.

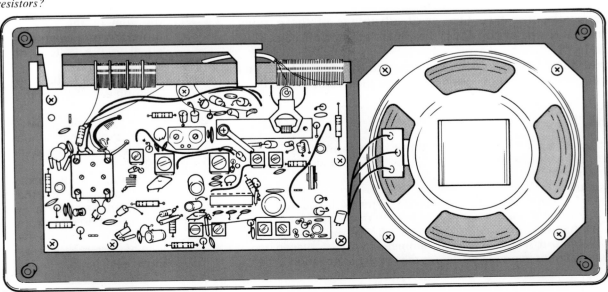

Power

Power is a measure of the rate at which energy is being generated or used up. In equation form it is expressed as

$$\text{power} = \frac{\text{energy}}{\text{time}}$$

that is, power is the amount of energy used up per unit time. Power is expressed in **watts** (W) when energy is expressed in **joules** (J) and time in seconds (s). It can be shown that the power of a device is equal to the voltage across it times the current that flows through it:

$$\text{power (W)} = \text{voltage (V)} \times \text{current (A)} \quad \text{or} \quad P = IV$$

Power stations generate electrical energy using various techniques. Some stations use fossil fuels, e.g. coal or petroleum, to convert chemical energy into heat energy. Others use nuclear reactors in which small amounts of mass from the nucleus of the atom are converted into tremendous amounts of energy by a process called **fission**. Uranium fuel is used in this latter process. Four kilograms of this fuel produce as much heat as three million gallons of oil. The heat energy produced by either process is used to convert water in boilers into steam. The energy in the steam is converted into mechanical energy by steam turbines. The turbines are connected to large dynamos which convert the mechanical energy into electrical energy. These large amounts of electrical energy generated per second are measured in megawatts (MW).

In some power stations the mechanical energy needed to turn the dynamos is obtained from water flowing down from a high reservoir. This is the **hydro-electric** system.

Solar cells can convert the Sun's energy directly into electricity. Solar cells are therefore useful in powering space devices such as communications satellites.

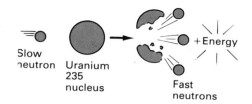

A fission reaction releases vast amounts of energy

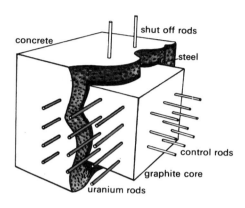

Nuclear reactor. The graphite core slows down neutrons for uranium fission

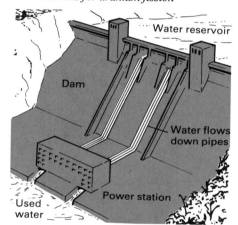

The hydroelectric system (above)

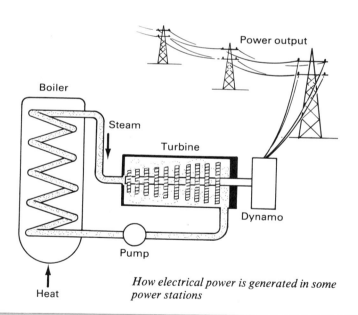

How electrical power is generated in some power stations

Questions

1 A current of 0·6 amps is flowing through a correctly operated 4·5 V lamp.
   (a) What is the lamp's power?
   (b) How much electrical energy does the lamp use up in 3 hours?
   (c) What is the lamp's resistance?
   (d) What is the electrical energy converted to in the lamp?
2 In a fossil fuel power plant, what energy change takes place in:
   (a) the boiler;
   (b) the turbine;
   (c) the dynamo (generator)?

Activities

1 Measure the resistance of a filment lamp (of an unknown low resistance) using a voltmeter and an ammeter.
2 Connect up a solar cell to a milliammeter to show that light can be converted into electrical energy.
3 Make a model hydroelectric system using a small generator. (A milliammeter can be used to show that electric current is generated as the water turns the generator.)

35

Mrs Singh's electricity bill

Mrs Singh was never satisfied when her electricity bill arrived. Why was it always so high? Her neighbours used more electrical appliances than she did and yet their bills were lower. Mrs Singh became furious when, one day, she received a bill for nearly double the amount she was accustomed to paying. 'The electricity rates have not gone up,' she told the cashier. 'I have bought no new appliances. I keep using my appliances as usual. I pay my bills regularly. Somebody is making money by false pretence here. I can't accept this bill. I want to see the manager.'

Learn to read your meter

The customer relations manager invited Mrs Singh into her office and showed her two electricity meters. 'Which one do you have, Mrs Singh, an analogue or a digital meter?', she asked.

'The analogue,' Mrs Singh replied, pointing. 'But why do you want to know?'

'I only want to make sure you know how to read your meter. We want our customers to be able to check for themselves that their meters are being read correctly. The digital meters are very easy to read. To read a meter like yours, however, you have to look carefully at the little needles and dials. If a needle is between two numbers, you must read off the number that the needle has just passed. These two demonstration meters have been set to show the same reading.'

Learn how to estimate your bill

'OK', Mrs Singh replied. 'Even if I know how to read the meter, I still don't think that will solve my problem. Look at this bill. I do not understand how you arrive at these high figures.'

Mrs Austin examined the bill. 'You have used 97 kWh of electricity.'

'What are kWh?'

'kWh stands for **kilowatt-hours**. The energy you use up registers as kWh on your electricity meter. The fuel charge is calculated at 31¢ per kWh. There is no charge for the first 50 kWh of energy used up. But there is an energy charge of 41¢ per kWh for each unit of energy after that. There is also a meter rental charge of $2·30 per month. Let's do the calculation together.'

Mrs Austin asked Mrs Singh what electrical appliances she used and made an estimate of the **power** of each appliance. She then used the formula 'energy = power × time' to calculate the energy such appliances could use up in 20 hours.

'But how can I tell the wattage of my appliances?' Mrs Singh asked Mrs Austin.

'It's marked on them. A bulb marked 110V 60W is rated at 60 watts. Some appliances may have VA (volts amps) marked on them instead of W (watts), though. VA is equal to 1W.

Know which appliances have large power ratings

Mrs Singh had calmed down. She looked at the calculation without saying a word and then shook her head. 'So, it's the iron that is responsible for half the bill. Then the fridge. Then the lights. The radio doesn't even use 1 kWh during 20 hours! And just think, I always tell the children

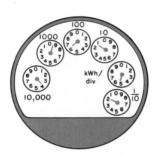

Analogue meter

Digital meter

CARIBBEAN ELECTRIC COMPANY LTD

Meter reading (kWh)		$
Present........ 3327	Energy charge	19·27
Previous....... 3230		
kWh used..... 97	Fuel charge	30·07
	Balance from previous account	—
	Meter rental	2·30
	Pay this amount	51·64

Mrs Singh's electricity bill

to turn off the radio hoping that will save on the bill. But when I try to cook and iron at the same time and leave the iron running, that's when the money goes down the drain. And when I leave the lights on when I am not using them, that's wastage too.'

'Yes Mrs Singh. Some devices use a lot of energy. But it's not only money. It is also dangerous to leave an iron on without making use of the heat. It can overheat and start a fire.'

Practice energy-saving habits

Mrs Austin could see that Mrs Singh was now very interested in cutting down on energy wastage. So she added, 'As for the fridge, if you open it often or leave it open for long, more energy will have to be used up to keep the things inside cold. And if the rubber seal (the gasket) around the edge of the door does not fit tightly, heat from the surroundings will get into the fridge and so the fridge will have to use up more energy again to keep the things inside cold. The fridge has an automatic switch (a thermostat) which will cut off the fridge motor only when the fridge has reached a certain coldness. Most high energy bills result from a badly fitting gasket on a fridge. Look, you don't have an air conditioner. But for some people it is *very* costly to run because they keep their windows and doors open. It's the same as for the fridge. Heat gets in. The appliance has to use more energy to maintain a certain coldness. Also if an appliance has a partial short across the wires, e.g. through build-up of rust, a circuit will be formed and some current will flow through the short. So, some energy will be wasted in the short circuit. It will not be used by the appliance.'

'Does CEC operate a repair service?'

'No, Mrs Singh. But we can send a technician to check your house and advise you what repairs need to be done to your appliances. Then you can consult a competent servicing company in your community about the repairs.'

'Can you send one today?'

'I should think so.'

Mrs Singh left Mrs Austin's office determined that her electricity bill would be lower next month.

appliance	Power	Energy used in 20h	Energy in kWh
3 lamps	3×60W	180×20Wh	3·6 kWh
1 refrigerator	300 W	300×20Wh	6 kWh
1 iron	700 W	700×20Wh	14 kWh
1 radio	2W	2×20Wh	0·04 kWh

Calculating the energy used by different appliances over 20 hours

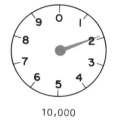     

10,000   1,000   100   10   kWh

Questions

1. What is the reading on the electricity meter above?
2. On 4 January and 4 February an electricity meter read 18431 and 18511 kWh respectively. If the energy charge is 30¢ per kWh and the fuel charge is 40¢ per kWh, and the monthly meter rental is 1·80 dollars, calculate the electricity bill for the month. (Assume all kWh units to be paid for.)
3. Name two household electrical appliances that operate at high powers and two that operate at low powers.
4. What are two ways of avoiding wasting electricity when using a refrigerator?

36

Fuses, plugs, flexes and transformers

Carefully remove the outer insulation

Carefully remove the insulation from the inner wires

Twist the copper strands together

Bend the bared ends in a clockwise direction to go with the turn of the screw, and attach to the CORRECT pin

Wiring a three-pin plug

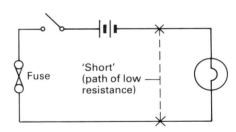

Fuse

'Short' (path of low resistance)

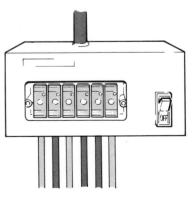

Household fuse panel

When using electricity in the home and at work there are four items that we often come across—fuses, plugs, flexes (drop cords) and transformers. This section will show you how to use them correctly.

Plugs

Some electrical appliances are sold without plugs. This is because there are so many kinds of plug and socket system in use today that manufacturers feel it is better to leave the customer to put on the right type of plug. The diagram on the left shows how to connect a standard three-pin plug to a three-wire flex.

A two-pin plug is not the right plug for appliances whose power cables have three wires inside. A three-pin plug *must* be used. Two of the wires, the 'live' and the 'neutral' carry the electricity. The third, the 'earth', is put there for safety. The colour-code used nowadays by most manufacturers is this: the **brown** wire is to be connected to the part of the plug marked L (live), the **blue** to the part marked N (neutral), and the **yellow/green** to the part marked E (earth).

Fuses

Many three-pin plugs contain a second safety feature—a cylindrical device called a **fuse**. The fuse melts and breaks the circuit if too much current passes through it, and so protects the appliance itself from receiving too much current.

The action of a fuse can be demonstrated by a fresh dry battery or power pack connected to a lamp. Place a suitable fuse wire in series with the lamp, as shown (*centre left*). The lamp offers some **resistance** in the circuit and therefore a not very large current flows when the bulb is lighting. The fuse remains intact. If, however, there is a 'short' across the lamp (e.g. if two wires touch each other, or a strand from one wire touches the other wire) a path of **low resistance** is created and a large current flows around the short circuit. This large current will cause the battery, the fuse and the wires to get hot. This is a dangerous situation. However, the fuse is constructed so that it quickly melts and breaks the circuit. The fuse can thus protect the circuit from overheating caused by large currents.

To maintain this protection it is important to replace a blown fuse with one of the correct current rating. The approximate current rating, *I*, of a fuse suitable for a circuit can be calculated from the equation

$$I = \frac{W}{V}$$

where *W* represents the maximum total power in watts of the appliances being used in the circuit, and *V* the supply voltage. Thus, in 115 V circuit, a 800 W freezer should be protected by a 7 amp fuse, by calculation. A suitable fuse would be a 10 amp fuse, allowing for voltage variations. A 20 amp fuse is unsuitable since this will allow nearly three times the 7 amperes of current to flow through the freezer. This current could damage the freezer before the electricity is shut off. A 5 amp fuse will blow each time the freezer is switched on. (Why?)

The electrical power points in a building are also connected to fuses. If many appliances are plugged into *one* of them, e.g. by using some adaptors, the total current drawn in that circuit becomes large. If the circuit is protected by a suitable fuse, the fuse will blow. Replacement of a blown fuse is cheap. If the fuse rating is not correct, a very large current will flow which may overheat the wires connected to the point and so start a fire. Before replacing a blown fuse, the electrical supply must be turned off at the main switch. The fault which caused the fuse to blow must also be corrected.

Flexes

Like fuses, drop cords or flexes also have ampere ratings. A flex that has an ampere rating of 3 A will conduct 3 A of electricity without overheating. If the flex is connected to an appliance that uses 7 amps, say, the flex will overheat. When you are selecting a suitable flex for an appliance you should first calculate the current the device will use, and then ask the person at the store for a flex of slightly higher ampere rating. If the person at the store does not know the ampere ratings of the flexes on sale, you will need to consult a competent electrician for advice, or visit a different store!

Transformers

How sad it is to buy a cassette tape tecorder which is set to operate from the 110 volt mains, plug it in to 220 volts and see smoke. All that was needed was a **transformer** to convert 220 volts mains electricity into 110 volts. But be careful! Transformers have also got current ratings. This is because transformers are made from coils of wire, each of which has an ampere rating. However, instead of stating the current rating of a transformer, the manufacturer usually gives the current × voltage rating. This is called the **power rating** of the transformer. A 1000 W polisher, for example, should be used with a 1000 watt (or greater) transformer. A transformer of a lower power rating will overheat and burn out. Why?

One final point about transformers. You must know where to connect the **input** and **output** voltage wires on them. The manufacturers usually indicate this. A transformer connected one way may **step down** 220 volts to 110 volts. Connected the reverse way it will **step up** 220 volts to 440 volts. A man once borrowed a 110 volts projector to give a film show in a 220 volts area. He used a 110/220 volt transformer. When he switched on the projector its lamp blew and the projector went up in smoke. Can you explain how it happened?

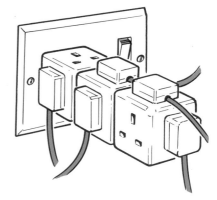

An overloaded power point!

Symbol for transformer

Questions

1 A certain wire is rated to conduct up to 3 amps without overheating. Is this wire suitable for a 110 V circuit consisting of:
   (a) three V-100 W lamps;
   (b) one 600 W refrigerator?

2 Stout wire cables and thin wire flexes are usually seen in household electricity circuits.
   (a) Where do the stout cables go?
   (b) Why isn't the entire house wired with either stout cables or thin cables only?

3 'Fuses protect circuits from shorts and overloads.' Explain this statement.

Activities

1 Connect fresh dry battery (or a freshly charged alkaloid battery) to a suitable fuse and lamp. Short out the lamp and notice how the fuse blows.

2 Use an a.c. voltmeter and a low voltage a.c. service (*not exceeding 12 V a.c.*). Connect up a 110/220 V transformer to the 12 V a.c. to show how stepping up or stepping down of the 12 V will take place depending on how the transformer is connected.
   NB: This activity is best done by a qualified physics teacher.

3 Collect pictures of various sizes of electrical cable and find out their ampere ratings. (You can enquire at a store or ask a qualified, competent electrician.)

220V

110/220V

110V

37

Electric lighting

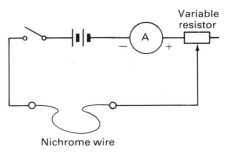

The filament lamp

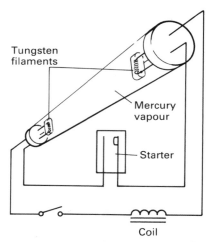

This apparatus demonstrates how the filament lamp works

Electricity can be made to produce light in a variety of ways, e.g. filament lighting, fluorescent lighting, the discharge tube, the electric arc, light-emitting diodes and laser beams. In this section the principles involved in the production of filament and fluorescent lighting will be described.

The filament (incandescent) lamp

This type of lamp is in common use in most households. A piece of nichrome wire connected in a series circuit with a variable resistor and a battery or power pack illustrates beautifully how it works (see *left*).

When the variable resistor is set at a maximum, very little current flows in the circuit. The nichrome wire feels cool or barely warm to the touch. As the resistance is reduced and more current flows in the circuit, as indicated by the ammeter, the nichrome wire glows first orange-red, then a bright red. A very large current might even make it look white and very bright. Electric current produces both the heating and lighting effects in the wire. This is the principle on which the filament lamp operates. Tungsten wire is usually used instead of nichrome in bulbs because it can reach higher temperatures without melting. Tungsten lamps are usually filled with a mixture of nitrogen and argon which helps to preserve the filament. If air were used the hot metal would burn up rapidly. If there were a vacuum inside the lamp the tungsten would evaporate quickly when hot.

Filament lamps are usually specified by their **wattage** and **operating voltage**. The higher the wattage, the brighter the lamp. Thus a 110 V 100 W lamp is brighter than a 110 V 40 W lamp.

Unfortunately, only a small percentage of the electrical energy is converted to light in this **incandescent** method. Most of it is radiated from the filament and lost as heat. In the fluorescent lamps there is much less energy loss.

Activity

Connect a piece of nichrome wire with a rheostat and a power pack. By adjusting the rheostat, show how the electric current produces a lighting effect in the wire.

The fluorescent lamp

Inside a fluorescent tube there is a gas, usually mercury vapour, at low pressure (mercury is very poisonous, so if a fluorescent tube breaks, you should provide plenty of ventilation and try not to inhale the vapour). The diagram (bottom *left*) shows how the fluorescent lamp works.

The light given off by a mercury lamp looks an eerie, bright, greenish white. A large amount of invisible, dangerous ultra-violet (UV) light is also given out which not only can damage the retina of the eye, but also represents a wastage of energy. The inside of the tube is therefore coated with a powder which glows white when it is hit by UV light. The powder is said to **fluoresce**, and this is how the fluorescent lamp gets its name. The powder used in some types of fluorescent lamps is highly poisonous due to the presence of berylium compounds.

The fluorescent lamp. The starter causes the coil to produce a momentary high voltage, triggering a flow of electrons between the tungsten filaments. When these electrons collide with atoms of mercury vapour, light is given out

Activity

Shine a narrow beam of light from a UV lamp with a test tube containing fluorescent solution. The solution glows where the UV light hits it. This glowing is called fluorescence.

Quality of light

Household fluorescent light looks white, but if you ever take colour pictures under fluorescent lights you will find that the pictures come out greenish. Why is this so? Fluorescent white light has a lot of green light in it, more than natural light has. Household incandescent white light has a lot of yellow in it, so the pictures taken in this light come out orangish. **Colour temperature** (the temperature of a hot filament) is sometimes used to describe the *quality* of a light. To produce light that resembles daylight in quality, an incandescent lamp filament has to be run at the very high temperature of 6000 K. That is why the incandescent **photoflood** lights used by TV cameramen and in photo studios do not last long. The very high temperature at which they have to operate destroys the tungsten filament very quickly.

Because the quality of light depends on the colour temperature, it is not surprising that a garment bought in a store lit by fluorescent lamps looks a slightly different shade when taken home and viewed in natural daylight. Fluorescent lights used in the store display make the garment look a tinge greener. The store walls also have an effect. They reflect light of their colour onto the garment. When buying colour film, too, it is wise to look on the box to see the colour temperature for which the film is made. You will then be able to decide whether to use the film for outdoor or indoor scenes, or with what kind of lighting. Some film may be used at more than one colour temperature provided that appropriate colour filters are used.

Photoflood lights in a TV studio

A comparison between incandescent (filament) and fluorescent lamps

INCANDESCENT (Filament)	FLUORESCENT
Waste a lot of energy as heat. Hence expensive to run.	Not much wastage of energy. Cheaper to run.
Filament usually small. Hence sharp shadows.	Usually long, hence very soft shadows.
Brightness easily controlled with a variable resistor or variable inductor.	Brightness not easily controlled.
Very yellowish light unless driven at high temperatures, in which case do not last long.	Light resembles daylight in quality, though slightly greener. Will maintain this quality of light for a long period of time.

Questions

1   What type of lighting (filament or fluorescent) would you use in the following situations and why?
    (a) To light up the subjects being photographed in a photo studio.
    (b) To light up a classroom being used for evening classes.
    (c) To light up a theatre stage.
2   Why do colours of objects look different in incandescent light and in fluorescent light?
3   Which is brighter, a 40 W fluorescent light or a 40 W incandescent light? Give a reason for your answer.

38

Using electricity to communicate

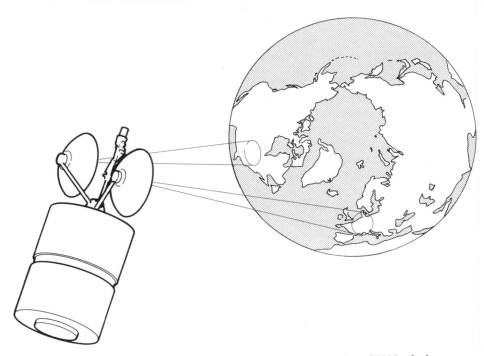

The Intelsat IV satellite provides circuits for 12 colour TV channels and 9000 telephone conversations between Europe and America

Apart from making our daily chores easier and providing us with clean light at night, electricity is also very useful in communicating. The communication is carried along wires or through the air, or even through space.

The telephone

When you speak into a telephone **mouthpiece**, the sound of your voice causes a light **diaphragm** to vibrate. These vibrations produce varying compressions on some carbon powder behind the diaphragm. The compressions cause the resistance of the carbon powder to vary in step with the variations in sound received by the diaphragm. The carbon powder is connected in a series circuit with a battery. Therefore a current flows through it. The varying resistance of the carbon powder causes the current in the wires to vary in step with the variations of the sound. This varying **electric current** is carried along the telephone wires. The device in the mouthpiece is called a **microphone**. A microphone therefore converts sound into electrical energy. A microphone is not, as some people believe, a device for making sound louder.

The electric current from your telephone's microphone is directed to the person you are calling by means of relay switches in the telephone exchange. When you dial, you are opening or closing these switches until you are connected to the person you are calling. But a person cannot hear an electric current. It has got to be converted back into sound. This is where the telephone **earpiece** comes in.

Inside the earpiece is a permanent magnet and two pieces of soft iron which pull on a thin iron alloy diaphragm. Two connected coils, each of hundreds of turns of insulated wire, are wrapped in an opposite manner on the two soft iron pole pieces. When the varying current from

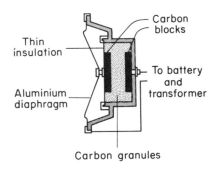

Carbon microphone in the telephone mouthpiece

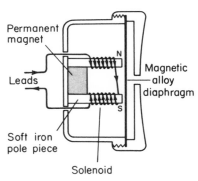

Telephone earpiece

100

the microphone passes through these coils they become varying electro-magnets. The varying magnetism produced adds to the magnetic pull already acting on the diaphragm. This makes the diaphragm vibrate and it is this vibration against the air that produces the sound.

Activity

Examine the inside of a telephone handset to observe the parts of the microphone and the earpiece.

Radio

Communicating along wires has the advantage that the communication can be kept private. The person dialling decides who will hear what he or she is saying. But what if we would like many people to hear us? Or what if the distances involved are great, e.g. from continent to continent or from Earth to the Moon? Or what if the terrain is difficult to access, e.g. a mountainous jungle? Electromagnetic waves have the advantage here, because they can travel through the air or through space.

Electromagnetic waves are so called because they have electric and magnetic properties. Radio waves, infra-red (heat) waves, visible light, ultra-violet light, X-rays and gamma rays are all electromagnetic waves. Although their frequencies and wavelengths are different, they all travel at the same fast speed, 3×10^8 metres per second through air and space.

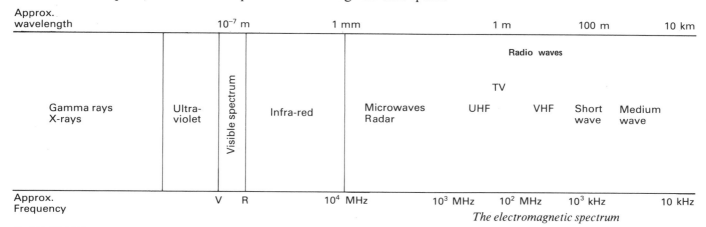

The electromagnetic spectrum

AM/FM

Radio waves are produced when electricity is made to go at high frequencies up and down a wire. When a person speaks into a microphone at the broadcasting station, a varying electric current, corresponding to the variations in his or her speech is produced. This varying current is combined with radio **carrier waves** at the transmitter. The result is either a variation in the amplitude (strength) or a variation in the frequency of the carrier wave. The former is called **amplitude modulation** (AM), the latter **frequency modulation** (FM).

Amplitude modulation can be used on all radio frequencies, but frequency modulation broadcasts work well only with high frequency radio waves (e.g. VHF, UHF and microwaves). High frequency waves have short wavelengths and therefore tend to travel very straight, so FM cannot be picked up more than about 20 km from the transmitter because of the Earth's curvature. Most local broadcasts are therefore done on *medium wavelength* AM as these waves tend to follow the curve of the Earth by a kind of spreading effect called **diffraction**. The range of most local AM broadcasts is about 200 km.

While AM has the advantage of range, FM has the advantage of quality. Whenever lightning flashes or a faulty appliance is sparking, these electrical effects can modulate the amplitude of radio waves. This will be heard on an AM radio as scratches unless the radio is equipped

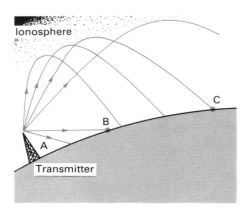

Medium wave broadcasts, reflected by the ionosphere, can be picked up anywhere between A and C, a distance of about 200 km

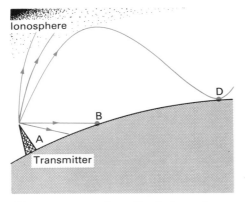

Short waves are reflected by the ionosphere only at a certain angle but can travel over 1000 km by repeatedly bouncing, as shown at D. No signal is received between B and D

with special filters. Since the *frequency* of the radio waves is not affected by these electrical disturbances, the scratches will not be heard on an FM broadcast. Music will therefore sound very clean on FM. In FM, too, because very high frequencies are used, it is possible to accommodate all the frequencies the ear can hear (from about 20 Hz to 20 kHz) on one FM radio wave. In fact, *two* sets of these frequencies are quite easily accommodated on the FM carrier wave and this makes **stereo** broadcasting possible. Since the carrier wave in AM broadcasts operates on low frequences it is not possible to accommodate the full range of frequencies we can hear on the carrier wave without making its bandwidth too large.

Activity

Set up a ripple tank to show that short wavelength (high frequency) waves hardly diffract, but that long wavelengths (low frequency) waves do.

Short wave

Somewhere between the medium wave band (MW) and the very *short waves* of FM is a very useful band of radio waves called short waves (SW). Their wave lengths are from 10 m to 90 m. Short waves tend to travel in straight lines like VHF FM waves and therefore are not usually used for local broadcasting. However, they are reflected by the ionosphere above the Earth. (VHF waves pass right through the ionosphere.) Short wave broadcasts can therefore be beamed to the ionosphere and reflected across oceans and continents, and so SW is often used in intercontinental broadcasting. Because the ionosphere is not steady, however, short wave broadcasts tend to 'come and go' sometimes. Nowadays important international broadcasts are transmitted on special very high frequencies which are reflected by satellite. These satellite broadcasts are steadier. In fact, when you make an international phone call, the electrical signals produced in your telephone by your voice are usually sent out of your country on extremely high frequency FM through the ionosphere, and reflected by satellite to the country you are calling.

Activity

Making a simple radio
You can make an AM radio quite simply by connecting up the pieces as shown in the diagram opposite. You might be able to find nearly all the parts needed for this simple radio inside a condemned pocket radio.

When radio waves reach the coil, they set up electric currents in it. By turning the variable capacitor C, which is connected to the coil, different currents can be selected, and so different stations are picked up by rotating the capacitor knob. This first stage is called the **tuning stage**.

The diode D is able to extract the audio signal from the carrier wave of an AM broadcast. This is called the **detecting stage**. If you live near to the broadcast transmitter, you can simply connect the headphones to convert this current into sound. You will need no batteries to operate this simple radio!

If you live far from the transmitter, however, the radio waves picked up will be weak. You will need to add an **amplifying stage** to amplify the current that is detected. If the amplifying stage is powerful enough a small loudspeaker can be used to convert the varying electric current into sound. Otherwise, headphones can be used.

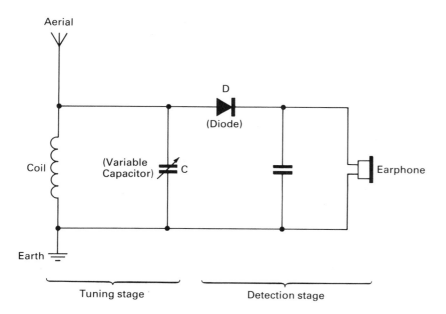

Tuning stage   Detection stage

A simple radio

Television

Television is broadcast on very high frequency waves, and so the range for television broadcasts is about 20 km, unless a very tall TV aerial is used. The television set which converts these electromagnetic waves into picture and sound has two very great dangers. First, there are parts inside the TV set that operate at a few thousand volts and could kill a person who touched them. And secondly, the screen may give off X-rays which are dangerous. We should therefore *never* attempt to open a TV set and should not view the picture from close to the screen. Even a disconnected TV set can be dangerous when opened because there are capacitors inside which can store charge at a few thousand volts.

The international telephone receiving station, Georgetown, Guyana

Questions

1 A carbon microphone is sometimes referred to as a 'variable resistance microphone'. Comment on this name.
2 When reporting on outdoor events live not far from a radio station, the broadcast is usually sent first by FM waves from the mobile broadcast van to the studio, from where it is then rebroadcast in AM. Explain why these two types of waves are used in these two situations.
3 Why are microwaves used when sending telephone messages to and from communications satellites?
4 What are the AM, FM and SW broadcasting frequencies being used
  (a) in your territory;
  (b) in your neighbouring territories?

39

Oil is important

Oil is important because it is the major source of energy and of organic compounds. It is found soaked into rock under the Earth's surface. Although oil has been in use for at least 6000 years, serious exploration for this commodity did not begin until 1859 when Edwin Drakes sunk the first oil well in Titusville, Pennsylvania.

How did the oil get there?

It is believed that oil was formed from the remains of plants and animals which became trapped between layers of sedimentary rocks millions of years ago. As time passed these remains became buried deeper and deeper. Under the high pressure and temperature that exist at these depths, and in the absence of air, oil and other fossil fuels were formed.

Gradually this oil soaked into layers of permeable (porous) rock, and was trapped in between layers of impermeable rocks.

Crude oil is a mixture of many **hydrocarbons** (compounds containing hydrogen and carbon only). Energy is stored in the chemical bonds of hydrocarbons. When hydrocarbons are burnt the energy is released. We use the released energy in many, many ways, for example, to light our homes, to cook our food, to power our cars, to run machines in factories, etc.

From crude oil to useful fractions

Crude oil is a mixture of many liquids. **Fractionating columns** like the one shown in the diagram are used to **purify** the crude oil (partially), i.e. separate it into fractions which boil at different temperature ranges. In a fractionating column the temperature varies from 350 °C at the bottom to 180 °C at the top.

The crude oil is heated to 350 °C and pumped into the lower levels of the column. At 350 °C many of the liquid fractions change to vapour. The lightest fractions rise to the very top of the column where they condense to liquid and are removed. Other fractions that are vapours at 350 °C rise up the column until each reaches the temperature at which it condenses. When they become liquid again they, too, are removed from the fractionating column.

In this way the crude oil is separated into its different components, with heavier fractions being drawn off at lower levels of the column.

The process by which a complex mixture such as oil is separated into its constituents is known as **fractional distillation**. If the fractions have widely different boiling points, good separations are achieved.

The origins of oil go back millions of years

Oil refinery at Pointe à Pierre, Trinidad

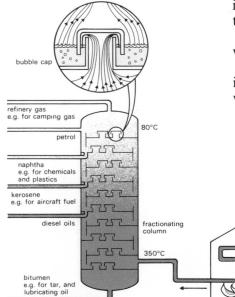

Fractionating column

Gasoline

Gasoline is one of the fractions of crude oil. It is the fuel on which cars and other motor vehicles run. But the gasoline fraction by itself is not large enough to satisfy the need for motor fuels.

Fortunately, it was discovered that if molecules of kerosene (another fraction) are broken down, gasoline molecules are obtained. The process by which kerosene molecules are converted to gasoline molecules is known as **cracking**.

The average kerosene molecule is twice as big as the average gasoline molecule. It is cracked by heat alone, or by the combination of heat and a catalyst. In this way sufficient quantities of gasoline are obtained.

'Untreated' gasoline misbehaves. It causes **knocking** in the engines of motor vehicles.

This problem can be overcome in a number of ways. One method is to increase the proportion of the branched hydrocarbon, iso-octane, in the gasoline mixture. The engine behaves better if the gasoline contains a high proportion of iso-octane. A second method of preventing knocking is to add lead compounds to the gasoline. The exhaust fumes of cars which use this gasoline will contain lead, a poisonous chemical, which will mix in the air we breathe.

Fraction	Use	Number of carbon atoms per molecule
Gases		1–4
Petrol		4–12
Kerosene (paraffin)		9–16
Diesel oil		15–25
Lubricating oil		20–70
Fuel oil		>10
Bitumen		>70

Petroleum fractions and their uses

LPG and LNG

The refinery gas which comes off at the top of the fractionating column during crude oil distillation contains hydrocarbons with from one to four carbon atoms. This fraction is a gas. However, it can be compressed and cooled until it liquefies, and then be stored under pressure, rather conveniently, in cylinders. The compressed pressurized liquid is known as **Liquefied Petroleum Gas** (LPG). LPG can be easily transported from one place to another.

Natural gas is found on its own in the Earth's crust as well in association with oil. Natural gas also contains hydrocarbons with from one to four carbon atoms. It can be compressed and stored in the same way as refinery gas. The compressed product is called Liquefied Natural Gas (LNG). Natural gas is transported to the refinery in this form, and takes up much less storage space as a liquid than as a gas.

Most Caribbean countries import oil and oil products such as gasoline, diesel oil and fuel oil. These imports place a severe financial burden on these countries, some of which have turned their attention to alternative sources of energy such as solar energy, wind energy and biogas to reduce their total dependence on oil. Some may consider following the example of Brazil which uses **gasohol** to run its cars and other vehicles.

Brazil grows large quantities of sugar cane. During sugar manufacture, molasses is produced. Molasses, when fermented and distilled, produces alcohol. **Gasoline** mixed with **alcohol** is known as **gasohol**. By using this gasoline/alcohol mixture Brazil is able to reduce its fuel import bill. (Starchy crops such as cassava, corn (maize) and potato can also be used in alcohol production.)

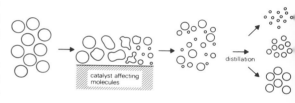

The process of 'cracking' molecules using a catalyst

Activity

Write a short paragraph to show you understand the meaning of each of the following terms. (You may consult any book, but as far as possible use your own words.)

1 Sedimentary rocks
2 Permeable rocks
3 Chemical bonds
4 Fractional distillation
5 Knocking

40

From oil to plastics

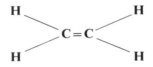

Containers made from plastics

Plastics and their uses

Oil is a major source of organic compounds which are used as fuels and to produce plastics.

Oil
— Gasoline, Kerosene
— Other chemicals, including those which are starting materials for preparing

Polythene	Nylon
PVC	Dacron
Perspex	
Synthetic rubbers	

The cracking of certain oil fractions produces a class of organic compounds known as alkenes. Ethene, formula C_2H_4, is an example of an alkene.

The alkenes are very reactive molecules, and many alkene molecules may link up to form compounds containing large numbers of carbon atoms. These compounds are called **polymers** and the process by which they are formed is known as **polymerization**. The word polymer literally means 'many units' (poly = many; and mer = units).

When ethene molecules link up we get polythene

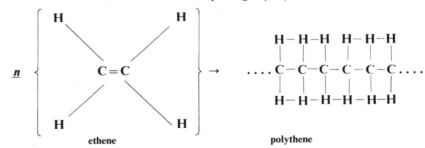

ethene → polythene

(n = large number greater than 1000)

In the same way

| propene | polymerizes to produce | polypropene |
| vinyl chloride | polymerizes to produce | poly(vinyl chloride) or PVC |

Polymers can be prepared from starting materials other than alkenes, but these starting materials are also derived from oil fractions.

The products of polymerization reactions must be processed or refined before they can be used by the consumer. The refined or processed materials are called **plastics**.

Plastics are widely used because they:

1   are light in weight;
2   can be made rigid or flexible as required;
3   do not corrode easily;
4   are relatively resistant to wear;
5   can be so made that they are very strong;
6   can be coloured during manufacture;
7   can be easily moulded into most shapes;
8   are often cheaper than wood, stone or metal;
9   are good insulators.

The ethene molecule, C_2H_4

Unfortunately plastics are difficult to dispose of. They are not **biodegradable**. This means that they do not rot, since they cannot be broken down by the action of bacteria. When burnt, plastics often produce acrid, poisonous smoke.

Because plastics burn easily they can be serious fire hazards. Moreover burning plastics can cause serious burns.

Oil and the environment

The extraction and use of oil and its products leads to pollution. The pollution can be either direct or indirect.

Direct pollution

This occurs when

(a) oil is being drilled;
(b) oil tankers are being loaded and unloaded;
(c) there are accidents at sea and on land.

Indirect pollution

When oil and its products are burnt (used) pollutants are produced and oxygen is used up. These pollutants affect the quality of the air we breathe, the quality of the water we drink, our buildings, etc. The pollution of the air is the most serious. Some pollutants are described below.

Carbon dioxide
Carbon dioxide is a product of the combustion of fuels.

$$\textbf{fuel} + \textbf{oxygen} \rightarrow \textbf{carbon dioxide} + \textbf{water} + \textbf{energy}$$

It is believed that the resultant build-up of carbon dioxide in the atmosphere could lead to a rise in the temperature of the Earth's surface.

Carbon monoxide
This pollutant is produced when gasoline and other fuels are incompletely burnt. Carbon monoxide is highly poisonous as it combines with haemoglobin of the blood, and prevents the uptake of oxygen.

Sulphur dioxide
This pollutant, which is often dissolved in rainwater, affects trees, concrete buildings, etc. It also causes respiratory problems.

Nitrogen oxides
Nitrogen oxides cause respiratory problems in humans; and induce excessive growth in microscopic water plants called algae. The rapid growth of algae decreases the oxygen content of the water, and so the fish population dies.

Lead compounds
Lead compounds are added to gasoline to reduce 'knocking'. When vehicles burn up the gasoline in their engines the lead compounds come off in the exhaust gases, polluting the air.

Lead compounds are poisonous. They accumulate in the body and interfere with the proper functioning of cells.

Oil and the future

Oil is a **non-renewable resource**, i.e. the oil we take from the ground to supply our energy needs is not replaced. At present oil supplies about 90% of the world's energy needs. It is clear that we should not continue to depend so heavily on an energy source which the experts say could run out sometime in the next century.

In addition to using the remaining oil more wisely, we need to develop methods of making efficient use of alternative sources of energy, for example solar energy, wind energy, and biogas, which do not depend on fossil fuels.

Questions

1 Perspex is preferred to glass for making windows for aircraft. Find out as much as you can about the physical and other properties of these two materials: Perspex and glass.
2 State three advantages of Perspex over glass.
3 Obtain pieces of Perspex and glass and determine, by experiment, which scratches more easily.
4 Identify four different uses for the material PVC.
5 Write a short essay entitled 'Plastics: a blessing and a nuisance.'
6 Describe an experiment you would carry out to compare the strengths of different plastics.

Questions

1 What is meant by the term **fuel**?
2 The three factors required to produce a fire are a **fuel**, **oxygen** and **heat**. This can be shown in the form of a triangle.

(a) Identify three ways of preventing a fire from spreading.
(b) What steps would *you* take if a fire broke out in your home?
3 Identify three glaring examples of pollution in your country.

41

The Sun has the power, we need the energy

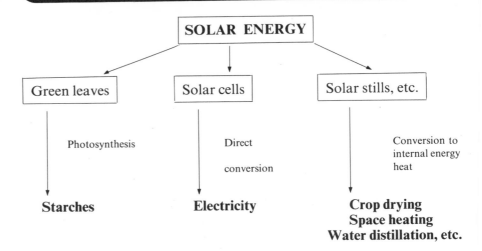

```
                      SOLAR ENERGY

        Green leaves      Solar cells      Solar stills, etc.

        Photosynthesis      Direct          Conversion to
                            conversion      internal energy
                                            heat

        Starches          Electricity       Crop drying
                                            Space heating
                                            Water distillation, etc.
```

The high cost of fuel, for example gasoline, diesel oil and fuel oil, has forced the world community to consider alternative sources of energy.

Solar energy is the most attractive alternative for tropical countries such as ours because:

(a) the Sun shines for at least 9 hours each day in the region;
(b) the supply of solar energy is inexhaustible;
(c) using this energy source does not cause pollution.

But the region and the world need the 'know how' to make use of the Sun's power. There are some solar power devices in use already.

Use of solar power

Solar stills

Solar stills

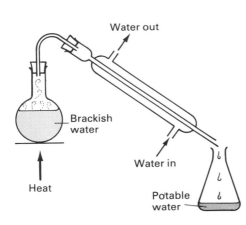

In some parts of the world the major water source consists of brackish water or sea water. The people in these areas need a cheap and reliable method of obtaining purer water from these sources. The solar distillation apparatus or **solar still** may be part of the answer to their problem.

Solar stills generally consist of a box-like structure with a transparent top (which may be made of plastic or glass). The inside of the 'box' is painted black. The stills are filled with water and mounted so that they face the midday sun. The Sun's radiant energy enters the box, and is trapped inside. This raises the temperature of the water in the box until it evaporates. The water vapour condenses on the inner surface of the transparent top, then runs off and is collected in a trough as pure water.

Stills made entirely of plastic, or those with transparent tops may be cheaper or lighter than those shown here, but they do not last as long and are less efficient.

Samples of potable water can also be obtained from sea water or brackish water using the distillation apparatus shown on the left.

Solar cookers

Solar cookers have been used for hundreds of years. These devices are essentially parabolic reflecting surfaces which are turned towards the Sun. The devices collect the Sun's rays and concentrate them, either at a point or over a small area, where the pot of food is placed.

Solar driers

Simple solar driers may consist of a wooden box fitted with a tray which holds the crops, for example, and a transparent top like the one on the right. The box should be properly insulated. Holes drilled in the walls of the box allow warm air to flow over the material being dried.

Solar panels

Solar power can be used to heat and cool buildings and to provide hot water for domestic and other uses. Solar heating panels such as those shown in the diagram are attached to the roofs of buildings. Water which is heated in the panel is pumped to a spiral coil where it is used to heat the water in the tank. This water is fed to where it is needed. Once the water in the coil has given up its energy to its surroundings it is returned to the panel so that it can receive more energy and continue the process.

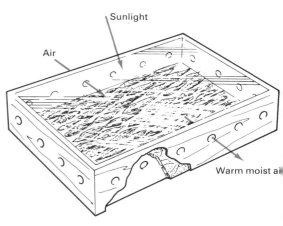

Solar drier

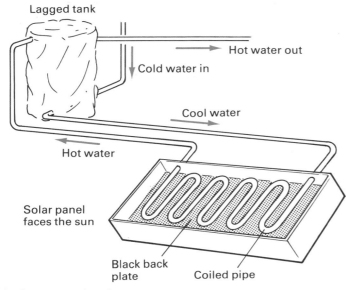

How a solar heating panel works

The solar cell

A solar cell is a device which converts light energy directly into electricity.

When light falls on a semiconducting material such as silicon, it is converted with 10–15% efficiency to electrical energy.

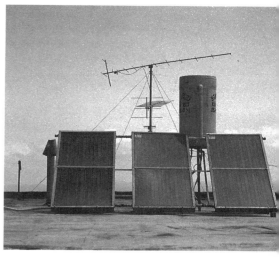

Solar panels on the roof of a house

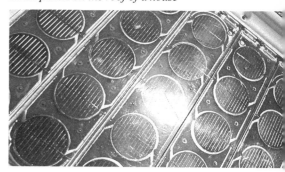

Banks of solar cells

Questions

1 What happens to the other 85–90% of the 'incident' energy falling on a solar cell?
2 Is it wise to build a power plant that draws its electricity entirely from solar cells?
3 Find out about at least two applications of solar cells in which the cells are connected together to generate a significant amount of electricity.
4 Why do you think solar cells work better in space than on Earth?
5 What are some of the disadvantages of depending on solar power to cook your meals?

Activity

With the help of one or two classmates, design and construct a working model of a device for heating water using solar energy.

Panels of solar cells mounted on satellites collect large quantities of the Sun's energy (right)

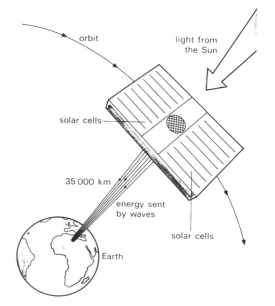

42

Metals and Us!

Metals in use

Metals have played a large part in the progress of many societies. They are used in a wide variety of ways: for tools, weapons, ornaments, in machinery, and so on. The most popular of these metals are aluminium, copper and iron. Their main features are summarized in the table below. The major physical properties of metals can be inferred from this table.

METAL	PROPERTIES	MAJOR USES
Aluminium	Low density (light) Good conductor of heat Does not corrode readily Alloys easily with other metals. Has a highly reflective surface, when pure.	Aircraft manufacture, cooking utensils, window frames, engines, in cables, as wrap or foil in cooking
Copper	Good conductor of heat and electricity Does not corrode easily Malleable—easy to bend	Electrical cables, cooking utensils
Iron/steel	Very strong but rusts easily	Reinforcement for concrete buildings, bodies of cars, tools, girders in bridges, cooking utensils

Physical properties of metals

Most metals

1 are **solids** at room temperature. (Can you think of any exceptions?);
2 are **shiny**;
3 have **high densities**;
4 are **malleable** (easily hammered into sheets)
5 are **ductile** (easily drawn into wires);
6 are **good conductors** of heat and electricity;

Alloys

Pure metals are sometimes brittle, or have other undesirable characteristics. However, when these metals are **alloyed** their properties are improved. An alloy is a mixture of two elements, at least one of which is a metal. This mixture has metallic properties. For example, iron can be mixed with other metals such as chromium, nickel, manganese and vanadium, so as to increase its range of uses.

Stainless steel, an alloy of iron and carbon, is not easily corroded, and can be used for making teapots, cutlery, tools etc. Pure iron could not be used for these purposes because it is too brittle and would rust when wet.

When copper is alloyed with zinc the product is called **brass**. Brass is easy to shape and conducts electricity well. It is used in the manufacture of door handles, nuts, screws and bolts, plugs, sockets and water taps.

The alloy of copper and tin is called bronze. Bronze finds many decorative and ornamental uses.

Aluminium alloyed with copper is very durable (strong). This alloy, which has a low density, is widely used in the bodies of spacecraft.

Corrosion can be useful

In Section 43 you will read about the rusting (corrosion) of iron, and discover that billions of dollars are spent each year fighting corrosion, or in replacing articles that are lost through corrosion. But corrosion is not always a bad thing. For example, when brass and bronze objects tarnish or corrode they develop a green patina (coloration) which can be very pleasing to the eye.

Aluminium, aluminium oxide and anodizing

Strictly speaking, aluminium is a reactive metal. But it does not normally behave as such. This is because aluminium develops a thin, evenly distributed, compact oxide coating when it is exposed to the air.

This oxide coating protects the underlying layers of aluminium metal from corrosion. A thick overcoat can be put onto aluminium by a rapid process known as **anodizing**.

The chemical properties of metals

1 Metals form mainly basic oxides. However, zinc and aluminium oxides are described as **amphoteric** because they dissolve readily in both dilute acid and alkali.
2 The active metals react with dilute aqueous acids to form a salt and hydrogen; heat is liberated in these reactions.
3 Metals alloy readily with other metals.
4 Metals decompose water or steam, if they are sufficiently active.
   The table below summarizes the chemical properties of selected metals when reacting with oxygen, water (or steam), alkali and acid.

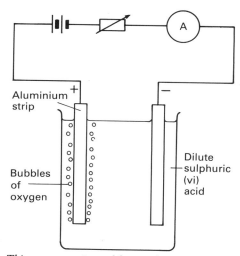

This apparatus is used for anodizing aluminium. When the current is switched on, oxygen gas escapes and reacts with the positively-charged aluminium strip, forming an oxide coating

METAL	REACTION WITH OXYGEN	REACTION WITH WATER (OR STEAM)	REACTION WITH DILUTE ACID	REACTION WITH DILUTE ALKALI
Aluminium	Rapidly tarnishes in the cold. A thin coating of aluminium oxide forms.	If pure, reacts with water, liberating hydrogen and a lot of heat.	Liberates hydrogen, salt is formed.	Dissolves, liberating hydrogen.
Zinc	Zinc oxide forms, slowly in the cold, but more rapidly when heated.	Displaces hydrogen from steam.	Liberates hydrogen, salt is formed.	Dissolves, liberating hydrogen
Iron	Forms an oxide if heated. Rusts in the cold, if moisture is present.	Reacts with steam to produce hydrogen.	Liberates hydrogen, salt is formed.	No reaction.
Copper	Forms black copper oxide if strongly heated.	No reaction.	No reaction.	No reaction.
Silver	Forms silver oxide (tarnish).	No reaction.	No reaction.	No reaction.

Activities

1 (a) Describe an experiment you would carry out to determine whether iron rusts more rapidly in sea water than in pipe water.
   (b) From the results of your experiments, state whether you would expect the iron gate of a home near the seaside to rust faster than a similar iron gate at a home inland.
2 Obtain as many examples of abrasives and scouring powders as you can. Compare the effectiveness of each abrasive and each scouring powder in cleaning (polishing) household articles made of
   (a) aluminium, (b) copper, (c) iron, (d) zinc.

Questions

1 Name two alloys and their uses.
2 Find out all you can about the properties and uses of the metals calcium, magnesium and lead. Present your findings in a table.
3 What common household chemicals are used to clean silver jewellery?
4 Compare the physical properties of a metal such as iron with a material such as PVC—a plastic.

Aluminium is the most abundant metal in the Earth's crust. It is found chiefly as bauxite, a mixture of aluminium oxide, silica and oxides of iron. Some Caribbean countries have large bauxite deposits. Here bauxite is being dug from the ground at a mine in Jamaica

43

Rusting and its prevention

When does rusting occur?

Look carefully at the diagrams and captions below. What can you deduce from them about the conditions necessary for rusting to occur? Why does more rust develop in tube III than in tube IV?

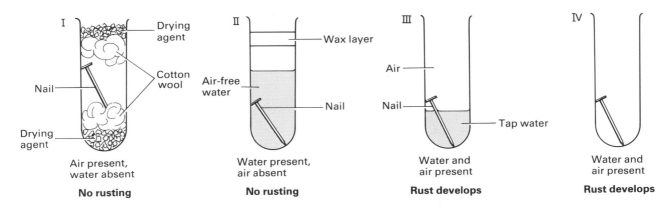

I	II	III	IV
Drying agent, Cotton wool, Nail, Drying agent	Wax layer, Air-free water, Nail	Air, Nail, Tap water	copper wire, Iron nail
Air present, water absent	Water present, air absent	Water and air present	Water and air present
No rusting	**No rusting**	**Rust develops**	**Rust develops**

The results indicate that moisture and oxygen are necessary for rusting. Now consider the diagrams below. From them you can see that

(a) rusting of iron is speeded up if the iron is attached to a metal less reactive than itself;
(b) rusting is prevented if iron is attached to a metal more reactive than itself;
(c) rusting is also speeded up if the iron is in contact with acid or dissolved salts or if the temperature is raised.

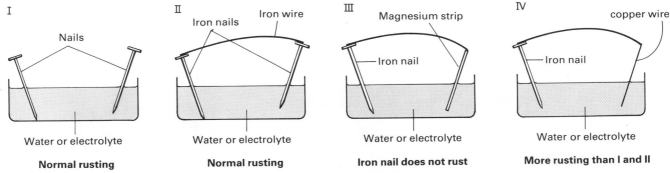

I	II	III	IV
Nails, Water or electrolyte	Iron nails, Iron wire, Water or electrolyte	Magnesium strip, Iron nail, Water or electrolyte	copper wire, Iron nail, Water or electrolyte
Normal rusting	**Normal rusting**	**Iron nail does not rust**	**More rusting than I and II**

What is rusting?

When rusting takes place iron is converted to iron oxide.

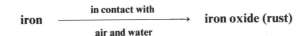

$$\text{iron} \xrightarrow[\text{air and water}]{\text{in contact with}} \text{iron oxide (rust)}$$

This conversion is often described as **oxidation**.

The iron oxide (rust) which forms does not adhere (stick) to the metal surface; it flakes off, leaving fresh metal open to air and water. This leads to more and more rusting until the metal has completely rusted away.

Between 10% and 25% of the iron and steel manufactured each year is lost through rusting. The replacement of the iron and steel lost in this way costs billions of dollars. The rusting of iron and steel can also lead to loss of life, for example when

(a) railway lines rust through and trains are derailed;
(b) rusted boilers and machinery in factories malfunction.

Since rusting is both troublesome and costly it is important to discover some ways of slowing it down or preventing it.

Iron can be protected from rusting by coating it with zinc—a process known as **galvanizing.** One way of galvanizing iron involves first cleaning it with sulphuric acid and then dipping it into molten zinc. In a galvanized object, the zinc is oxidized instead of the iron, which is not exposed to the air. In this way the iron or steel object is protected.

Tin is also used to reduce corrosion. Tin cans are not made of tin alone—they are steel containers which have been coated with a thin layer of tin. Tin cans are widely used for the storage of food and beverages. Tin salts are **non-toxic.** If small amounts of tin are transferred from the can to its contents, the consumer will not be harmed. In contrast, zinc salts are toxic, so galvanized cans are not used for food storage.

Other methods of reducing rusting in iron and steel objects include:

(a) painting;
(b) coating the object with organic plastics, rubbers and greases;
(c) dipping the object into dilute solutions of chemicals such as sodium nitrate(III) ($NaNO_3$) and potassium dichromate(VI) ($K_2Cr^2O_7$);
(d) electroplating or electrodeposition.

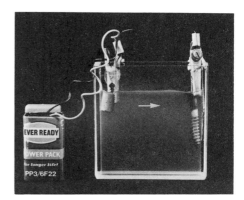

The apparatus shown in the photograph can be used to silver plate articles such as spoons. The article to be plated is connected to the negative end of the battery. A silver rod is connected to the positive end of the battery. When the current is switched on silver atoms leave the silver rod and, at the same time silver atoms are deposited on the rod to be plated, so that a thin, evenly distributed layer of silver is deposited on a less precious metal such as copper.

Many articles are either chromium (chrome) plated or nickel plated. Chromium plated articles are widely used for decorative purposes. Chromium plating also increases the strength of tools and machinery and helps to preserve them from rust.

Summary

1 Rusting is the conversion of iron metal to its oxide.
2 Rusting takes place if air and water are present.
3 Rusting is speeded up by acids, bases, dissolved salts and by raising the temperature.
4 Rusting can be slowed down or prevented by:
 (a) galvanizing;
 (b) tin plating and chrome plating;
 (c) electroplating;
 (d) the use of paints, plastics and rubbers.

Activities

1 If you were given the following chemicals:
 sodium carbonate (washing soda), sodium hydrogencarbonate (baking soda), ethanoic acid (vinegar), ammonia, citric acid (lemon juice), and ethanedioic acid (oxalic acid)
 how would you determine which of them removes rust stains from clothing and kitchen utensils?
2 Using a suitable reference book, find out what steel is made from.
3 Given that aluminium, magnesium and zinc are more reactive than iron, and that lead, copper and tin are less reactive, would you use aluminium to protect the steel hull of a ship from rusting? Give a reason for your answer.
4 Describe an experiment to show that the rusting of iron is speeded up in the presence of an acid or a base.

pH, acids, bases and salts

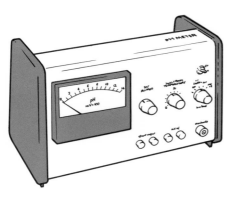

pH meter

pH and indicators

You have met the terms pH, acids, bases (alkalis) and salts before. **pH** is simply a measure of how acidic or basic (alkaline) a substance is. Substances which dissolve in water can be tested using pH paper, or by another suitable method, and so placed into one of three groups—acids, bases and salts.

Substances with pH less than 7 are called acidic, those with pH greater than 7 are called basic. pH of 7 indicates that the substance is neither acidic nor alkaline, i.e. it is neutral. Many, but not all, salts dissolve in water to give a solution with pH 7. This solution of a salt in water is commonly called an **aqueous solution**.

The pH meter gives a precise value of the pH of aqueous solutions of substances but indicator paper can be used on solutions to determine whether the substances are neutral, alkaline or acidic. Indicators are dyes which show one colour when in an acid substance and another when in contact with a base, and so give an approximate value of the pH of aqueous solutions.

pH	DESCRIPTION	COLOUR WITH UNIVERSAL INDICATOR	HOUSEHOLD SUBSTANCE	CHEMICAL IT CONTAINS
14 13 12	Strongly basic	Deep blue	Oven cleaner	May contain sodium hydroxide
11 10	Weakly basic	Green	Household ammonia	Ammonia
			Milk of magnesia and other antacids	Magnesium hydroxide
9 8			Baking powder	Potassium hydrogencarbonate
7	Neutral	Yellow	Blood, milk, water	
6 5 4	Weakly acidic	Orange	Vinegar	Ethanoic acid
3			Oranges, health salts	
2 1 0	Strongly acid	Red	Lemon juice	Citric acid

Experiment A : To find the pH of toothpaste

Obtain as many different brands of toothpaste as you can. Using pH paper or universal indicator determine the pH of each brand. What is the pH range of the brands of toothpaste examined? Why do you think manufacturers produce toothpaste in this range?

Acids

Acids can be solid, e.g. ethanedioic acid; liquid, e.g. sulphuric acid; or gaseous, e.g. sulphur dioxide. Apart from their pH, acids can be detected by the following properties.

1. Their reactions with carbonates and hydrogencarbonates. When an acid is added to sodium carbonate (solid or in solution) there is a vigorous effervescence (bubbling) and the gas carbon dioxide is given off. Sodium hydrogencarbonate will react in the same way.

   acid + carbonate (or hydrogencarbonate) $\longrightarrow$ carbon dioxide + water + salt

   Carbon dioxide is easily identified because it turns lime water milky.
2. Their sour taste. **It is unsafe to taste chemicals.** Do not do so unless you are told to do so by your teacher.
3. Their reaction with active metals. Acids react with active metals such as magnesium and zinc to produce hydrogen gas:

   acid   + active metal   → salt (aq)   + hydrogen (gas)
   hydrochloric acid + magnesium   → magnesium chloride + hydrogen (gas)

   Hydrogen gas, in a test tube, can be identified by the popping sound it makes when a lighted splint is held in the mouth of the tube.
4. Acids turn moist blue litmus red. They also develop definite colours with other indicators.

Bases (alkalis)

Some bases are soluble in water, others are not. Soluble bases are commonly called alkalis. Examples of soluble bases are potassium hydroxide and sodium hydroxide. Insoluble bases include copper(II) oxide (a black powder) and iron(III) hydroxide. Apart from their pH, alkalis have the following properties.

1. They turn moist red litmus blue. They also develop definite colours with other indicators.
2. They have a slippery feel. Do not touch alkalis unless told to by your teacher. They can be caustic.
3. They do not react with sodium carbonate or sodium hydrogen-carbonate.

Volumes of aqueous acid and aqueous alkali can be accurately measured using the pipette, burette and the volumetric flask. These pieces of apparatus are all made of glass, and should be handled with care. Each piece of equipment is intended for use in a particular way. During your science lessons your teacher will tell you what to do with them.

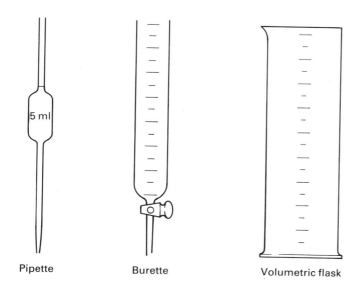

Pipette   Burette   Volumetric flask

Salts

Applying fertilizers

> ### Experiment B: To prepare a salt
>
> Place about 5 cm³ of dilute sodium hydroxide solution on a watch glass. Add dilute hydrochloric acid, drop by drop. Stir continuously, and test the pH of the mixture (using pH paper) at the same time. Continue to add the acid until the test paper indicates a pH of 7. Evaporate the solution you have obtained and note the white crystals that appear on the watch glass. You have just prepared a salt.

$$\text{acid} + \text{alkali} \rightarrow \text{salt} + \text{water}$$

acid (hydrochloric acid) + alkali (sodium hydroxide) → salt (sodium chloride) + water

The reaction type in which an acid is added to an alkali (base) to produce a salt and water is known as a **neutralization reaction**. Neutralization reactions are widely used in the home, in the school laboratory and in industry.

Sodium chloride is a neutral salt, i.e. when it dissolves in water its solution has pH 7. But some salts, when dissolved in water, have pH less than 7. For example, ammonium sulphate (a fertilizer) dissolves in water to give a solution with pH about 5·5. You can now appreciate why repeated applications of ammonium sulphate to the soil leaves it acid. Other salts, when dissolved in water, have pH greater than 7, e.g. sodium carbonate and potassium ethanoate.

Salts used in everyday life

SALT	COLOUR AND OTHER CHARACTERISTICS	USES
Ammonium chloride	White crystals	Dry cells, fertilizers
Ammonium sulphate (sulphate of ammonia)	White crystals	Fertilizers
Calcium carbonate (marble, limestone)	White but can be coloured	Decorative stones, manufacture of cement and line
Calcium sulphate (plaster of paris, gypsum)	White powder	Plastering walls; making casts, etc.
Magnesium sulphate (Epsom salts)	White crystals	Purgative
Copper (II) sulphate	Blue crystals	Fungicides
Sodium carbonate (washing soda)	White crystals or powder	In cleaning, in laundry as a water softener, in the manufacture of glass
Sodium hydrogen-carbonate (baking powder)	White powder	Raising agent (in cakes), to remove some fruit stains, cleaning silver jewellery

Neutralization reactions at home

1   *Reducing indigestion*   Acid indigestion is suffered when too much acid builds up in the stomach. The discomforts of excess acidity can be relieved by neutralizing the excess stomach acid with a mild alkali such as milk of magnesia or sodium hydrogencarbonate. Most antacid tablets contain a mild alkali. Strong alkali is not used to cure indigestion. Why?

2 *Calming bee and wasp stings* If you are stung by a wasp, vinegar (ethanoic acid) should be dabbed on the affected part; if you are stung by a bee it is advisable to use sodium hydrogencarbonate. What do these treatments suggest about the nature of the substances in the wasp sting and the bee sting?

3 *Cleaning toilet bowls* The active ingredient in some toilet bowl cleaners is sodium hydrogensulphate which dissolves in water to produce a solution of pH less than 7. This suggests that many of the stains in the toilet bowls are alkaline in nature.

4 *Removing fruit, wine and tea stains* The substance disodium tetraborate (common name borax) is a base. It is widely used to remove tea, fruit and wine stains; suggesting that these stains might be acidic in character.

Questions

1 Black coffee is known to have pH 5. What does this tell us about the nature of the substances in black coffee?
2 Do you agree with the statement 'the solutions of all salts have pH 7'? Justify your answer.
3 Calcium oxide or calcium hydroxide is used to treat soil which has become too acid. What does this suggest about the nature of calcium oxide and calcium hydroxide?

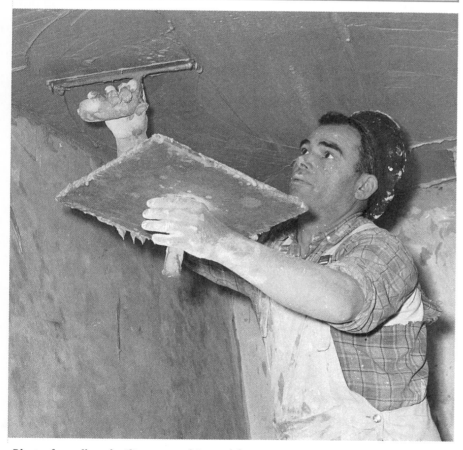

Plaster for walls and ceilings uses calcium sulphate

45

Analysis – what is there and how much?

Naming salts

sodium hydroxide + hydro*chloric* acid → *sodium chloride* + water
(base)　　　　　　(acid)　　　　　(salt)

potassium hydroxide + *nitric* acid → *potassium nitrate* + water
(base)　　　　　　(acid)　　　　(salt)

copper oxide + *sulphuric* acid → *copper sulphate* + water
(base)　　　　(acid)　　　　(salt)

It can be seen from the above equations that the name of a salt has two parts: one part derived from the base and the other from the acid from which it was formed.

Identifying substances

When salts dissolve in water they usually (but not always) break up into two charged parts called **ions**. For example, sodium chloride in water produces the sodium ion (Na^+) and the chloride ion (Cl^-). Substances can be identified by finding out which ions they are composed of.

Oxygen escaping

Testing for oxygen

Carbon dioxide escaping

Testing for carbon dioxide

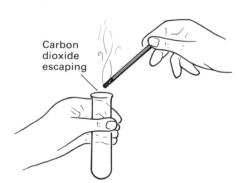

Calcium hydroxide (lime water)

Dilute hydrochloric acid　　Sodium carbonate

Producing carbon dioxide

Activities

1 To identify oxygen

Place 2 cm³ hydrogen peroxide in a test tube. Add a very small amount of manganese(IV) oxide and immediately place a finger over the open mouth of the test tube (this traps any gas that is formed). Note the vigorous bubbling of the solution which indicates that a gas is being given off. When the bubbling stops hold a glowing splint in the test tube. Observe that the splint relights. This indicates that oxygen was produced in the reaction.

2 To identify carbon dioxide

Using a drinking straw, bubble exhaled air into a solution of lime water in a test tube or other suitable container. Note that the lime water soon turns cloudy.

Exhaled air contains carbon dioxide. It is reasonable to assume that carbon dioxide caused the lime water to go cloudy. Continue to pass exhaled air through the solution. What do you observe?

3 What produces carbon dioxide?

Add some dilute hydrochloric acid to some powdered sodium carbonate in a test tube and allow the gas produced to bubble through lime water in another test tube (see the apparatus in the diagram). Observe that the lime water turned cloudy, indicating that carbon dioxide was evolved.

Repeat the above experiment, but this time use calcium carbonate, copper carbonate and sodium hydrogencarbonate instead of the sodium carbonate.

You should have found that in each case the lime water initially turned cloudy. Therefore in each case carbon dioxide was given off.

All carbonates and hydrogencarbonates react with acids to produce carbon dioxide.

If a lighted splint is plunged into a container of carbon dioxide the flame goes out. This property of carbon dioxide is used in firefighting.

4 Testing for hydrogen

Place a small amount of powdered magnesium in a test tube, and add a little dilute hydrochloric acid. You should notice that the test tube gets hot and steady bubbling shows that a gas is evolved.

Place a lighted splint at the mouth of the test tube. You should hear a loud 'popping' sound. That noise indicates that the gas given off was hydrogen.

Repeat the experiment using powdered iron and aluminium. Record your observations. Now try it again using copper powder and dilute hydrochloric acid. Is it true to say that *all* metals react with acids to produce hydrogen?

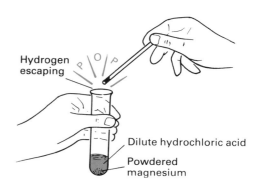

Testing for hydrogen

Testing for the hydroxide ion

When solid sodium hydroxide is dissolved in water a clear solution containing the hydroxide ion (OH^-) is obtained. The hydroxide ion can be detected since it forms a precipitate (suspension) with most metal ions, e.g.

with copper ions (Cu^{2+}) it forms a blue precipitate;
with calcium ions (Ca^{2+}) it forms a white precipitate;
with iron(II) ions (Fe^{2+}) it forms a green precipitate; and so on. . . .

Finding out how much base is present

The **concentration** of an aqueous solution of sodium hydroxide can be determined by **titrating** a fixed volume of it with an acid of known **concentration**. Concentration is a measure of the quantity of substance dissolved in known volume (usually 1 litre) of solution. Titration is the process of adding a solution from a burette to another solution in a conical flask or other container.

The procedure for determining the concentration of a sodium hydroxide solution is outlined below.

1 Pipette 25 cm³ of a solution of sodium hydroxide into a conical flask.
2 Add two drops of the indicator—screened methyl orange is used here. The contents of flask should turn a green colour.
3 Using the burette, slowly run in the acid, e.g. sulphuric acid, until the colour of the mixture just changes to a very light pink. At this point the aqueous solution in the flask has a pH of (approximately) 7.

The process of adding an acid to a base until the pH is 7 is called **neutralization**. In this case the salt formed is sodium sulphate.

sodium hydroxide + sulphuric acid → sodium sulphate + water

The products of neutralization are always salt and water.

Given the concentration of the acid, and knowing the volumes of acid and base which combined to form the neutral solution, it is possible to calculate the concentration of the base. The concentration of some other substances dissolved in water can also be determined by titration.

A solution is a **homogeneous** mixture of two or more substances. Look up your glossary of terms to find out the exact meaning of the word homogeneous.

A solution is formed whenever one or more substances dissolve completely in a given substance. The substance that does the dissolving is called the **solvent**, and the substances which dissolve are called **solutes**.

A solution, then, is a homogeneous mixture of solute(s) and solvent. When water is the solvent the solution is said to be **aqueous**. If another solvent is involved the solution is described as **non-aqueous**. Examples of non-aqueous solutions are grease dissolved in kerosene and nail polish dissolved in acetone. Both aqueous and non-aqueous solvents can be used to extract pigments or dyes from plant tissue.

Questions

1 What is the name of the salt formed when sodium hydroxide reacts with carbonic acid?
2 Describe how you would attempt to prepare a solid sample of the salt potassium nitrate.
3 Describe an experiment you would carry out to determine which of the metals zinc, copper, iron, tin and lead react with dilute hydrochloric acid to produce hydrogen.
4 'Kerosene is used to remove grease stains from clothes.' Why do you think that this is possible?

46

Using chemicals with care

Symbols warning of corrosive chemicals

Be careful—that chemical may be dangerous

Some chemicals are toxic, others are corrosive, flammable or explosive . . . that is why warning labels are placed on containers to tell users of the dangers associated with using that particular chemical.

Corrosive chemicals

These chemicals include caustic soda (sodium hydroxide), nitric acid, sulphuric acid and hydrochloric acid (commonly obtained from the drug store as muriatic acid).

Corrosive chemicals are very unkind to the skin. If your hand or skin comes into contact with a corrosive chemical you should (except if the procedure on the label states otherwise) wash it immediately with lots of water.

Bleach

If bleach is swallowed, milk or the white of an egg should also be consumed. Milk of magnesia may also by used. **Do not** administer either sodium hydrogencarbonate or anything acidic.

It is very unwise to mix bleach and ammonia. These preparations, when mixed, produce fumes which affect the regularity of our breathing.

Ammonia

This substance is very irritating to the eyes and nose. It is also caustic to the skin. If ammonia is swallowed, large doses of lime squash or lemon juice should also be taken. If these are not available diluted vinegar may be used instead. Egg white, milk or edible oil will ease the distress felt.

If ammonia gets onto the skin or in the eyes it should be washed off with lots of water.

Poisonous substances

Most insecticides are **toxic**. Some are stomach poisons, i.e. they are dangerous when ingested, others are contact poisons, i.e. they can be absorbed through the skin. All insecticides should carry labels such as 'Keep out of the reach of children. If swallowed seek medical advice.'

Some insecticides contain heavy metals such as lead, mercury and arsenic which are all highly toxic. Others contain organo-chlorine compounds which are equally toxic. All too often, medical advice or attention reaches the victim too late. So you must be very careful with insecticides. Make sure they are always kept on a high shelf in a labelled bottle. Lock them away if you can.

Some of the chemicals used by jewellers are also toxic. In at least one Caribbean territory jewel making is often carried out in the home. To what extent are the householders and their families affected by the continued use of such chemicals as mercury and potassium cyanide?

Mercury is a cumulative poison which stays in the body and affects the nervous system.

Do not wait until there is a fire!

Find out where the fire extinguisher is and how to use it.

Carbon dioxide is a non-flammable gas, i.e. it does not burn, and it does not support combustion (things do not burn in it). Carbon dioxide is denser than air, and therefore tends to sink downwards. These two properties make carbon dioxide useful for fighting fires.

Some modern fire extinguishers contain carbon dioxide held under pressure. When the valve of the extinguisher is opened the gas rushes out and blankets the fire, excluding the air. As soon as the fire is deprived of air, it goes out. Carbon dioxide extinguishers should be used instead of water extinguishers for fighting electrical fires (remember that water conducts electricity—see p. 89) and fires involving oils, or gasoline (if water is sprayed onto burning oil or gasoline the oil or gasoline floats to the top of the water and continues to burn).

In the absence of a fire extinguisher, a box of dry sand should be kept in the corner of the laboratory, as an emergency measure.

Solutions, suspensions and colloids

A solution was defined on p. 119 as a homogeneous mixture of two or more substances, i.e. as a mixture which is the same all the way through. In a solution the particles of the solute break up so much that they are no longer visible.

In some mixtures the solute particles do not break up to this extent and can still be seen. The term **suspension** is used to describe such mixtures. In time the solid particles in the suspension settle to the bottom of the container in a process known as sedimentation. The particles can be separated out more quickly by using a centrifuge.

Colloids

In these mixtures the size of the solid (solute) particles lies between those of true solutions and those of suspensions. The particles of colloids are too small to be separated from the solvent by filtration and also too small to be seen by the unaided eye; but they scatter a beam of light which falls on them.

Emulsion

Salad dressing is a good example of an **emulsion**. In this mixture both media (vinegar and oil) are liquids. A little mustard must be added to keep the oil in very small drops.

An emulsion is a special sort of colloid—it is a liquid-in-liquid colloid.

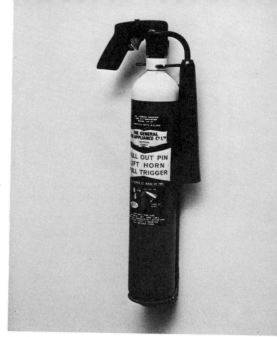

Carbon dioxide fire extinguisher

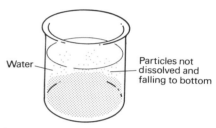

A suspension

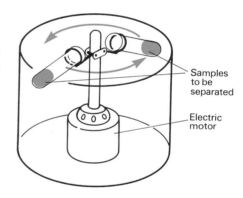

A centrifuge is used for separating particles in suspensions

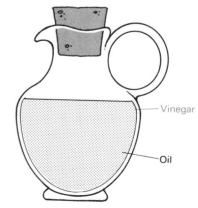

An example of a colloid is oil and vinegar. If mixed with mustard and shaken they form an emulsion

---

Activity

Using as much help as required, make a working model of a carbon dioxide extinguisher.

Questions

1 Distinguish between colloids, suspensions and solutions.
2 Give two examples each of colloids, emulsions and suspensions.
3 Why do you think the particles of a colloid stay apart?

Cleaning it up

Detergents, of which soap is an example, are now so commonplace that you probably think they have always been readily available. Although the principle of soap-making has been known for hundreds of years it is only in the last 80 years that detergents have become cheap enough for most people to afford them.

Detergents are cleaning agents which are used for dishwashing, laundry, in personal care products and in industrial cleaning. The word 'detergent' is derived from the Latin *detergere*, meaning to clean. Detergents are of two types:

1 *Soapy detergents (soaps)*   These are made from fats and oils and an alkali (sodium hydroxide or potassium hydroxide).
2 *Soapless detergents*   These are made from chemicals obtained from petroleum.

Making a soapy detergent (soap)

The materials used in the production of soapy detergents are animal fats or the oils of plants and sodium hydroxide. The steps in the commercial manufacture of soap are as shown in the block diagram below.

Saponification is the breaking down of the oil or fat by the action of an alkali into the fatty acids. In this process the fats or oils are mixed with sodium hydroxide and heated under high pressure. The products are then washed to remove the glycerol which is formed during saponification. In the finishing stages other unwanted products are removed. Finally, substances are added to give the soap its attractive properties. These may include: perfume, colour, bleach and brighteners.

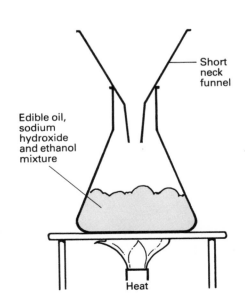

Activity

You can make your own soap in the following way.

1 Place 25 cm³ edible oil (e.g. corn oil or coconut oil) in a suitable conical flask.
2 Add 25 cm³ of 30% aqueous sodium hydroxide (as supplied) and 15 cm³ of ethanol. Be careful—sodium hydroxide is caustic.
3 Place a short neck funnel in the mouth of the flask and boil the mixture very gently for about one hour. Add a little water from time to time to replace that lost through evaporation.
4 When heating is complete, add a little water and stir until a smooth paste is obtained. Then add 40 cm³ hot concentrated aqueous sodium chloride. Stir vigorously, then set the flask aside for 2 to 3 hours.
5 Skim off the material that floats on top of the mixture and put it in a beaker.
6 Add water to the skimmed-off material and heat the beaker.
7 Add a suitable dye and a few drops of your favourite perfume.

Now try out your soap!

Manufacture of soapless detergents

The first soapless detergent was made in 1831. But soapless detergents did not become popular until 1950, when it was discovered that petroleum (oil) contained a group of compounds (alkylbenzenes) that could be converted to soapless detergents.

$$\text{alkylbenzenes} \xrightarrow[\text{at 50 °C}]{\substack{\text{conc.}\\ H_2SO_4}} \substack{\text{soapless}\\ \text{detergents}\\ \text{(raw material)}}$$

As with soaps, a number of substances are added to the raw material to produce detergents with attractive properties.

Uses of soapless detergents include:
(a) cleaning raw wool, cotton and fibre in the textile industry;
(b) laundering clothes, etc.;
(c) cleaning of machinery;
(d) suppressing dust in the mining industry;
(e) in the leather industry.

How do detergents work?

Water is a poor cleansing agent because:

(a) it has poor wetting properties;
(b) it does not have a grease-loving molecule.

Detergents improve the wetting properties of water and help to disperse grease and dirt.

The detergent molecule can be described as shown on the right:
The water-loving head attaches itself to the water, while the grease-loving tail attaches itself to the soilants in the fabric to be cleaned.

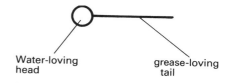

Water-loving head   grease-loving tail

Which detergent to use?

Soap is excellent for laundry purposes if soft water is available, but hard water wastes soap. Some of the soap added to hard water is used up in softening the water and so there is less soap available for cleaning. Soapless detergents do not react with the calcium or magnesium salts which are dissolved in hard water. Soapless detergents are therefore unaffected by the hardness of the water.

Soap is degraded by bacteria, while detergents are not. These latter can accumulate and cause serious pollution problems such as the clogging up of sewer systems. However, some of the detergents manufactured nowadays are biodegradable.

Phosphates are sometimes added to synthetic detergents to increase their cleaning power. When the phosphates in waste water enter lakes and ponds, etc., they enable the algae (microscopic plants) in the water to multiply rapidly. The algae use up most of the dissolved oxygen in the lake water and other aquatic organisms die of oxygen starvation. This is another harmful effect of detergents.

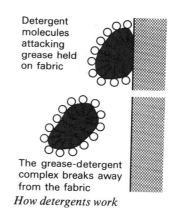

Detergent molecules attacking grease held on fabric

The grease-detergent complex breaks away from the fabric

How detergents work

Questions

1 Write brief notes on (a) the manufacture of soaps; (b) the manufacture of a soapless detergent.
2 Discuss the advantages and disadvantages of using a soapless detergent as compared to a soap.

Pollution of water by detergent foam

48

Ventilation

Discotheques often suffer from poor ventilation

Air supports life on Earth, enabling all living things to breathe. Outside our buildings the air is in continuous circulation and its composition remains relatively constant. But indoors, especially where there are physically active people, the composition of the air is different. It is not only different from the air outside, it changes according to the number of people present, etc. As people respire in an enclosed area, the following changes are likely to occur to the air:

1   The temperature steadily increases, chiefly due to **radiation** of body heat to the surrounding air.
2   The moisture content rises markedly, thus increasing the **relative humidity**.
3   The carbon dioxide content gradually increases.
4   The oxygen content progressively decreases.
5   Pollutants, such as cigarette smoke or odours, may accumulate.

The result is that the air becomes stuffy, damp and stale; the people in it feel sweaty and uncomfortable, and soon become listless and drowsy. The principal factors responsible for such feelings of discomfort are:

(a) the increased **temperature**,
(b) the increased **humidity**, and
(c) the poor **ventilation**,
      rather than the change in the oxygen and carbon dioxide content.

If the room is badly ventilated and contains still, humid air, sweat cannot evaporate quickly enough to cool the people and remains on their skin as liquid. As their body temperatures rise, their brains and nervous systems function more slowly and they soon become drowsy.

The need for ventilation

What has ventilation to do with stuffiness in a room and the discomfort and drowsiness experienced by the people in the room?

Ventilation is the continual replacement of hot, stale air with cool, fresh air, i.e. air circulation into and out of the room. Circulating air also makes air move over the skin surface. This increases the rate of evaporation of sweat, and consequently lowers the people's body temperature. The air circulating in a well-ventilated room also removes polluting odours, smoke, dust particles and spores. So if the ventilation is poor, the risk of inhaling harmful agents increases. These agents could cause respiratory and other infections, and induce allergic reactions.

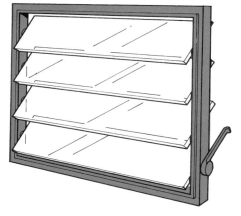

Louvre-type window

Methods of ventilation

Natural ventilation of buildings occurs through windows, doors, ventilation bricks and woodwork, and roof vents. A properly ventilated building has the following features:

(a) Large windows, about six feet high, which can be swung open. This allows hot, stale air which rises to the top of the room to flow out through the top of the window; cool air is then drawn into the room through the lower part of the window.
(b) Windows and doors placed on opposite sides to encourage the flow of air through the building.
(c) High ceilings to accommodate the rising hot, stale air, until it is expelled from the room.
(d) Space around the building with trees which encourage air circulation and provide shade and cooler air temperatures.
(e) Fanlights, or smaller windows or vents, which allow air to flow out at night when the doors and large windows are shut.

Casement-type window

Artificial ventilation is used in large buildings (e.g. airports, stores and supermarkets) where doors must be kept closed to reduce noise or pollutants. Air conditioners are then used to keep the place cool, but these often have a drying effect on the skin and linings of the nasal passages.

Extractor fans provide a better method of ventilating artificially since they cool the room by taking in air from the outside.

Summary

Good ventilation is especially necessary in classrooms, offices, factories, cinemas and other places where large numbers of people are likely to gather at the same time. It is particularly important during the hot summer months, when temperatures may exceed 34°C, with consequent increased sweating.

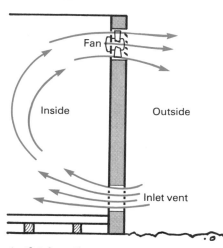

Artificial ventilation using an extractor fan

Questions

1 Explain the way in which ventilation can lower body temperature.
2 What physical process is used to circulate air in the houses B, C and D below?
3 Would you select a louvre or a casement window to provide better ventilation? Explain why.

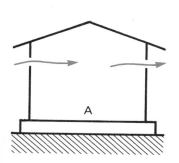

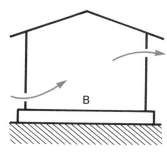

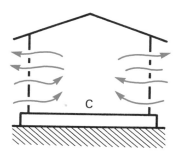

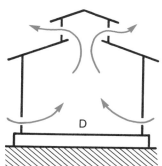

49

How hot is it?

Temperature is a measure of the hotness or coldness of an object while **heat** is energy in process of transfer from one body or region to another. Here is a simple explanation of the difference between heat and temperature. If you heat two beakers of water, one large and one small, using the same amount of heat energy (from a bunsen burner) for a fixed time (about two minutes), you will find that the temperature is higher in the small beaker than in the large one. The same amount of heat energy has been transferred to each beaker, but this energy has had a different effect on the temperature of the water in the beaker.

Measuring temperature

Temperature is measured by an instrument known as a **thermometer**. The most commonly used thermometers are made of mercury trapped in glass. When the temperature of mercury rises the metal expands; when the temperature is lowered it contracts. This change of volume is used to measure temperature.

Alcohol is sometimes used in thermometers instead of mercury. It is much cheaper and has a lower boiling point and freezing point than mercury (mercury: b.p. 360°C, f.p. −40°C; alcohol: b.p. 78°C, f.p. −115°C).

Calibration of a thermometer uses two fixed temperatures: ice melts at 0°C at atmospheric pressure of 760 mm mercury; and water boils at 100°C at atmospheric pressure of 760 mm mercury. The space on the thermometer between these two fixed points is divided into 100 divisions or degrees.

There are two main types of mercury thermometers: **laboratory** and **clinical**. The clinical thermometer differs from the laboratory thermometer in that it is designed to measure, to a high degree of accuracy, the temperature of the human body.

In structure the clinical thermometer differs somewhat from the laboratory one, as shown in the diagram. After use the clinical thermometer must be sterilized.

All thermometers are delicate and expensive instruments. Great care should be taken to handle them properly.

Keeping the temperature constant

Many household appliances, such as irons, ovens, hot water tanks, refrigerators, etc., must be kept at about the same temperature. This is achieved by using a thermostat. The most commonly found thermostat contains a **bimetallic strip**, and uses the linear expansivity of metals.

All materials expand when their temperature is raised, however, the amount of expansion differs from material to material. Although expansion takes place in all directions, if the material is formed into a bar or tubular structure, such expansion can be thought of as linear.

The differential expansion of two metals is utilised in bimetallic strip thermometers. Two metals with different linear expansivity are riveted together. As a result of the differential expansion, when the temperature of the strip is raised, one side expands more than the other and the strip bends; on cooling it regains its original (straight) position. The bimetallic strip can thus act as a switch, breaking contact when it reaches a given temperature. The metals used in the bimetallic strip may vary, but the important principle of differential expansion is still essential.

Laboratory thermometer (left) *and clinical thermometer* (right)

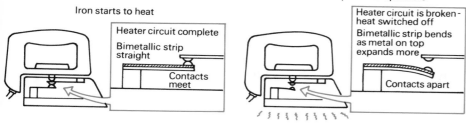

Iron starts to heat

Heater circuit complete
Bimetallic strip straight
Contacts meet

Iron reaches preset temperature

Heater circuit is broken - heat switched off
Bimetallic strip bends as metal on top expands more
Contacts apart

The bimetallic strip acts as a thermostat, switching off the heat when the iron reaches a pre-set temperature. On cooling, the strip straightens again to complete the circuit

Water in the air

Humidity is a measure of the amount of water vapour in the air. The **relative humidity** refers to the degree to which the atmosphere is saturated with water vapour, that is, it represents the amount of water vapour present in the air as a percentage of the amount the air can hold.

Temperature and relative humidity are important factors, among others, in the transpiration rate in plants (p. 54). A high temperature supplies latent heat of vaporization which facilitates evaporation. The lower the relative humidity of the air the greater the space available in the atmosphere for water vapour, and the more easily the water evaporates from the leaves.

The evaporation of perspiration is used to cool the body of animals in the same way. Air conditioners and refrigerators also produce their cooling effect by evaporation. The diagram below shows how evaporation is used to cool a domestic refrigerator. A volatile liquid such as freon is pumped through the tubes round the walls of the freezing compartment. As it passes through, the freon evaporates rapidly and takes up heat from the air in the compartment next to the tubes, and cools it down. This cool air sinks down to keep the rest of the refrigerator cold. The freon releases the heat again outside the appliance and the cycle is repeated.

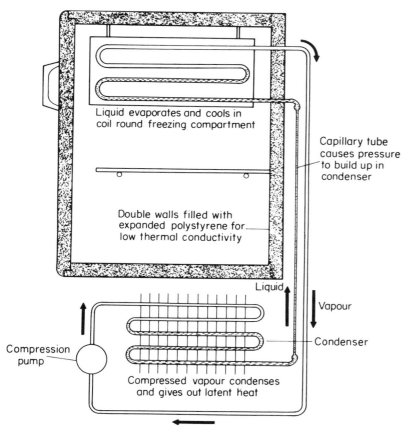

Liquid evaporates and cools in coil round freezing compartment

Capillary tube causes pressure to build up in condenser

Double walls filled with expanded polystyrene for low thermal conductivity

Liquid

Vapour

Condenser

Compression pump

Compressed vapour condenses and gives out latent heat

50

Air-borne diseases

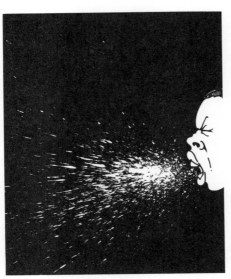

Sneezing sprays droplets of saliva and mucus into the air which can carry infection

The respiratory tract is open to the atmosphere at the nostrils and the mouth. Fungal spores, pollen, dust, animal hair, smoke, the germs of a number of infectious diseases and other suspended particles are normally present in the atmosphere. These may enter the body through the respiratory tract, and infect the nasal passages, throat, sinuses and the lungs.

If you are in a room that is properly ventilated, there is very little risk of infection since most disease-causing germs soon die in fresh, circulating air and sunlight. Where ventilation is poor, however, bacteria and viruses collect and travel as 'passengers' on particles of dust, on hair, or in tiny droplets of saliva and mucus. Fine droplets of saliva and mucus are forcibly sprayed into the atmosphere each time someone coughs or sneezes without covering the mouth and nostrils.

In poorly ventilated surroundings, healthy persons may inhale enough germs to catch a serious illness. The **smallpox** virus, for example, may be present in the skin of infected persons. When layers of dead skin, which contain the virus, scale off, they can be carried in the air for long distances. These scales could later be inhaled by other persons, who would then be infected. Similarly, the **tuberculosis** bacterium can remain active in dried spit (saliva) for several weeks, and be blown about in dust. If this germ-laden dust is inhaled by people in poorly ventilated areas they could become infected. Other diseases which may be spread by air-borne droplets are: the common cold, influenza, diphtheria, whooping-cough and measles.

Activity

Draw up a table in your book to show (a) the causative organism, (b) the method of transmission, (c) the symptoms and (d) the treatment for each of the diseases mentioned in this section.

Allergies

The term **allergy** refers to the increased or **'hyper' sensitivity** shown by body cells to specific substances or **allergens**. An allergen is always a protein, and may be present in spores, dust, chemicals and even drugs. Any of these can come into contact with the body, either externally to the skin or internally with the respiratory surfaces during breathing or the digestive tract. When this happens the protein could initiate an **allergic reaction** in persons sensitized to the allergen. An allergic reaction is an acquired ability of a tissue to react violently to the allergen. The reaction may range from rashes and swellings, coughing and sneezing, to fever, nausea, vomiting and diarrhoea, or there may be even more serious symptoms.

Two common allergies caused by inhaling air-borne particles are asthma and hay fever.

Asthma is an example of a bronchial allergy caused by inhaling dust, pollen, fungal spores, animal hairs, or chemicals produced by plants such as the 'White Christmas Flower' (*Euphorbia alba*). The allergic reactions typical of asthma are difficulty in breathing, wheezing and tightness of the chest, which are the result of muscle spasms which constrict the walls of the bronchioles. The membranes lining the bronchioles may also swell. These reactions decrease the oxgyen supply, causing headaches, dizzyness and nausea. The asthmatic person has distressing feelings of suffocation and requires adrenaline or cortisone to relieve the symptoms.

Hay fever is also induced by pollen. In this allergic reaction the membranes of the upper part of the respiratory tract are affected by contact with the allergen. The eyes, nostrils and mouth cavity are affected, in contrast to asthma which affects the deeper, non-ciliated parts of the lungs. Symptoms of hay fever are irritation of the eyes, which therefore appear red and watery; inflammation of the nasal and mouth membranes; nasal discharges and profuse sneezing.

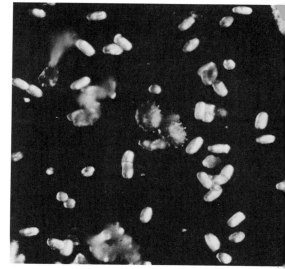

Rough and smooth pollen grains magnified × 75

Special clinics for patients with respiratory diseases like tuberculosis are often located in mountainous areas where the air is purer

51

Smoking and respiratory diseases

Would you knowingly inject tar, like that shown in the picture, into your body? If you are smart, your answer will be 'No!' Yet many so-called smart persons do just that every day—in fact, they do it several times! Each time you smoke a cigarette 35 mg of tar is left in your lungs. After you have smoked 20–30 cigarettes in a day, about 1 gram of tar has collected in your lungs. Imagine then, how much tar would accumulate in your lungs after one year of regular smoking!

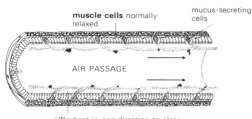

Experiment: To investigate cigarette smoke

Set up the apparatus shown in the diagram and use it to 'smoke' cigarettes.

Questions
(a) What colour is the substance that collects in Tube A?
(b) What do you think this substance is?
(c) What does the substance collected in Tube B look like?
(d) What has caused the colour change in Tube C?
(e) What does Tube D smell like?

Harmful chemicals present in cigarettes

Cigarettes are made from dried and processed tobacco. **Nicotine** is the most harmful substance in tobacco. It is a powerful poison if ingested in its pure form. Nicotine makes the blood vessels narrow which raises the smoker's blood pressure; it also speeds up the pulse considerably. Nicotine is therefore believed to be a significant factor in **hypertension** (high blood pressure) and heart-attacks.

Both nicotine and other substances in cigarette smoke irritate the membranes of the nose, throat, trachea, bronchioles and lungs. Particles of ash and various gases in the smoke settle on the moist ciliated membranes, damaging the cilia. The cilia are thus unable to perform their function of sweeping particles out of the bronchioles and lungs. As the membranes are further irritated they become swollen, narrowing the air passages. The muscle cells also contract, further reducing the diameter of the small tubes. So, breathing becomes severely restricted as less air passes through these narrowed air tubes.

The smoker also develops a persistent cough as the body tries to clear the air tubes of the excess mucus which collects in them. As the cough worsens, the thin tissues of the lungs become torn, causing a condition called **emphysema**. People who suffer from chronic emphysema have great difficulties in breathing, walking, working and may even have to carry their own oxygen supply with them.

Other substances in cigarette smoke are methane, propane, acetone, formaldehyde, formic acid, phenol, toluene and carbon monoxide. Some of these substances accumulate in the lung tissues of smokers, and are believed to be contributory causes of **lung cancer**.

Carbon monoxide is one of the poisonous gases produced as tobacco burns. It readily combines with haemoglobin in red blood cells, preventing them from carrying their full amount of oxygen to the other body cells. This reduction in the oxygen supply could seriously damage brain cells, heart muscles and other tissues.

muscle cells normally relaxed

mucus-secreting cells

AIR PASSAGE

cilia beat in one direction to clear the **mucus** and any trapped **dust particles** from the lungs

Healthy bronchiole (above) and infected bronchiole (below)

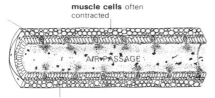

muscle cells often contracted

AIR PASSAGE

most **cilia** stop beating. this causes **mucus, bacteria, dust,** and **smoke particles** to accumulate in the bronchioles

Smoking and health

'Tars' produced when tobacco is smoked have been shown in experiments to cause cancer. Such cancer-causing chemicals are known as **carcinogens**. Cancer of the lungs, larynx and lips have been linked to the carcinogens found in cigarettes.

Studies concerned with the dangers of smoking have shown:

1 The risk of developing lung cancer increases with the length of smoking-time and the number of cigarettes smoked daily.
2 Heavy smokers who started smoking at an early age are more likely to have high blood pressure and to suffer heart-attacks.
3 The risk of lung cancer and of high blood pressure lessens if smoking is stopped.
4 Cigarette smoking is the most common cause of cancer of the larynx and of chronic bronchitis.
5 Chronic bronchitis and emphysema are more likely to occur among smokers than non-smokers.
6 Smaller babies, more miscarriages and more still-born babies are the results of smoking during pregnancy.
7 The lungs of children who smoke may not develop properly.

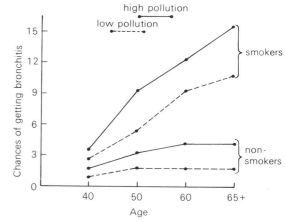

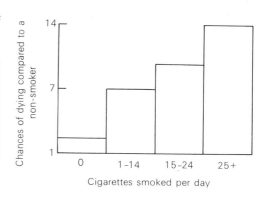

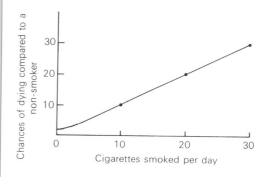

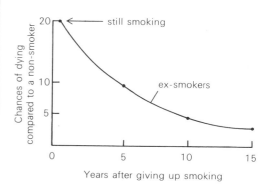

Activities

1 The following warning appears on cigarette boxes packaged in the UK.

DANGER: HM GOVT. HEALTH DEPT'S WARNING
CIGARETTES CAN
SERIOUSLY DAMAGE YOUR HEALTH
LOW TO MIDDLE TAR

   (a) Examine various brands of cigarettes produced in your country. Is there a similar warning on the cigarette boxes?
   (b) Discuss the value of including such warnings on cigarette boxes.
   (c) Write a warning about the hazards of smoking which you would like to see placed on cigarette boxes produced in your country.
2 The first graph shows how bronchitis is affected by smoking and atmospheric pollution.
   (a) Comment on the relationship between high atmospheric pollution and the chances of getting bronchitis for (i) a 40-year-old smoker; (ii) a 40-year-old non-smoker.
   (b) Compare this to the chances for 60- and 65-year-old smokers and non-smokers.
3 The second graph shows the chance of dying of a heart attack for males under 45 years of age.
   (a) If you smoked 1–14 cigarettes daily, how many times would you increase your risk of dying from a heart attack?
   (b) By how much more would you increase your risk of dying if you smoked 30 cigarettes per day?
4 The third graph shows the chances for men of dying from lung cancer.
   (a) From the graph estimate the chances of dying from lung cancer for a man who
      (i) does not smoke;
      (ii) smokes 25 cigarettes per day?
   (b) What is the relationship between the number of cigarettes smoked per day and the chances of dying from lung cancer?
5 The fourth graph shows the chances of dying from lung cancer of ex-smokers.
   (a) What is an ex-smoker?
   (b) From the graph, deduce the benefit gained by the ex-smoker.
   (c) If a man gave up smoking for 5 years, how would this affect his chances of dying from lung cancer?

52

Sanitation

Hygiene is concerned with the various conditions that affect our health and the ways in which we can control these conditions to prevent diseases. Hygiene includes knowledge of personal cleanliness, as well as cleanliness of the environment.

Personal hygiene

This is achieved by regular washing with soap and water, which removes organisms which cause ill-health.

Cleanliness of the body

The skin is a breeding ground for all kinds of germs. Some of these cause infections such as ringworm, others produce unpleasant odours. To avoid these unpleasant effects you must wash your skin daily, with soap, water and a rag when necessary. This removes layers of dead epidermis, stale perspiration, and the natural oils or **sebum**. It also keeps the pores open, so that sweat can be properly excreted. The best method is to bath in warm, soapy water, especially after vigorous exercise. A cold water rinse after a warm bath closes the pores and improves blood circulation.

Periodic exposure to sunlight is necessary to keep the skin healthy. The ultra-violet rays in the sunlight make the skin form calciferol (Vitamin D). However, overexposure to sunlight dries the skin and causes sunburn, especially in fair-skinned people.

Hands are the chief transmitters of infection, because they come into contact with all kinds of pathogens, even without our knowing. These can easily be transferred to the mouth, eyes and nose when they are touched, scratched or handled.

Wash your hands several times daily, especially after using the latrine, after handling garbage or poisonous substances, or after gardening. At these times pathogenic organisms or harmful substances can be spread on your hands or become lodged under the fingernails. When washing your hands, use soap and water and a nail brush to remove dirt from around and under the nails, and between fingers.

Feet should be given similar attention, particularly if you walk bare-footed. 'Athlete's foot' is a common foot infection caused by a fungus called **tinea**. Sweat and dirt between the toes provide a good breeding-ground for the fungal spores.

Toenails should be trimmed neatly, and dirt and dead skin under the nails removed with a nail brush.

Make sure that your shoes are the correct size and fit properly. Pointed-toed shoes cause malformation of the foot bones, especially when worn by the young. 'Corns' and bunions are formed where the badly-fitting shoes rub against the foot. Do not buy shoes with very high heels since they upset your centre of gravity as the weight of the body is tilted forward. This causes bad posture, an awkward walk and strained leg, back and abdominal muscles.

Your hair needs special care, especially in hot, tropical countries. Dirt easily settles on the scalp and the hair, mixing with sweat and the oil secreted by the scalp. This can cause unpleasant odours, and encourages fungi, dandruff, and headlice.

Lice live among the hairs on the body, either on the head or in the pubic region. They thrive on the bodies of persons who are careless about personal hygiene. Lice feed by piercing their host's skin to suck the blood.

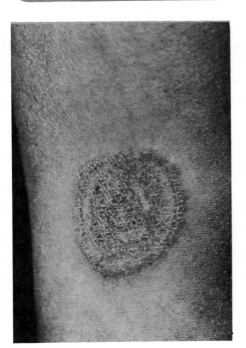

Ringworm infection

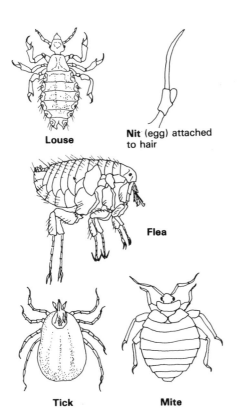

Louse

Nit (egg) attached to hair

Flea

Tick

Mite

Other parasites which live on the body and scalp are itch-mites, bed bugs, fleas and ticks.

The hairs in the **nostrils** filter out dust particles from the air before it enters the respiratory tubes. The dust is trapped by mucus which is secreted by cells lining the nostrils. This debris should be removed daily with a soft tissue or damp cloth.

The **ears** produce and secrete a brown wax which helps to trap crawling insects and dust particles. Many persons adopt the bad habit of pushing hair-pins and match-sticks into their ears, to try to clean out this wax. **This is a highly dangerous practice which may damage the ear and should not be done.** Excess wax will eventually work its way to the opening of the ear, when it can be removed with a soft, damp cloth, or tissue. If there is a serious build-up of wax it should only be removed by a doctor or nurse who will use a syringe.

Teeth are meant to last a lifetime, but will only do so if they are properly cared for. In Section 14, you learned about the effects of bacterial activity on teeth. Frequent brushing, especially after meals, is important to prevent tooth decay.

Clothing not only protects your body from dirt and temperature extremes, it also absorbs perspiration. It is important to wash clothes to remove stale perspiration, as well as traces of urine, faeces, dirt and unpleasant smells. Underwear should be changed and washed daily. Combs and brushes, wash-cloths and towels must also be washed and disinfected frequently.

Wastes

People produce a variety of domestic and industrial waste as a result of their daily activities.

1 **Domestic waste** is either solid, from the kitchen and the yard, or liquid, as **sewage**. Each type must be disposed of in specific ways. Solid wastes can be disposed of by:

  (a) burning;
  (b) compost heaps;
  (c) public garbage disposal system.

  Sewage is disposed of through:

  (a) private latrines;
  (b) public sewage system.

2 **Industrial wastes** A wide range of waste products are produced by industrial processes. Many are not pollutants in themselves, but when passed out in large quantities, and dumped in specific limited areas, they may then be considered pollutants in the environment.

  Depending on the type of process involved, some industrial waste can be recycled for later use.

Summary

Personal hygiene relies chiefly on keeping the body surface clean by regular use of soap and water. If a wash-cloth is used, the abrasive action removes dead skin and the harmful microorganisms which live in the dead cells.

Questions

1 Why is it advisable to take a warm shower after vigorous exercise?
2 Discuss methods of preventing athlete's foot.
3 Why is it dangerous to attempt to clean the ears with match-sticks and hair-pins?
4 Explain the correct techniques for brushing and generally caring for the teeth.
5 Give specific examples of waste which can be safely, and hygienically, disposed of by burning or composting.

6 Discuss some important considerations when selecting a site for a garbage dump.
7 Comment on the suitability of the design of the garbage disposal trucks in your area, as a hygienic means of transporting garbage to a dump.
8 List the waste(s) produced from any *one* industry in your country. Comment on the effectiveness of the disposal of these waste(s).
9 Justify the need for the safe and hygienic disposal of domestic and industrial waste.

53

Easing our daily chores

Many of our daily tasks are made easier by **machines**. A machine is any device that enables a small force to overcome a large force, or that enables a force to be applied from a convenient position.

Levers

The simplest machine is the lever, which is merely a rod that turns about a pivot (or fulcrum). The piece of wood the carpenter is using to get out the stuck post is an example of a lever. The force the man is applying is called the **effort**. The total force he is trying to overcome is called the **load**. The carpenter cannot pull the post out directly because the load is too great. But by using this machine, the little effort he can manage can overcome the large load. This machine arrangement is used as a 'force multiplier'.

Law of Levers

A metre rule, a round pencil and a set of weights can be used to illustrate the law of levers. Balance the rule on the pencil. Place a weight W_1 at a distance X_1 from the pivot, then place weight W_2 on the rule so that the rule balances again. You should find that, within experimental limits, $W_1X_1 = W_2X_2$.

This Law of Levers must be satisfied when a small force overcomes a larger force. The equation tells us that by means of a large lever arm (X_2) a small force W_2 can be used to overcome a large force W_1. If the rule is not pivoted at its centre of gravity the weight of the rule must be taken into account:

$$W_1X_3 = WX + W_2X_4$$

where W is the weight of the rule and X the distance from its centre of gravity to the pivot.

The products W_1X_1, W_2X_2 and WX are called **moments** or turning effects. The Law of Levers can also be called the **Law of Moments**. For a rule to balance, or for a load to be overcome, the clockwise moment about the pivot must be equal to the anticlockwise moment about the pivot.

Mechanical advantage

If a machine uses a small effort to overcome a large load we say that the machine has a large force multiplying effect. This force multiplying effect is called **mechanical advantage**. Mechanical advantage (MA) is defined as the ratio of the load (L) to the effort (E). Hence,

$$MA = \frac{L}{E}$$

If a load of 80 N is raised by applying an effort of 20 N, the mechanical advantage of the machine is 4.

Classes of levers

Lever arrangements are classed according to the arrangement of the load, pivot and effort. In a **Class 1** lever system the load and effort are on opposite sides of the pivot. In **Class 2** levers the load and effort are on the same side of the pivot but the effort is further away than the load.

Anticlockwise moment   Clockwise moment

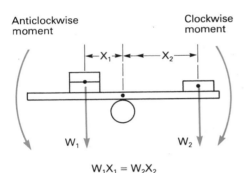

$$W_1X_1 = W_2X_2$$

*Illustrating the law of levers (*above *and* below*)*

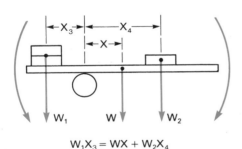

$$W_1X_3 = WX + W_2X_4$$

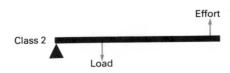

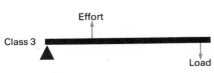

Classes of levers

The effort must therefore be smaller than the load. In the **Class 3** lever system the effort and load are again on the same side of the pivot, but this time the effort is nearer to the pivot and therefore is *larger* than the load! In this class of levers the mechanical advantage is less than 1, i.e. there is a mechanical disadvantage. The advantage of the arrangement is convenience of handling, usually there is no large force to be overcome.

Levers of all three classes can be found in the human body. The base of the skull, the foot and the forearm are all examples of Class 1, Class 2 and Class 3 levers, respectively.

Pulleys

A pulley is a wheel, usually grooved, that is pivoted at the middle. The diagram shows a simple pulley being used to hoist a load upwards. The rope is pulled downwards. The pulley is being used here mainly to allow the force to be applied from a convenient position. Using a spring balance to measure load and effort, you can show that a simple fixed pulley has a mechanical advantage of approximately 1. That is, the load lifted and the effort applied are about equal. In a block and tackle system of pulleys, the mechanical advantage is greater than 1. That is why the block and tackle system is used when heavy objects are being hoisted.

Inclined planes

The inclined plane is yet another simple machine. If you pull a loaded trolley up the plane with a spring balance you can show that the mechanical advantage of this system is also greater than 1. That is, the effort applied is less than the load being overcome. However, inclined planes are also used for the convenience they provide. It is easier to roll a heavy drum up a plank into a truck than to lift it from the ground into it.

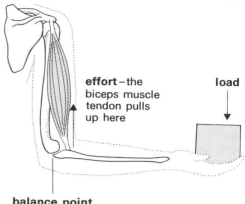

Class 3 levers are common in the body. How can the effort exerted by a biceps muscle in lifting a load be estimated?

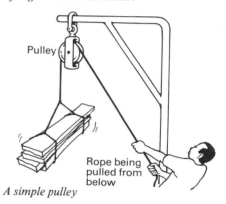

A simple pulley

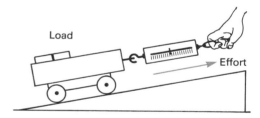

Measuring effort in moving a trolley up an inclined plane

Questions

1 If a pivot is placed at the 20 cm mark of a metre rule, the rule does not balance. What is the reason for this?
2 Name one kitchen utensil which is
   (a) a first class lever;
   (b) a second class lever;
   (c) a third class lever.
3 Is the simple fixed pulley a force multiplier, a machine used for the convenience of applying a force, or both? Give your reasons.
4 What type of machine (e.g. lever, pulley, inclined plane) could you use in the following situations
   (a) to get a heavy box from the ground to the first floor of a house;
   (b) to send a flag up a flag pole;
   (c) to remove a nail that is stuck in a piece of wood.

Activities

1 Using a metre rule, pencil and a set of weights, verify the law of levers (law of moments).
2 Using a known mass, a metre rule and a pencil, devise a means of finding the mass of the metre rule.
4 Using a spring balance and a set of weights, show that the MA of an inclined plane is greater than 1.

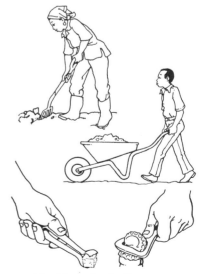

Can you identify the load, effort and pivot in these levers?

54

Using simple machines

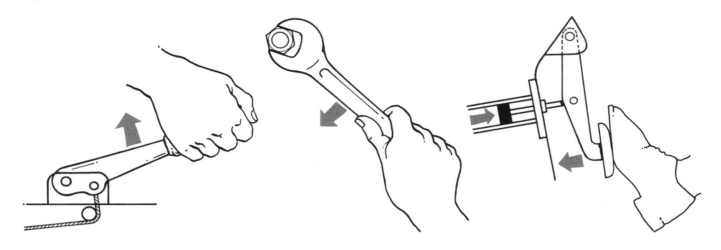

Using levers (left to right) *car handbrake lever, spanner, car brake pedal*

Simple machines are used extensively in vehicles. They may be parts of vehicles, or they may be tools used to make or mend them. Five such simple machines will be looked at in this section.

Levers

Look at the pictures carefully. They all show levers in action. Can you identify the load, the effort, the load arm, the effort arm, and the pivot? Can you tell whether the levers are first class, second class or third class? (See Section 53.) Are the levers being used mainly for their force multiplying effect or mainly to apply the effort from a convenient position?

Pulleys

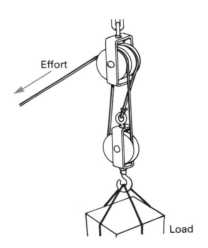

Look at the picture of a block and tackle pulley system being used to hoist a very heavy load in a ship. The block is fixed and the tackle can move. The effort is applied along *one* rope which passes over the block. This rope passes three times between the block and tackle (this number depends on the number of pulleys in the block and tackle system). So the load is held up by three portions of the rope. The system has a mechanical advantage of approximately three since the effort applied along a single rope end is applied to the load three times—once along each portion of the rope which suspends the tackle.

Wheel and axle

The steering wheel and column of a motor car form an example of another kind of simple machine found in vehicles—the wheel and axle. In the diagram the effort E is smaller than the load L because the effort arm R is large and the load arm r is small. For the load to be lifted the equation $E \times R = L \times r$ must hold. Thus a load of 800 N can be overcome by an effort of 100 N if $R = 40$ cm and $r = 5$ cm.

Screwdrivers also make use of the wheel and axle principle. The fatter the handle, the less effort has to be applied to overcome the opposing frictional load.

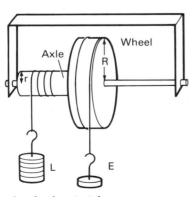

Wheel and axle principle

Screw

The screw is yet another simple machine associated with vehicles. Some aeroplane wing flap movements are controlled by a long screw. Some motor vehicle jacks are designed round the screw. When the effort E is moved through one complete revolution, the load L moves a tiny distance equal to the **pitch** of the screw. The energy converted by the effort is equal to the effort × distance moved by the effort. The energy gained by the load is equal to the load × distance moved by the load. Assuming that the energy applied is equal to energy gained,

$$E \times 2\pi R = L \times p$$
$$\therefore \quad E = \frac{Lp}{2\pi R}$$

Where R is the length of the effort arm and p is the pitch of the screw. So although the load may be very large, the effort will be small as long as the pitch p is very small and R is large.

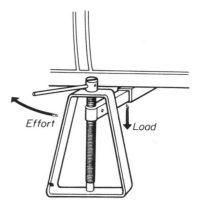

Hydraulic braking system

Hydraulic press

The hydraulic press is used in the hydraulic jack and in hydraulic braking. In the hydraulic press, the pressure (force per unit area) is constant throughout the fluid. A small force applied on a piston in a tube of small diameter can therefore overcome a large force in a connected tube of large diameter. When the brake pedal of a hydraulic brake is pressed a cylinder with a piston at each end forces out the brake shoes. An advantage of this system is that equal effort can be exerted on all four wheels at once.

Efficiency and care of machines

The efficiency of a machine can be defined as the ratio of the useful energy converted to the energy supplied. It can be expressed as a percentage:

$$\text{efficiency} = \frac{\text{useful energy converted}}{\text{energy supplied}} \times 100\%$$

$$= \frac{\text{load} \times \text{distance moved by the load}}{\text{effort} \times \text{distance moved by the effort}} \times 100\%$$

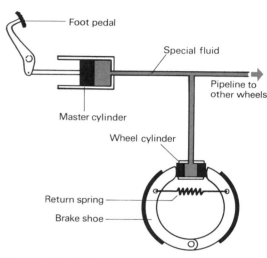

Motor vehicle jack

If an effort of 5 N is needed to lift a load of 4 N through a distance of 2 m, using a simple pulley, then the efficiency of the machine is 80%. 20% of the energy supplied is wasted. Where has it gone? It was probably used at the pivot. If the pivot is rusty or corroded the effort must overcome a lot of friction. A drop of lubricating oil at the pivot is usually all that is needed to reduce friction and hence reduce the effort. This increases the efficiency of the machine. Oiling or greasing not only helps to reduce friction, but also helps to prevent the bearings at the pivots rusting. Replacing worn bearings with new ones also helps to increase efficiency, since worn bearings are rough and cause more friction than smooth new bearings.

Questions

1 What type of machine is each of the following:
   (a) a door knob;
   (b) the steering wheel of a car;
   (c) the wheels on the top of a dragline;
   (d) the tray and the two handles of a donkey cart.
2 (a) How much energy is converted in raising a 300 kg car engine through a height of 0·8 m? (*Note*: a mass of 1 kg has a weight of approximately 10 N.)
   (b) If a force of 800 N is used to raise the car, what is the mechanical advantage of the machine used?
   (c) What is a suitable simple machine that can be used to lift the engine?

55

Soil – its formation and components

The soil is one of our most important natural resources. It provides the medium in which plants grow, which is the source from which all animals derive their food. Without the soil and without growth of healthy plants animal life would be in jeopardy.

Soil is formed from rocks. The rocks are transformed into these finely divided particles by factors such as **weathering**. The changes in weather conditions, from hot to cold and back again, make the rocks expand and contract. These movements cause the rocks to break into finer particles.

Factors which influence soil formation

Soils are formed mainly by the action of the weather. The most important aspects of the weather which affect the process are rain, sun, wind and ice (in temperate countries).

When rain falls it beats down onto the surfaces of the rocks. The falling water loosens rock particles, eventually breaking them into smaller pieces. The rain water may also dissolve certain gases in the atmosphere, e.g. carbon dioxide. This results in the formation of weak acids which could help to break down solid rocks. The whole question of 'acid rain' is a major talking-point in highly industrialized countries. Apparently waste gases like sulphur dioxide dissolve in rain water. The resulting solution defaces buildings and statues, and destroys crops.

The sun heats the rocks, making them expand. When they cool again at night they contract. This alternate expansion and contraction makes the rock break up. The formation of sand in deserts is directly due to intense heat during the day, followed by near freezing temperatures at night.

Wind by itself might not be very effective as an agent of weathering. However, when a gust is 'armed' with grit and small pieces of materials it easily breaks down the rocks. Weathering by wind is well demonstrated on rocks near beaches.

Components of the soil

Soil is made up of the following components: **mineral particles** formed by weathering of rocks; **organic particles** from decaying plant and animal remains; **air**; **water** containing dissolved salts; **living organisms**.

Mineral particles

The mineral salts available for plant growth usually depend upon the nature of the parent rock. Fertile soil contains most, if not all, of the elements necessary for healthy growth. These elements have been found by experimentation to include carbon, oxygen, sulphur, potassium, magnesium, calcium, hydrogen, nitrogen, iron and phosphorus. Certain elements are required in small (trace) amounts, e.g. zinc, cobalt, boron, silicon and molybdenum. All of these, except carbon, must be taken in by the roots. The nitrogen, absorbed as nitrates, is produced by nitrogen-fixing bacteria in the nitrogen cycle (see p. 188).

Soils have several distinct layers. The fertile layer is the topsoil, derived from weathered particles of parent rock plus organic material from decayed plants and animals, air and water

138

Organic Particles

When plant and animal parts decay they form a sticky, colloidal, organic compound called humus. The decay is caused by microorganisms such as fungi and bacteria. This is one example of microorganisms that are beneficial to man. Humus supplies the nitrates which are important in protein synthesis. Because of its fibrous properties it absorbs water easily, and is used, in the form of compost, to improve the crumb structure of sandy soils.

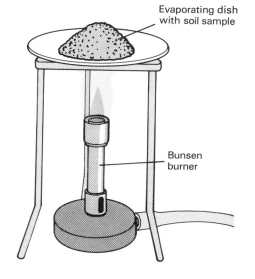

Evaporating dish with soil sample

Bunsen burner

Experiment A: To estimate the organic content of a soil sample

What you need
Dried soil, evaporating dish, Bunsen burner, tripod.

What you do
1 Put some of the oven-dried soil in the evaporating dish.
2 Weigh the dish and its contents.
3 Heat the contents of the dish until there is no further weight loss.
4 Reweigh the dish and its contents.
5 Calculate the organic content of the soil using the following equation:

$$\frac{\text{loss in weight}}{\text{weight of original sample}} \times 100 = \text{percentage of organic matter}$$

6 Repeat the experiment using samples of soil from other locations. Is there any difference in the percentage of organic matter found? Which had the greatest? Which had the least?

Experiment B: To show the solid components of soil

What you need
Measuring cylinder, soil sample, water, salt.

What you do
1 Shake the sample of soil in the water in the measuring cylinder.
2 Allow the mixture to stand for some minutes.
3 Measure the width of the various 'bands' or layers which you can see. Which is broadest? Which is narrowest?
4 Shake the cylinder again, and then add some salt. Does the soil 'settle' more quickly this time? What are the implications of your finding for soil-laden river water entering the sea?

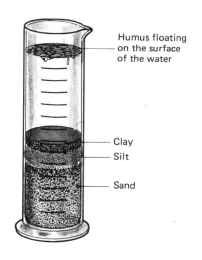

Humus floating on the surface of the water

Clay
Silt

Sand

Soil air

Soil air is found in the spaces between the soil particles. Since different soils have different sized particles (see below), the amount of air present in a soil sample depends upon the size of its particles. The soil air is necessary for the aerobic respiration of the myriad of soil organisms, and for the plant roots themselves. Waterlogged conditions in certain clay-type soils preclude the presence of air. Under these conditions only anaerobic organisms can flourish.

PARTICLE SIZE	SOIL TYPE
2–0·02 mm	sand
0·02–0·002 mm	silt
<0·002	clay

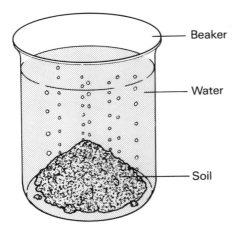

Beaker

Water

Soil

Experiment C: to show the presence of air in a soil sample

What you need
Beaker or jam jar, soil samples, water.

What you do
1 Put a sample of soil in the beaker and add water.
2 Observe what happens and report.
3 Repeat the experiment using samples of soil from other locations. Which sample has most air?

Soil water

Soil water forms a thin layer around the inorganic particles of the soil. This water is essential for plant nutrition since it provides a medium in which mineral salts can dissolve, and so can be taken up by the plants. The amount of water that a soil holds is a measure of the size of the inorganic particles and also of the crumb structure of the soil.

Experiment D: To measure the water content of a soil sample

What you need
Soil sample, tin, oven.

What you do
1 Record the weight of the tin and the weight of the tin with the soil sample in it.
2 Heat the tin and its contents in the oven for about 6 hours at about 100 °C.
3 Cool the tin and its content in a desiccator.
4 Weigh the container and its contents again. Record the weight. The percentage of water in the soil can be calculated using the following equation:

$$\frac{\text{loss in weight}}{\text{original wet weight}} \times 100 = \text{percentage of water in soil}$$

5 Compare the percentage water in different soil samples using the above procedure. Which soil has most/least water?

Questions

(a) Why is the soil sample cooled in a desiccator?
(b) What are the implications of your findings for growth of plants?

Living organisms

These are mainly, but not exclusively, microorganisms. The following microorganisms are usually found in fertile soil: bacteria, fungi, protozoa and algae. Besides these there are centipedes, millipedes and earthworms. The presence of earthworms is a good indication that soil is fertile. These earthworms help in the mechanical breakdown of humus in the soil. They also, by burrowing, increase the **aeration** of the soil, as well as bringing fresh subsoil to the surface. The microorganisms help the decomposition of dead and decaying matter, releasing nutrients that are essential to plant growth.

Physical properties of the soil

Soils are usually classified as **sand**, **clay** and **loam**, depending on the size of the mineral particles of which they are formed. This is a product of the nature and structure of the parent rock. Clay is derived from silicates and is rich in plant nutrients; sands are largely made from quartz; loam is a mixture of sand and clay, with the properties of both. Loam is considered the most fertile soil.

Several features could be measured to find out more about the properties of the three soils: (a) the feel; (b) the water retention capability; (c) permeability; (d) air content; (e) capillarity.

The feel or texture can be determined by rubbing the soil between the fingers. This indicates whether the mineral particles are loose, dry, or sticky; and smooth or gritty. This texture test also gives a fair indication of some of the other properties.

The ability of the soil to hold water is very important if the soil is to support healthy plants. Waterlogged soils encourage anaerobic conditions which could be disastrous for plants. Of course, the ability to retain water is intimately related to the nature and size of the mineral particles, as well as to the percentage of organic materials present.

Experiment E: To measure water retention in three soil samples

What you need

6 measuring cylinders, cotton wool, funnel, 3 soil samples of equal weight—one each of sand, clay and loam.

What you do

1 Measure 50 ml water in a measuring cylinder. Add this quantity of water to each soil sample, as shown in the diagram.
2 Measure the quantity of water that drains out of each sample.
3 The quantity of water retained by each sample equals the amount poured on (50 ml) less the amount drained out.

This same experiment could also be used to measure the permeability of the soil samples. In this case it would be necessary to measure the quantity of water that drains through over specific time intervals.

The quantity of air in the soil is also a measure of the size of mineral particles. Generally speaking, sandy soils have large particles and large spaces between them. As a result the air content is high. The size of the air spaces also influences the water retention property of soils, and so influences the drainage.

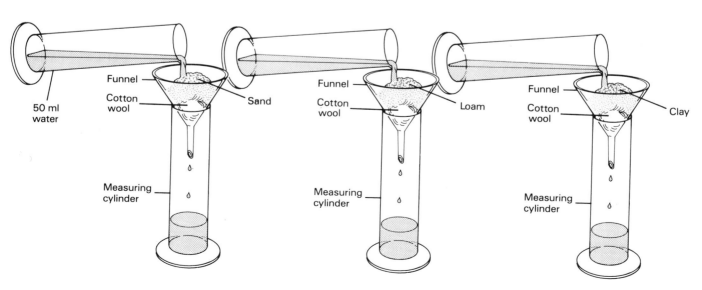

Capillarity was mentioned in Section 17 when the forces responsible for upward movement of water and mineral salts in plants was looked at. Capillarity also takes place in soils which have large air spaces. These spaces form the narrow channels through which the water moves. This action takes place especially in sandy soils. In some cases the water brings with it valuable nutrients which are needed for plant growth.

The physical properties of soils

| | PROPERTIES | | | | |
SOIL	SIZE OF MINERAL PARTICLES	PERME-ABILITY	RETENTIVE ABILITY	AIR CONTENT	CAPIL-LARITY
Clay	Small	Low	High	Low	Slow
Sand	Large	Very high	Low	High	Rapid
Loam	Mixture of large and small	Moderate	Very high	Moderate	Moderate

Soil acidity and alkalinity

Soils may be acid, alkaline or neutral, according to their pH value. The acidity or alkalinity depends on the nature of the parent rock, and so is linked to some of the physical properties listed above.

Generally speaking, acid soils are those which are waterlogged, while alkaline soils are associated with limestone, and others rocks high in calcium and sodium. The soil's pH can be determined using a pH meter or by using universal indicator.

Plants are usually very specific as to the type of soil on which they grow.

Gulley erosion of hillsides

What is soil erosion?

The loose mantle of soil which is found at the top of a soil profile is called the **top soil**. This is the main medium in which plants grow since it contains the nutrients, etc., which are vital to growth. The mantle is produced from the parent rock over several hundreds of years, or is transported from one point to another over a long time. However, man's careless and reckless use of the soil could destroy the top soil in a very short period of time. The removal of top soil by wind, rain and running water is called **soil erosion**. Clearly, the reduction of the top soil could be disastrous for man and his environment. Some of the practices which lead to erosion include clearing vast tracts of land for housing and non-agricultural purposes; over-grazing, and intensive cropping.

The causes of soil erosion

Wind is a very powerful agent of erosion in some environments. These include areas that are treeless, and those in which the soil is light and loose enough to be carried by the wind.

Rain and **running water** are perhaps the most widespread causes of soil erosion. They attack almost all exposed areas, irrespective of particle size and the weight of the soil. The rain drops, by constantly beating on the soil, remove particles by splashing. However, it is running water that causes most damage.

During the seasonal rains that we experience in the Caribbean, floods may be caused. These form large sheets of water which take away the soil when they drain away themselves. This is usually worst on relatively flat or slightly sloping land. Flowing water on steeper slopes tends to form channels which make the water's descent easier. These vary in width and are called rills or gullies. The draining flood waters wash tons of fertile soil away and deposit it on the beds of rivers or in the sea.

Preventing soil erosion

Erosion by the wind could be prevented by erecting windbreaks at the edge of fields. Irrigation could dampen the loose soil and reduce the amount blown away, while more permanent anchors for the soil could be made by introducing grasses and other plants which bind soil particles together with their roots.

Erosion by water (rain and running water) could be prevented by various conservation methods. **Contouring** the land involves ploughing across the slope rather than up and down. The furrow thus made blocks water flowing down the slope.

Strip cropping involves planting row crops, e.g. corn and potatoes, in strips alternating with cover crops like grass. This combines two methods: contouring the land and covering the soil to prevent it washing away.

Terracing erects a series of banks on a slope, giving the appearance of steps. Each bank is held together by plants or rocks.

By far the most successful method of soil conservation is the prevention of erosion. Methods are varied but they depend on the terrain and related aspects. At all costs we must make sure that the mantle of soil is not abused as man makes an impact on the environment.

56 Food chains and ecosystems

All living things are interdependent, and any break in the complicated web of relationships results in catastrophe.

The study of the relationship of plants and animals to their environment is called **ecology**. Ecology seeks to establish why a particular organism is found in a particular environment.

All the living components (plants, animals, microorganisms) together with the non-living factors in an area are called an **ecosystem**. An ecosystem may be large, e.g. a forest, or it may be small, e.g. a jar containing organisms and non-living components in balance.

In each ecosystem there are usually organisms which produce—**producers**. These are the green plants which provide the basis of all interdependence. Animals, which do not contain chlorophyll and so cannot manufacture food from sunlight, are not producers but are rather **consumers**. Animals may be primary or secondary consumers, depending on whether they eat plants directly, or eat the animals which eat the plants.

(a)

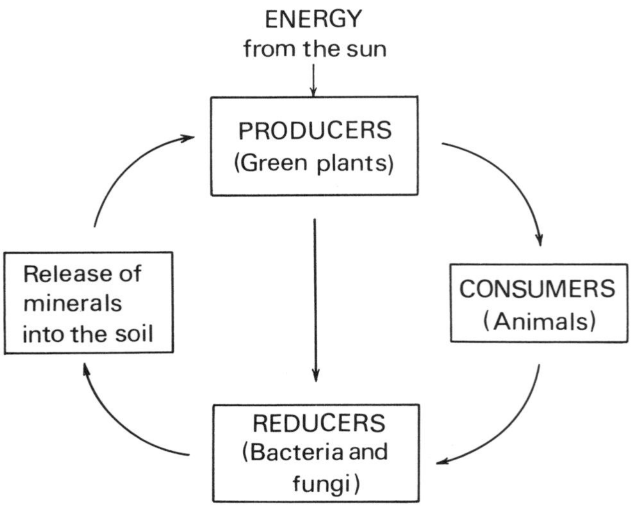

(b)

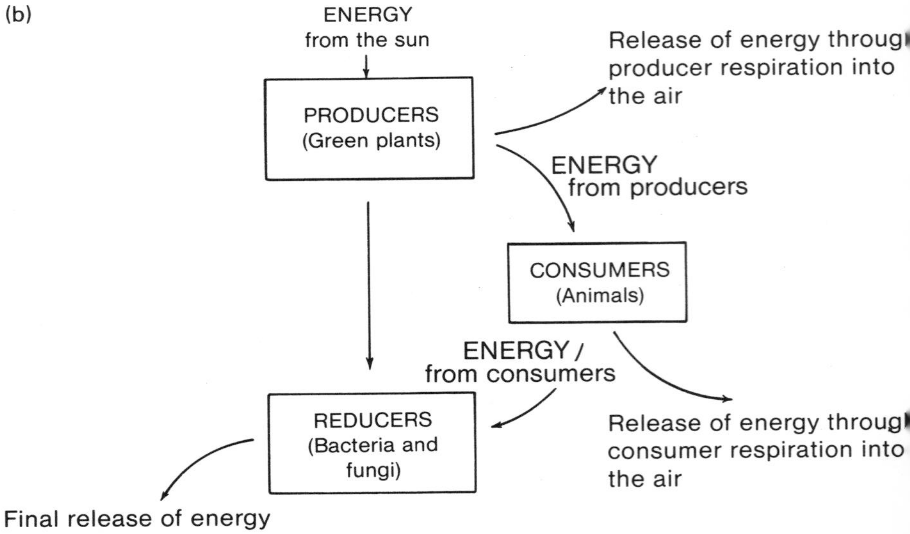

a) The circulation of materials in an ecosystem

b) The flow of energy through an ecosystem

As important as the producers are the **decomposers** or **reducers**. These break down any dead and decaying matter so that it can be used by the producers. Decomposers are vital to the nitrogen cycle.

The particular area of the environment in which an organism lives and interrelates is called its **habitat**.

Animals are classified by the type of food that they eat. **Carnivores**, e.g. cats, eat mainly the flesh of other animals, and their dentition and the structure of their digestive tracts are related to this function. **Herbivores**, e.g. goats and sheep, eat mainly plant materials and their dentition and digestive activities are suited to this. **Omnivores**, e.g. man, eat both plants and animals. Their dentition and digestive activities are designed to transform both types of food into a form in which it will be most useful.

All life is delicately bound into a network of food and energy relationships. For example, man cannot make his own food from its component parts, but derives it, directly or indirectly, from the green plants which can. Man may eat the plant, or the animal, e.g. a cow, which lives on the plant. Wherever the food comes from, a set of food relationships called a **food chain** is set up. The chain discussed above may be represented thus:

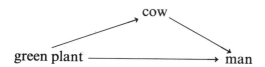

The food chain represents a linear summary of food and energy relationships within a particular ecosystem. Many interrelated food chains may be present in a single ecosystem. This network is called a **food web**. The diagram below shows a simple food web:

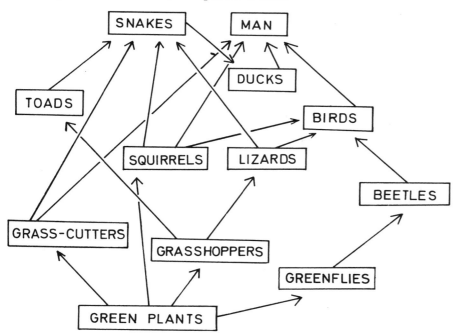

57

Our aquatic environment

The rapid increase in the human population of the Earth is making it more and more difficult to provide food from traditional terrestrial sources. However, the oceans are relatively under-utilized as a source of food.

Food from the sea

The oceans cover about three-quarters of the Earth's surface and contain a large amount of food suitable for humans. Fishing and fish farming are important industries all over the world, particularly in the Caribbean.

There are several different types of fish. Some of them live in fresh water, some in estuaries, where the water is partly salt (brackish), and others in the sea, which, of course, contains salt water.

There are two main types of fish which supply us with protein: (a) those with skeletons made of cartilage (gristle), such as sharks, and (b) those with bony skeletons, such as flying fish.

Methods used in fishing

If you live near the sea, you will be able to find out for yourselves what methods the fishermen in your area use for catching fish. They will depend on the habits of the fish (whether they live near the surface or deep down in the sea, whether they move about in shoals, or tend to gather only in small numbers) and, of course, on the skill of the fishermen and the kind of equipment they have.

Much of the fishing done in the Caribbean is carried out from small boats, often by only one or two men, and only enough fish is caught to supply the local market. The chief methods used are as follows:

1 Line fishing   Hand lines or long lines may be used. The use of hand lines is time-consuming and the catch is often small. Long lines consist of several thousands of baited hooks placed at 2 metre intervals and hung at a suitable depth in the water. These are checked at regular intervals and the bait replaced.

Line fishing in a lagoon in the Bahamas

2 Net fishing Some nets are called drift nets. They are used to catch fish which swim near the surface to feed on tiny floating creatures. These nets may be very large—sometimes 15 metres deep and 3 or 4 kilometres long. They are left floating overnight. They are usually thrown over the side of the boat and are hung where there is likely to be a large number of fish. The fish swim into the nets and are trapped in the meshes. The nets are then hauled in and the fish shaken out on the deck.

Not all nets are placed near the surface. Some are hung near the bottom of the sea so as to catch deep-sea fish. These nets are called trawl nets. They consist of a bag, shaped something like a cone, the mouth of which is kept open by two boards. The net is attached to a trawler which drags it slowly across the bottom of the sea. After trawling for about an hour the net is hauled aboard and the fish turned out on deck.

Fish farming

Just as farmers keep animals on land, the 'farming' of fish in ponds and lakes is one way of getting more fish. Young fish are put into the ponds, from which they cannot escape. There they can be grown to a certain size and then 'cropped' for the market. They can also be allowed to breed so that the stock is maintained. All this is done scientifically, care being taken to stop the fish from becoming diseased by treating the water with chemicals, and also providing the fish with the proper food so that they grow quickly to the biggest size. Fish farming is becoming increasingly important for breeding 'luxury' fish for hotels, but as the world population grows and the demand for food becomes greater and greater, this method will help to supplement the fish caught from the sea for general use.

Fishermen in the Grenadines hauling in their nets

A fish farm in Jamaica

58

Physical activity and body functions

Physical activity involves some form of movement. Most people enjoy some form of physical activity, whether in performing routine tasks or taking part in recreation or sport. During physical activity the brain directs various muscles and glands to work together, so that parts of the body are used. This helps to keep the body in good working condition.

The effects of physical activity

Physical activity has specific beneficial effects on various body functions.

1 The respiratory movements, inhalation and exhalation, become deeper as the lungs are used to their fullest. This enables the maximum exchange of oxygen and carbon dioxide across the thin alveoli walls to take place. Body cells thus obtain a ready supply of oxygen for cellular respiration, and waste carbon dioxide is also rapidly removed. This exchange is especially important in preventing fatigue in muscle cells.
2 The rate at which the heart beats is considerably increased and blood pressure is raised. The circulation of the blood is improved, especially the movement of blood through the veins. Food and oxygen therefore reach the body cells more quickly, and wastes are also rapidly removed.
3 Food stores in the cells are oxidized or burnt up more rapidly, which helps to prevent the formation of fatty tissue. Continuous exercise therefore brings about rapid weight loss, especially in fat or over-weight persons.
4 Peristalsis (the movement of food through the digestive tract) is improved by the muscular movements of exercise. This helps to prevent constipation.
5 Without exercise, muscles become flabby, fat begins to accumulate in them and they get out of condition, or lose **muscle tone**. Muscle tone, the slight state of tension in which muscles are held, enables them to respond rapidly when necessary.
6 The sweat glands become more active in their removal of wastes in the sweat.
7 The nervous system benefits by the increased circulation of blood to the brain. When the nervous system is working perfectly, muscles can be more properly controlled. So nerve–muscle coordination increases as a result of physical activity.
8 Sound, restful sleep often follows a period of physical activity.

Meals and physical activity

A balanced diet, taken at regular meal times, is important for physically active people. The food we eat provides the reserves which are later oxidized to release energy for muscular activity.

Food should be taken at regular intervals during the day. As discussed in Section 11, soluble sugars, amino acids and fatty acids are absorbed into the blood stream following digestion. After a heavy meal a large proportion of the circulating blood is diverted to the stomach and intestines to facilitate absorption. This blood is then unavailable to skeletal muscles, so vigorous physical activity should not be undertaken less than one or two hours after a full meal. This allows enough time for digested foods to be passed out of the stomach, absorbed from the intestines, and for reserves to reach muscle cells.

Activities

1 Explain why:
   (a) you may suffer from cramps if you swim soon after a meal;
   (b) an athlete sometimes eats an orange with a spoonful of glucose between his races.
2 Select a vigorous activity, such as jumping on the spot quickly 50–100 times, or jumping on and off a chair 20–50 times.
   Copy this chart into your book and fill it in. Work with a partner if necessary.

CONDITIONS	PULSE RATE per minute	BREATHING RATE per minute
At rest		
After exercise		

Ask your partner to record your pulse rate, using a stop watch to time one minute accurately. You must sit quietly the first time that the pulse is recorded.
   (a) Your partner should place two fingers lightly on your wrist close to the base of your thumb. **Caution**—make sure he or she does not use their own thumb, since they might feel and record their own pulse, rather than yours. Relax and wait until a steady pulse beat can be identified.
   (b) Use a stop-watch to record the number of pulse beats felt per minute. Fill it in on your chart. Record your breathing rate also.
   (c) Do some vigorous exercise for 5 to 10 minutes.
   (d) Immediately record the pulse beat again over one minute. Then record the number of breaths taken per minute.
   (e) Below your chart write down any other changes you observed after your vigorous exercise (e.g. your complexion, any sweating or pain).

   Note You may want to record each rate three times and fill in the average value in your table.

Muscle fatigue

Excessive physical activity can have adverse effects on the body functions. When a muscle is working, foods stored in the muscle cells are oxidized or burned up to release energy for further cellular activity. During vigorous activity it is often difficult to get enough oxygen to muscle cells, so the muscles do not get enough energy to work properly. Anaerobic respiration will then begin to produce more energy for work. But lactic acid is produced during anaerobic respiration, and this accumulates within the muscle cells. The anaerobic breakdown of glucose can be summarized like this:

$$\text{1 molecule glucose} \xrightarrow{\text{anaerobic respiration}} \text{lactic acid} + 150 \text{ kJ energy}$$

The normal amount of lactic acid in the blood is about 70 mg per 100 cm³. As the lactic acid level rises above this, it starts to poison the cell and causes muscular pain and cramps, and severely impedes the activity of the muscle. The muscle then enters a state of **fatigue**.

When a muscle becomes fatigued after a prolonged period of physical activity, a period of **rest** is essential to allow the muscle to relax and the poisonous lactic acid to be removed. During the rest period, excess lactic acid is converted to glucose, in the presence of oxygen. Heart and respiratory rates slow down, the body temperature is reduced, and the nervous system gets a chance to recover.

Sleep is an excellent form of rest. After sleep the muscles are well rested, and the body is once again capable of carrying out all its physiological activities with maximum efficiency.

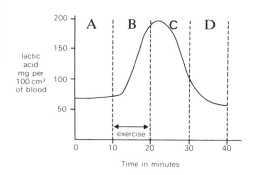

Activity

The graph shows the effects of 10 minutes vigorous exercise on the concentration of lactic acid in the blood of a trained athlete. Examine the graph carefully, then answer the questions.
   (a) What was the original level of lactic acid in the blood?
   (b) What was the greatest amount of lactic acid in the blood? Explain when it was present.
   (c) How long will it take for the level of lactic acid to return to normal?
   (d) Would you expect part C of the graph to be longer or shorter for an untrained person doing the same exercise? Why?

59

Drugs and the athlete

A pharmacist dispensing drugs at a clinic in Barbados

A drug is a chemical substance which exerts some effect on the normal functions of the body.

Drugs can be used to slow down or speed up body functions, to induce or to prevent sleep, to relieve pain, to reduce tension, to prevent a state of mental depression, to stimulate or reduce the appetite, and to fight disease-causing microorganisms.

Because of the variety of effects they can have on the body's activities, most drugs are **prescription drugs** and can only be obtained in set doses when prescribed by doctors, to be used for a specific purpose. Some drugs are sold 'over the counter' without a prescription for general use. These **non-prescription drugs** are usually supplied with information giving their proper dosage and use, but are often abused by purchasers.

Classification of drugs

All drugs act primarily through the brain and nervous system, to affect other body systems. Drugs can be grouped into five general classes, based on their ability to affect physical and mental activities.

1   **Stimulants** are used medically in small doses and for limited periods to combat fatigue, prevent drowsiness, and to reduce the appetite. They stimulate the nervous system, which in turn increases the heart and respiratory rates and raises the blood pressure. Soon after taking a stimulant drug, the user feels extremely energetic, has increased self-confidence and feelings of well-being. Many athletes are therefore tempted to take 'speed' or a 'pep pill' before taking part in an athletic event.

But as the stimulant effects wear off, feelings of depression and fatigue take their place and lead to the desire for another 'pep pill'. Very

soon, the user is in a cycle of 'up feelings' followed by 'down feelings.' In order to maintain the feelings of self-confidence and energy, he or she may take increasingly large doses. This finally results in mental dependence on the drug, headaches, diarrhoea, collapse of the circulatory system, coma and possible death.

Amphetamines (such as Benzedrine, Dexedrine and Methedine) and the drug **cocaine** are examples of stimulant drugs.

2 **Depressants and sedative drugs** have an overall opposite effect to stimulants. When used in prescribed doses they have a quieting effect on the nervous system, relieving mental strain. They are actually capable of 'shutting down' the nervous system, producing an alcoholic-like drunkeness followed by **sleep**, a state in which the brain ceases its conscious level functions. They slow down heart rate, lower the blood pressure, decrease the rate of breathing, and suppress reflex activity of the skeletal muscles.

Barbiturates (such as phenobarbital and seconal) are classified as sedatives, *but only when taken in prescribed doses*. They are especially dangerous when misused, since the effect of higher than medical doses cannot be predicted accurately for any one user. They can also cause extreme depression, distortion of vision and a slowing of nervous reaction. Some users become extremely violent, destroying objects in their surroundings and even committing brutal crimes, although they are unaware of their actions.

In addition, barbiturates are strongly addictive, with resultant physical and mental dependence. As the body develops a tolerance to the drug, the user needs to take continually increasing doses to prevent withdrawal sickness. Symptoms of withdrawal sickness are nausea, severe muscular cramps, convulsions, delirium and temporary insanity. Athletes who are tired after intense training and participation in sporting activities should never take such sedatives without medical advice, in case they become addicted.

Although it produces initial gaiety and loss of inhibition, **alcohol** really decreases or suppresses the activities of various body systems. It deadens nerves in the same way as an anaesthetic, and decreases the rate at which muscular responses can occur. It eventually causes blurred vision, slurred speech, loss of balance and final collapse into unconsciousness. *Alcohol is therefore a depressant*, and should not be used in an attempt to increase athletic ability.

3 **Tranquillizers** include drugs such as the phenothiazines, which also have a quieting effect on the nervous system. In prescribed doses, however, they do *not* induce sleep. A nervous athlete may be tempted to take a tranquillizer before an event, since there is no risk of falling asleep. Moreover, they do not produce hallucinations and are not

physically addicting, so the user may continue to use the drug on a regular basis. Eventually, however, he or she develops an emotional or a mental dependence, and then takes the tranquillizer to *prevent* anxiety, rather than to treat an existing state. Large doses of tranquillizers have similar effects to barbiturates.

4 **Hallucinogens** act on the nervous system in such ways as to confuse the senses, produce distortions in time and space, loss of memory, and cause the user to 'see visions'. Initially, the user feels relaxed and peaceful, with an exaggerated sense of well-being—a state called **euphoria**. There may also be visual confusion as objects seem to assume different and unreal shapes and colours. LSD and ganja are two common examples.

  When **marijuana (ganja)** is first smoked, the effects are usually felt less than fifteen minutes after inhalation. It also increases the heart rate. However, accompanying this is a lowering of the body temperature, and a reduction in the level of circulating blood sugar which is needed to supply energy during cellular respiration. Ganja smoking is often linked with religion; the smokers believe that it improves wisdom and insight, 'helps them to understand' themselves, and increases performance in physical activities. Thus footballers and other athletes may 'smoke weed' prior to a match, mistakenly believing that they will have increased stamina, and be able to 'read their opponents' thoughts' about the passes to be made during the game. But far from doing this, ganja impairs the judgment; the user soon becomes unsteady and has difficulty in co-ordinating muscular movements.

  The use of ganja, particularly by athletes, is thus to be abhorred, as it imparts no special powers—neither mental nor physical—to the user. In addition, its long-term effects are the emotional and psychological dependence of the user; it may also 'open the door' to the use of more dangerous drugs.

  LSD, known as 'acid' or 'sugar cubes', is the most potent and dangerous of the hallucinogens, exerting powerful influences on the brain.

  All hallucinogens, including ganja, are particularly dangerous because of the unpredictable effects they have upon body functions. Users have been known to suffer chromosomal damage (from LSD) and sterility (from ganja). It is also believed that the offspring of habitual users could suffer serious birth defects.

5 **Narcotics** are all addictive drugs. Users soon develop a psychological and physical dependence on the drug, suffering serious withdrawal sickness when deprived of it. Symptoms may range from sweating, nausea, shaking and diarrhoea, to abdominal pains and muscular cramps, especially in the legs. Opium, morphine, codeine, cocaine (also called 'coke' or 'snow'), paregoric and heroin are examples of narcotic drugs. Heroin, or 'junk', is the most dangerous and addictive of the narcotic drugs. Even in the medical profession, its use is forbidden by law.

Drug dependence

This is a state in which there is a psychological need for the effects which the drug produces. 'Pep pills', ganja (marijuana) and nicotine in cigarettes are some examples of drugs for which a dependence can readily develop. Many of the drugs may not themselves cause actual physical damage to the body, but are really 'habit-forming'. When the individual is deprived of the drug, there may be mental stress, anxiety, prolonged depression and other behaviour changes.

  Drug addiction is a state in which there is total dependence on the drug, and in which there are physical as well as psychological changes in the body. Alcohol (e.g. rum), heroin and morphine are common examples. When an addict is cut off from the drug supply, painful withdrawal symptoms are experienced.

Heroin addict

152

Who is to decide?

Male and female sex hormones cause the development of secondary sex characteristics, including the change of body shape seen during adolescence. Although hormones are not normally thought of as drugs, if they are taken in abnormal amounts for purposes other than those for which the body produces them, then they must be placed in this class.

Female athletes have been known to take the male reproductive hormones or steroids to promote muscular development. Other athletes have used adrenaline to 'promote a state of readiness for action'. Such practices are dangerous, because they may have harmful effects on the body's ability to function normally in later years. There are also serious moral and ethical questions surrounding the use of drugs and unorthodox methods to alter athletic performance. Should taking vitamin supplements be considered illegal or unethical? And what about the so-called 'tonics', special high-energy diets, consumed while the athlete is in training? Even smoking a cigarette, containing nicotine, to calm an athlete's 'nerves' just before the competition could be considered as drug-taking. There is also a technique called 'blood-boosting' in which red blood cells are injected into the bloodstream to increase the oxygen carrying capacity of the blood and so prevent muscle fatigue.

So stiff are the current athletic competitions, and so great are the pressures, especially on adolescent athletes, of winning a trophy, that athletes may ignore the immorality of using drugs and other methods to try to improve their performance in sporting competitions. The short-term advantages of winning a race or performing well in competitive sports are outweighed by the irreparable and long-term damage which can be done to body cells by the taking of drugs.

Because of their harmful effects, all persons, and especially those operating dangerous equipment or machines and driving motor vehicles, as well as athletes, should avoid taking drugs unless they are medically prescribed. Effects such as the sense of unreality, the variations in emotions, and the alteration of general behaviour could be responsible for loss of life, including that of the drug-taker!

Questions

1 Another name for Benzedrine tablets is 'speed' or 'wake-ups'. Why do you think they are called this?
2 Howard, a member of the school's track team, was encouraged by friends to take some amphetamine 'pep pills' to improve his athletic performance, and to keep him awake while studying at night after his training. Very soon however, he was feeling increasingly tired, falling asleep in class, taking more and more 'pep pills' and was eventually dropped from his school's team.
  How could you account for Howard's 'misfortune'?

60

Leisure and recreation

Because of the mental or physical effort involved in any form of physical activity, including even routine household chores, we each need some form of relaxation and change from that activity.

Choosing your recreation

Leisure time, and the recreational activities in which we become involved, provide a necessary period of relaxation. It focuses the mind on some alternative activity, and allows the body to rest some over-used muscles while using others. Leisure activities allow the heart and respiratory rates to proceed at a different pace. Fatigue of the nervous system, a condition which could result in uncoordinated nerve–muscle interactions, is prevented. Reading, listening to music, sewing, dancing and swimming are but a few of the leisure activities we can choose from.

Persons who work under considerable mental strain, taking little physical activity, are also in need of some form of recreation. More active forms of recreation, such as tennis, gardening, badminton, would be suitable or they may even choose to kick a football for an hour or so each day.

Leisure activities should relieve boredom and mental strain, should be different from repetitive tasks or routine activities, should ease muscular fatigue, and provide such relaxation and enjoyment that the individual looks forward to it.

When choosing recreational activities, the following important considerations should be taken into account:

(a) the type of mental or physical activity or routine tasks usually performed;
(b) the age of the individual, which has a bearing on skills possessed and the form of recreational activities the body can undertake. Young persons can choose more active forms of recreation, but older persons should pursue less strenuous activities to prevent overwork of the heart, the muscles and other body systems;
(c) climatic conditions. These will naturally limit the choice of recreational activity, and the time when they can be pursued. Persons living in tropical countries should try to avoid prolonged outdoor activities during the hot, dry months of the year. At these times the temperature is very high, and the air is dry and dusty. Any form of physical activity will generate a lot of body heat, which may cause heat stroke as the brain and other body cells become overheated. There could also be excessive sweating, which depletes body salts, especially sodium, and this could easily result in muscular cramps.

Similarly, prolonged outdoor recreational activities in cold climates could, especially if correct protective clothing is not worn, let the extremities, e.g. fingers and toes, get too cold, causing tissue damage.

Athletic ability

Your performance in sports depends on your athletic ability. High athletic achievement is the result of good co-ordination, short reaction times and constant practice.

Co-ordination

When the body is healthy, there is good muscle tone, mental alertness and all body systems function properly. In particular, muscles and nerves will work well together in perfect co-ordination, resulting in smooth, graceful, athletic movements.

Reaction time

All muscles respond to commands, which reach them as nerve impulses, by contracting or relaxing. The time taken for a whole muscle to respond to a specific command is the **reaction time**. The greater the nerve–muscle co-ordination, the shorter will be the reaction time. A fast reaction time is an asset to an athlete.

Experiment

A ruler is held vertically between the thumb and a finger at the bottom end. When the thumb and finger are spread apart the ruler falls, but it can be caught by quickly closing back the thumb and finger. The distance the ruler falls through before it is caught is a measure of a person's reaction time. Design and carry out an experiment to find out if the girls in your class have faster reactions than the boys.

Practice

The basic skills of running, jumping, kicking, throwing and catching are fundamental to all sports. Good performance in sports is dependent mainly on improving co-ordination and reaction times. This can only be achieved by practising the basic skills. Practice sessions must be frequent, but of short duration to avoid fatigue.

Summary

When drugs, hormones and other methods are used in an attempt to alter athletic ability, their effects eventually prove harmful to the physical and mental well-being of the user. The only guaranteed formula for excellent performance in sports is a well nourished body with muscles kept toned and healthy through regular exercise, proper diet and appropriate recreational activities.

Bert Cameron from Jamaica, 400 metres world champion

61

Projectiles

A **projectile** is any object that is thrown or projected into the air. A variety of projectiles are used in sporting activities. The javelin, discus, cricket or rounders ball, arrow, football, golf ball, shot-putt, and the human body in a broad jump all are projectiles. How do projectiles move through the air?

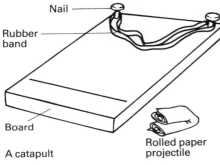

Nail

Rubber band

Board

A catapult

Rolled paper projectile

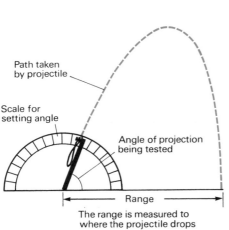

Path taken by projectile

Scale for setting angle

Angle of projection being tested

Range

The range is measured to where the projectile drops

Experiment: Making a catapult

The simple catapult shown in the diagram can be used to investigate projectile motion. (A movable inclined plane can be used in place of the board.) To conduct a proper *investigation* of the angle of projection which makes the projectile travel farthest, the following things must be done:

(a) The rubber must be stretched to the same position each time.
(b) The projection must be done several times for each angle and the *average* measurement taken for that angle.
(c) The same projectile must be used each time.

Why are these three precautions necessary in an investigation of this nature?

When a graph of horizontal range *vs* projection angle of the projectile is drawn, it is found that the range is the greatest for an angle of approximately 45°. In projectile sports this is an important angle as it may very well decide who wins the game.

If the target is far away and the person aims exactly at the bullseye, is he likely to hit the target? Why?

Effect of gravity

The main reason that projectiles behave as they do is that they are under the influence of **gravity** as they move through the air. Gravity tends to pull objects vertically downwards towards the ground. The moment a projectile is let go, therefore, it starts to fall—whether it is projected upwards or straight ahead.

Effect of the wind

As a projectile moves through the air it also encounters friction or air resistance which slows it down and therefore reduces its range. If a wind is blowing against the direction of travel, the range will be further shortened. However, the range will be lengthened if the projectile is travelling with the wind. Also, if the wind is blowing across the path of the object the direction of travel will be affected as shown. The effect the wind has on projectiles is similar to the effect of moving water on water vehicles.

How do kites and planes fly?

You wonder why a kite does not fall towards the ground as a projectile would. If you blow over a narrow strip of paper you will find that it tends to rise. It experiences an upward force (a **lift**) due to the unequal air speeds above and below it. (This is in fact how aeroplanes fly; the shape of the wings causes air to rush faster over the upper surface of the wings than over the lower, creating a lift.) When there are no wind currents, the kite will drop down. However, as long as there are wind currents which make air flow faster over the front of the kite than over the back, the kite will experience the lift necessary to keep it up. Sail boats can make use of this wind current effect to sail *against* the wind.

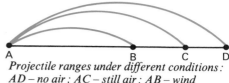

Projectile ranges under different conditions: AD – no air; AC – still air; AB – wind blowing against projectile

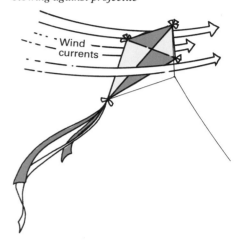

Producing lift in kites (above) and aeroplane wings (below)

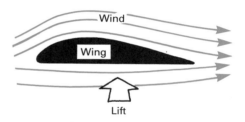

Questions

1 Draw a diagram to show the path a broad jumper must take from the ground through the air in order to jump the farthest.
2 Discuss two effects the wind has on a football kicked into the air at an angle, say, of 45°.
3 Explain how vultures are able to stay up in the air by merely keeping their wings spread out.

62

Materials used in sports

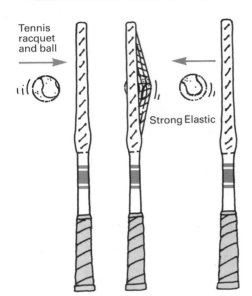

Tennis racquet and ball

Strong Elastic

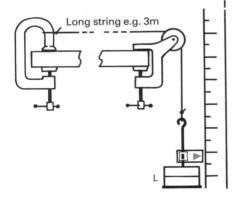

Long string e.g. 3m

L

Investigating elasticity of strings

How is the right type of material selected for use in a particular sport? There are two main approaches. One is to select any material, make the sports equipment with it, and then give the product a trial. This method has two main drawbacks. First, the equipment may take a lot of time to make, e.g. a floor for playing tennis indoors. If the item does not work properly, a lot of time will again have to be spent to make it from another material, until the right material is found. A second drawback is the possible danger in using inappropriate materials. A pole vault stick might break in use during a test. This will put the person trying it out in unnecessary danger.

A second approach is to ask what properties the material must possess for the use to be successful. Tests for these properties are then carried out on the material in a scientific way.

Strings

Lawn tennis racquets are made with strings. These strings must be strong (not easily broken when stretched) and elastic (must return to their original tight state after the ball has left the racquet).

The diagram shows some apparatus which can be used to test strings for elasticity and strength. Loads L are added *gently* (why gently?) to the hanger and the corresponding extensions E are noted. After each extension the loads are taken off to see whether the string returns to its original position. If it does, it means that the string still behaves as elastic after bearing that load. The experiment should be repeated with several equal lengths of the same string and the average values for E taken for each L. This compensates for the fact that the string might not be perfectly uniform. The largest load a string can bear and still remain elastic gives an indication of the useful strength of the string.

A graph can be plotted of extension against load. For most materials, the graph is a straight line through the origin, showing that the extension is *directly proportional to the load*; i.e. if the load is doubled, the extension is doubled, and so on. The point where the graph starts to curve enables the *elastic limit* of the string to be found. The elastic limit is the maximum load the string can take and yet return to its original state when the load is removed. Material A is the best to use for a lawn tennis racquet. It stretches the least, can take the greatest load and still remains elastic.

Rods

Materials to be used for rods can be tested for elasticity and strength. The depression is measured for each load and a depression–load graph plotted.

Playing surfaces

Playing surfaces can be tested for friction by using a horizontally operating spring balance and a fixed load L. The maximum force F exerted on the balance to make the load just move is the frictional force between L and the playing surface. The experiment is repeated on several parts of the playing surface and the average value of F taken. Why are several readings taken?

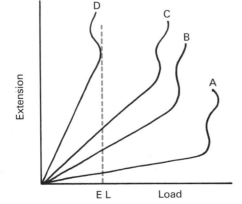

Extension-load graphs for four strings. The elastic limit EL of D is shown

Bounce can be investigated by dropping the same ball from a fixed height onto a sample of the playing surface (e.g. on to various parts of a playing field). Average readings taken for each kind of surface can be compared to see which surface has the most or least bounce.

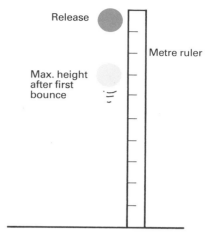

Testing a surface for bounce

Malcolm Marshall bowls a bouncer

Activity

Relating properties of materials to their uses
By considering the strength, elasticity and density of the following materials, can you comment on why they are used in the sporting items shown?

Can you also suggest methods of preserving these materials? By considering the springs in vehicles, can you suggest why a maximum number of passengers, or a maximum laden weight is assigned to a bus or truck?

Questions

1 A certain type of pole vault stick is made of an aluminium alloy. Explain, with reference to **three** properties needed by a pole vault stick, why the aluminium alloy is a good choice.
2 How would you design an experiment to find out which of two brands of tennis ball has a better bounce?
3 How would you design an experiment to find out if nylon strings are stronger than polythene strings?

63

The camera and the eye

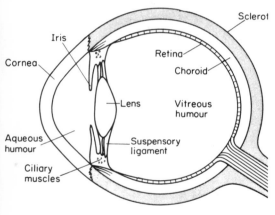

Focusing ring
(Alters distance
of lens from film)

Film
spool

Diaphragm   Film

Lens

Diaphragm
adjusting
ring

Shutter

The camera

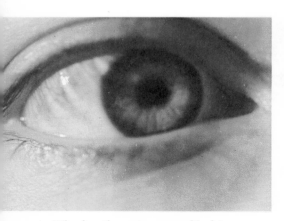

Iris

Cornea

Sclerot

Retina

Choroid

Lens

Vitreous
humour

Aqueous
humour

Suspensory
ligament

Ciliary
muscles

The eye

Why does the centre appear black?

The human eye is a marvellous sense organ which can in some ways be compared to the camera. Let us consider the simple box camera, for instance.

Focusing

Both the eye and the box camera use a **biconvex** lens to produce an image on a screen. In the eye, however, the curved transparent cornea also helps to focus the image. You can use a lamp and screen arrangement to show that a lens needs to be moved farther away from the screen to produce a clearly focused image of a nearby object. The lens should be moved nearer to the screen to accommodate distant objects. This is the effect of rotating the barrel of a simple box camera. The lens is either moved nearer to or farther away from the screen (the film) to get a sharp picture. In the eye, however, nearby objects are focused by contracting the **ciliary muscles** so that the lens is able to get fatter in the middle. To view distant objects, the muscles relax and the lens gets thinner, enabling a sharp image to be formed on the retina.

Controlling the amount of light

If too much light enters the eye it can damage the very delicate light-sensitive cells of the retina. In bright light the muscular **iris** automatically contracts to create a small hole which lets in less light. This hole is called the **pupil**. The colour of the iris in most people is brown, but it can also be blue or green.

In the box camera a lever is sometimes used to insert a diaphragm with a small aperture which reduces the amount of light reaching the film.

These photographs of a beach show over-exposure (above) and correct exposure (below)

Preventing scattering of light

Cameras are painted black inside to prevent light scattering onto the film. This would spoil the clarity of the picture.

In the eye there is a black **choroid** layer that absorbs any stray light and so prevents scattering. This black layer inside makes the pupil of the eye look black.

Receiving colour

On the retina of the eye are cells called **cones**, which are sensitive to colour. The colour information they pick up is converted to electrical impulses and sent to the brain along the optic nerve.

Colour film has three layers of dyes. Each layer is sensitive to either red, green or blue light. A **chemical change** takes place when a layer receives the appropriate colour of light. If paper treated with silver chloride solution is exposed to light, you can see a chemical change taking place. Scenes are reproduced in full colour because red, green and blue lights mix to produce a variety of colours depending on the proportion of the constituents in each mixture. In a TV camera the colour information is converted to an electric current by means of a photo-electric effect occurring at the screen. Thus a TV camera resembles the eye more nearly than the simple box camera.

Lens protection

The eyelid protects the cornea and lens from dust and, with the aid of tears secreted by a tear gland, constantly keeps the surface of the cornea clean. Tears also have a disinfectant effect, helping to kill germs that get to the retina. A lens cap is used to protect the lens of the box camera from dust. Box cameras should be kept in dry places to prevent a fungus from eating away the coating that is normally put on the lenses.

Colour correction

A lever in the box camera can be operated to place a **filter** behind the camera lens if the quality of the light does not suit the film. (Alternatively, the filter can be screwed on in front of the lens.) If the light is too green, say, an appropriate filter can be used to filter out the excess green light. In the eye there is no such filter. But the brain sometimes 'interprets' a colour based on past experience. The brain acts as if it were a filter to get the colour 'right'.

What colour do you see? Do you see it as yellow? It's not. It's orange. The brain sometimes attempts to do some colour corrections based on past experience

Questions

1 Name three structures in the eye that resemble structures in the camera.
2 Discuss two ways in which parts of the eye do not function in quite the same way as the corresponding parts in the camera.
3 It is good practice to store good quality microscopes in closed boxes in which there is some silica gel (a drying agent). How does the silica gel help to protect the microscope lenses?

Activities

1 Use a bicoloured lens and a screen to show
 (a) how focusing on near or far objects takes place by moving the lens;
 (b) how apertures (e.g. holes in cardboard) of various sizes placed in front of the lens cause images of various brightnesses.
2 Examine a model of the eye and a simple box camera and note similarities and differences as described above.

64

Colour

White light is made up of a variety of colours

White light, whether artificially produced or from the Sun, is really made up of a wide range of colours. If this were not so, our world would appear far less colourful than it is.

The colours of white light

A ray box, glass prism and white screen can be used in a darkened room to show that white light consists of a whole range of colours. Most people seem to see seven colours. But there are in fact an infinite variety of shades between the red and violet ends. A second prism, makes the colours recombine and produce white light. A colour wheel rotated very fast also appears white. This suggests that coloured light is again recombining (in the eye) to produce white light.

The rainbow

Like the glass prism, rain drops can also split white light into its component colours. You can make your own rainbow using a fine spray from a garden hose if you stand with the Sun behind you.

Primary and secondary colours

Three ray boxes (or flashlights) with colour filters in front of them can be used to investigate the effects of mixing coloured lights. Can you mix two colours of light together to give red, green or blue light? Try it! These three colours that cannot be produced by mixing coloured lights are called **primary** colours. Magenta, yellow, and cyan are the **secondary** colours produced by mixing primary colours in pairs. Notice that to produce light that appears white to the eye only the primary colours red, green and blue are needed. The entire spectrum is not necessary.

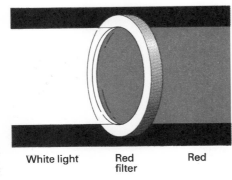

White light   Red   Red
             filter

A red filter lets through red light. The other colours are absorbed. What do you think a blue filter does?

How we see colour

A red dress seen in white light appears red. This is because red light is reflected by the dye in the dress. All other colours are absorbed by the dye. In red light the dress also looks red. But in blue light the dress looks black. Can you say why?

    Most of the dyes in common use are 'impure' in the sense that they reflect more than one colour of light. Yellow dyes, for example, reflect red and green light as well as orange and primary yellow. All other colours in the spectrum are absorbed. Blue dyes reflect mainly blue and green. Since green is reflected by both dyes, yellow and blue **paint** mixture looks green. Between them, the yellow and blue absorb all the colours of the spectrum except green. Can you suggest why red + green + blue **paint** gives nearly (but not exactly) black paint? Can you predict what colour you will get when secondary yellow **light** (red + green) is mixed with blue light? (The colour mixing diagram may help you.)

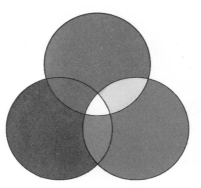

Mixing coloured lights

Mixtures of dyes

Unlike light the colour that results when paints are mixed is produced by **subtraction**. The colour seen is the colour of light not absorbed by any of the pigments. By using the **chromatography** apparatus shown, black ink from a felt-tip pen can be shown to be made up of a variety of coloured dyes. Other ink colours can be analysed in the same way to see what they contain. Flowers can be crushed and their dyes extracted using a suitable solvent, e.g. methylated spirits + a few drops of hydrochloric acid, or white rum. The dye can then be analysed by chromatography to see what colours are present. The same solvent should be used in performing the chromatography.

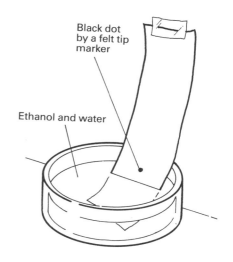

Applications of colour-mixing principles

A knowledge of colour-mixing principles enables us to predict roughly what colours will be seen when dyes are mixed. This is useful for those who wish to dye garments. People who operate stage lights will also benefit from knowing how coloured objects appear in coloured lights.

The colour-TV screen is made up of many tiny dots (or lines) of powders that glow red, green or blue when electron beams are swept across them. When these glow, the varying colours in a scene are reconstructed. If a printed colour photograph is examined under a magnifying glass dots of various colours can be seen. The colour picture is broken down into dots. First the magenta dots are printed, then the cyan, then the yellow, then the black. This produces the complete range of colours seen.

Magnified view of TV screen to show dots are made up from three powders

Questions

1 Why do white clothes feel cool and dark clothes hot?
2 How will the following look in secondary yellow light:
   (a) a white blouse with red polka dots;
   (b) a white blouse with green polka dots;
   (c) a blue blouse with black polka dots.
3 How can it be shown that the colours of flowers are due to mixtures of pigments?
4 A blue filter is placed in front of a beam of white light. The colour of light that passes through the filter falls on a red tablecloth that has green stripes. How will the tablecloth look in the filtered light?

Magnified view of colour photograph showing the breakdown into dots

65

Making light bend

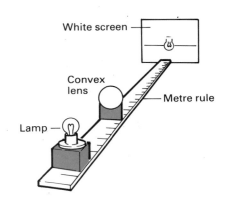

The bending of light

Although light travels in straight lines, it can be bent. Bending occurs when light travels from one medium to another, and takes place at the boundary between the two. It is known as **refraction**. Consider the tracks made by a fast moving car as it leaves the hard road and enters a sandy stretch at an angle. The tracks bend because one front wheel is slowed down by the sand before the other. In the same way the light bends at, for example, a glass/air boundary because glass slows it down.

Rectangular prisms

A ray box and a rectangular prism can be used to show light bending at an air/glass boundary. If a triangular prism is used a spectrum is formed because some colours are bent more than others. What does this tell us about the speeds of light of different colours?

The bending of light at air/water boundaries makes pools appear shallower than they really are. This effect can be shown by writing 'REFRACTION' on a piece of paper and standing a rectangular prism on one end over part of it. That part will appear nearer than the rest.

Convex lenses

If the glass is a convex shape some other effects of refraction show up. Parallel rays of light are brought to a **focus** by a convex lens. By moving the lamp along the ruler it can be shown that a large upside-down image will be formed on a screen if the lamp is slightly further away than the **principal focus** of the lens. A small upside-down image is formed when the lamp is a long way from the lens. Images that can be formed onto a screen are said to be **real**.

The ability of a convex lens to bring light to a focus is used to correct long-sightedness. A long-sighted person cannot see close objects clearly because his eyeball is too short (or his lens muscles too weak). A convex lens can be used to bend the light further so that it focuses sharply on the retina. A person suffering from short sight cannot see far away objects clearly because his eyeball is too long (or his eye lens too thick when relaxed). A **concave** lens helps to spread the rays outwards and so makes the rays come to a focus on the retina.

The ability of convex lenses to form large images on a screen is used in slide and movie projectors. The slide is lit up by a bright lamp with a concave reflector and convex lenses which help to focus the maximum amount of light onto the transparency. (A heat filter is necessary to prevent the heat of the lamp, which is also focused onto the transparency, from burning it.) The transparency is placed just outside the principal focus of the projection lens. A large image is therefore formed on the screen. Why must the transparency be inserted upside-down?

A convex lens does not always produce an image that can be caught on a screen. When used as a **magnifying glass**, the lens forms a large upright image on the same side as the object. You can see the image. But try as you may, you will not be able to see it on a screen. This type of image is said to be **virtual**.

The **camera** makes use of the ability of the convex lens to form a small image when the object is some distance away from the lens. The camera is described in Section 63.

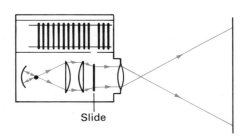

Investigating image foundation by a curved lens

White screen

Convex lens

Metre rule

Lamp

Slide

Large image on screen

How a projector forms a large, bright image

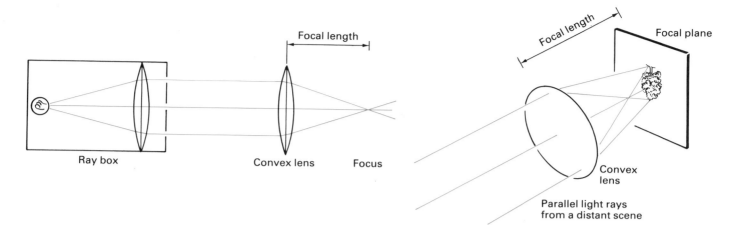

Focal length

Ray box   Convex lens   Focus

Focal length   Focal plane

Convex lens

Parallel light rays from a distant scene

Finding the focal length of a convex lens

Questions

1 How many focal lengths from a convex lens must an object be placed so that the following types of images can be formed:
   (a) real, enlarged, upside-down;
   (b) real, smaller, upside-down;
   (c) real, same size, upside-down;
   (d) virtual, enlarged, right-side-up.
2 A certain swimming pool appears to be 1 m deep when full of water. By means of a ray diagram explain why the pool appears shallower than it really is.

Activities

1 Using a ray box and rectangular glass prism, trace the bending of a beam of light as it crosses air to glass and glass to air boundaries (it would be helpful to draw a line perpendicular to the boundaries at the point of the bending to see if the light is bending towards or away from the perpendicular).
2 (a) Look down an opaque container, e.g. a tin can or paper cup, and observe that filling it with water makes the container appear shallower.
   (b) Use a pencil to locate the apparent position of the bottom of the container, while looking through the water from above.
3 Use a ray box and a triangular prism to show that when light bends, some colours are bent more than others.
4 Aim a biconvex lens at a far away object (e.g. the clouds). Move a screen until the image of this object comes into focus. Since approximately parallel rays of light will be received by the lens from far away objects, the screen will be at the *principal focus* of the lens when the image of the clouds is formed. Measure the focal length (the distance between the principal focus and the lens) of the lens. Then, using a small lamp, with the lens and screen, carry out experiments to find out the answers to Question 1.
5 Examine the lamp/lens/transparency system of a movie and a slide projector.

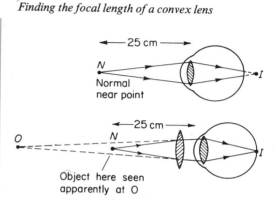

Long-sight correction. The eyeball is too short (above) so that an object at N, 25 cm away, will appear blurred and would be in focus only at I behind the retina. The convex lens (below) bends the rays in towards the eye so they are focused on the retina

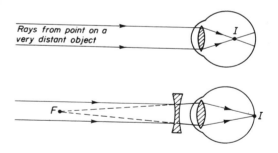

Short-sight correction. The eyeball is too long (above) so rays from a distant object would be in focus in front of the retina. The concave lens (below) spreads out the rays before they enter the eye so they can be focused on the retina

66

Bouncing light off surfaces

Reflection off a plane surface

When light bounces off a very smooth, plane (flat) surface, the **angle of incidence** of the ray of light is equal to the **angle of reflection**. It is this property that makes every point of an object appear to be the same distance behind a plane mirror as it is in front. This produces a **lateral inversion** effect—making left look like right and vice versa.

Clear images are not seen in rough surfaces like this paper. The tiny bumps on the surface reflect the light in all directions even though, at each point, the angle of incidence is equal to the angle of reflection. The air in our atmosphere also scatters light in all directions. That is why shadows on the Earth do receive some light and are therefore 'softer' than shadows seen on the Moon.

Using a ray box to show the angle of incidence (i) is always equal to the angle of reflection (r)

You can make a periscope by fixing two plane mirrors at an angle of 45° to the imaginary line between them. The top mirror will reflect the cricket match on to the bottom mirror so it is visible through the eye hole

Reflection from curved mirrors

Flashlights and car head-lamps make use of the fact that parallel rays of light can be made to emerge from a **concave** mirror (silvered on the inside) by placing the lamp at its focus (this effect is used in reverse in solar cookers (p. 108) where parallel rays from the Sun are reflected to a focus). A concave mirror can also be used to make something that is placed near to the mirror look larger. Make-up and shaving mirrors and dental mirrors make use of this effect.

Small images are always formed in **convex** mirrors (silvered on the outside). These mirrors can take in a wider field of view than a plane mirror. Concave mirrors can also form small images, but only if the objects are far away. The image formed is upside-down. Why are convex and not concave mirrors used as driving mirrors? The diagrams should help you decide. Why are some driving mirrors convex rather than plane? Which type of mirror would you recommend for use in stores so that an eye can be kept on a wide area?

The image in a plane mirror always seems to be the same distance behind the mirror as the object is in front of it. Why?

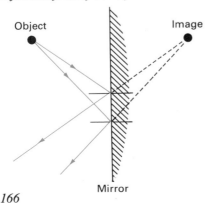

Questions

1 Draw a diagram to show how the letter J will look when viewed in a plane mirror. Which letters of the alphabet will not look different when viewed in a plane mirror?

2 Both concave and convex mirrors make small images of large, distant objects. Why are convex and not concave mirrors used as driving mirrors?

3 Draw a diagram to show how a large plane mirror placed by the roadside can help motorists see around sharp bends where view is obstructed.

4 Why are concave (dish) aerials used to send radio waves from Earth to satellites?

Activities

1 Use a plane mirror, a protractor and a ray box to show that when light reflects, the angle of incidence is always equal to the angle of reflection.

2 Use a pencil to locate the position of the image of an object (e.g. a small coin) behind a plane mirror. Measure the distance between the object and the mirror and the distance between the image of the object and the mirror. What do you notice?

3 Make a simple periscope using plane mirrors.

4 (a) Aim a concave mirror at the sun (but *do not* look at the sun). Move a match head in front of the mirror to a position where the match can be ignited. The match head is now at the principal focus of the mirror. Measure the focal length of this mirror.

    (b) Carry a mirror into a room and look at your face (or a pencil). How many focal lengths away from the mirror must you place your face (or the pencil) in order to obtain an image that is
      (i) smaller and upside-down;
      (ii) larger and upside-down;
      (iii) larger and upright.

5 Move a convex mirror away from you and notice that the image is always small and upright.

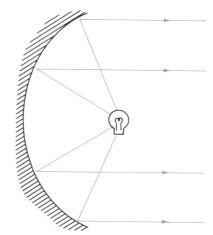

Car head-lamp principle. The bulb is placed at the focus of a concave mirror

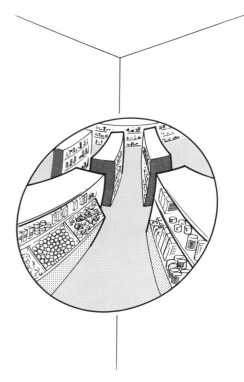

What kind of mirror is this?

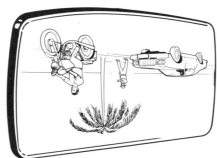

*Imagine you are driving a car and you want to see how much traffic is behind you. Which of these mirrors would be the most useful (*left to right*) plane, concave, convex? Why?*

67

Light and shadow

This picture was taken from above the surface of the Moon (foreground). In the distance is the curve of the Earth, lit by the Sun

Wherever there is light, there is likely to be shadow. The shapes of shadows provide good evidence that light travels in **straight** lines.

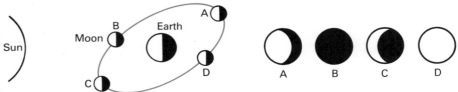

The phases of the Moon provide evidence that light travels in straight lines

Soft and sharp shadows

The apparatus shown in the diagram demonstrates that a round coin gives rise to a round shadow. A rectangular matchbox gives rise to a rectangular shadow. This shows that light does not bend around these objects. In other words, light travels in straight lines.

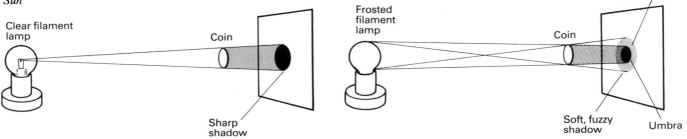

A small source of light throws sharp shadows. An extended source throws soft, fuzzy shadows. Tungsten bulbs will therefore give sharper shadows than fluorescent lamps

The diagram shows that the sharpness or fuzzyness of shadows depends upon the size of the light source. Fluorescent tubes are sometimes preferred to bulbs in factories and evening schools because they produce less shadow. Each time the eye has to focus on a bright region after a shadowed region, or vice versa, the iris has to close or open to let in the right amount of light. If the iris has a lot of work to do, eye fatigue results.

Phases and eclipses

Phases of the Moon occur because light falls only on the half of the Moon facing the Sun. The light does not bend over to light up the dark side. As the Moon revolves around the Earth we see different fractions of lighted and dark portions.

An **eclipse** of the Moon occurs whenever the Moon enters the Earth's shadow. An eclipse of the Sun takes place when the Moon lies in a straight line between the Sun and the Earth.

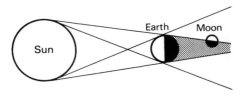

The Moon about to undergo a total eclipse. The Moon is, however, still visible because the atmosphere of the Earth acts like a lens and bends light round into the dark region. An eclipsed Moon looks brownish because of this effect

Warning   It is dangerous to stare at the Sun, either in its full state or in its eclipsed state. Dangerous UV rays are given off that can damage the retina of the eye. 'Sunshades' offer **no** protection against *these* rays. Only special glasses like those worn by arc welders offer some protection.

168

Pinhole camera

You can make a pinhole camera and observe an upside-down image of a bright scene on the screen. This provides further evidence that light travels in straight lines. The circles of light you see under trees are really images of the Sun formed by this pinhole camera effect as light passes through tiny holes formed between leaves. When the Sun is overhead, similar circles of light can be seen on the floor of a house which has small holes in the roof.

The pinhole camera can be used to measure the size of objects using the formula:

$$\frac{\text{height of object}}{\text{distance of object from pinhole}} = \frac{\text{height of image}}{\text{distance of image from pinhole}}$$

Solar eclipse

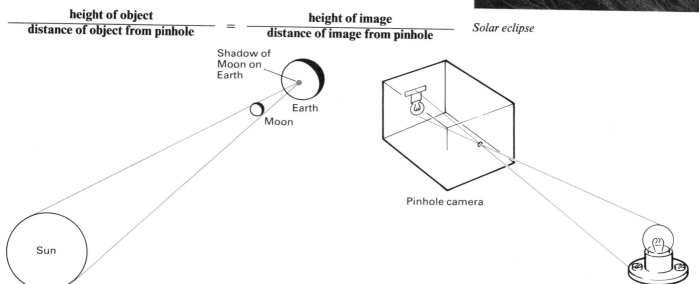

During a solar eclipse (left), the size and position of the Moon mean that it appears to block out the Sun when viewed from the position shown (see the photograph above). A pinhole camera (right)

Questions

1. Certain types of coloured glass or plastic help to reduce the quality of light reaching the eye. Explain why 'sunshades' made of these materials may harm the eye (a) on a bright day; (b) in a place where arc welding is being done.
2. What **two** precautions will you take following the breakage of a fluorescent tube?
3. In a pinhole camera, the shape of the image of the Sun is like this: O when the pinhole is circular. What will be the shape of the image of the Sun when the pinhole is square?
4. Although the Earth rotates daily on an axis, the Sun is visible for all 24 hours at the North Pole. Draw a diagram to show how this is possible.

Activities

1. Place a pencil about 2 m directly below a fluorescent lamp. Place a screen about 10 cm below the pencil. Observe the shadow of the pencil when the pencil is (a) parallel and (b) perpendicular to the fluorescent tube. Can you explain your observations?
2. Make models to show
   (a) phases of the Moon;
   (b) eclipse of the Moon;
   (c) eclipse of the Sun.
3. Make a pinhole camera and use it to measure the height of your school building.
4. Use a map of the world or globe on a fitted axis, and a torch light to show how one of the poles can have 24 hours of daylight and the other 24 hours of darkness.

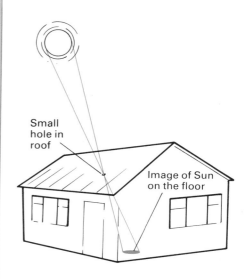

Pinhole camera effect caused by a tiny hole in a roof. Can you suggest how the diameter of the Sun can be found by making use of this image?

169

68

Making music

A new sound for the world—the pride of the Caribbean people! An orchestra made of musical instruments invented in the twentieth century. But how is music made with this steel pan?

Pitch

The playing surface of each steel pan is divided by channels into regions of differing areas. These areas vibrate when struck with a rubber tipped stick. The areas that are small give out a high-pitched sound. The large areas give out sounds of low pitch when they are struck. Each of the areas thus produces a distinct musical note. The frequency of each note can be measured by listening to the note and adjusting a calibrated signal generator until it produces the same note. It will be found that the high-pitched notes correspond to large frequencies of vibration and the low-pitched notes to small frequencies of vibration.

Other factors also affect the pitch in this fine instrument. The thickness or density of the vibrating surface is one factor. The tension the surface is under is another. If you look carefully at the first, tenor and bass pans, you will notice that the surface of the first is beaten in the most. Why do you think this is done?

Since musical instruments behave in similar ways, simple investigations into the factors affecting pitch can be performed with strings. A **sonometer** apparatus can be used to investigate (see diagram *below left*).

(a) how length of the string affects pitch. The same string must be used throughout the investigation, and its vibrating length varied (by moving X). The tension in the string should be kept constant (by keeping the weight of the bucket the same).

(b) how the higher density of the string affects pitch. First use a stout string, and then a thin string. What factors will you keep constant and how? What result do you expect?

How would you investigate how tension in a string affects pitch?

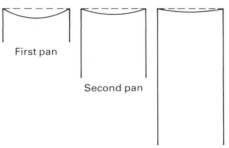

First pan

Second pan

Bass pan

The surface of the first pan is beaten in the most. Why?

Loudness

This feature is not too difficult to investigate! When a note on a steel pan is struck hard the note sounds loud. The same note struck more gently gives a softer sound. Using the sonometer and observing a plucked string (especially a heavy string) will illustrate what is happening. A loud sound corresponds to large amplitudes of vibration. A soft sound corresponds to small amplitudes of vibration. Thus the loudness of a sound is related to the energy output per second (power) of the vibrating object. However, the ear tends to hear very low and very high frequencies more softly. This is why there are bass and treble controls on amplifiers—so that these extreme frequencies can be given a boost and heard to the listener's satisfaction.

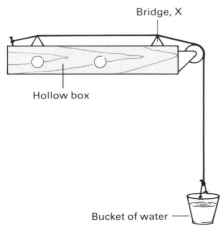

Bridge, X

Hollow box

Bucket of water

A sonometer apparatus

Quality

How is it that a note played on a piano or a guitar sounds different when produced on a steel pan? What is the same? What is different? If the wave form of the note is displayed on an oscilloscope the number of cycles

170

per second will be found to be the same. But the shapes in each cycle, as well as the overall shapes of a set of cycles, will be found to be different. This is because each note has a **fundamental frequency**, but other frequencies of vibration are produced also. It's these other high frequencies that add up and give each instrument its distinctive sound. We say that each type of instrument gives sound a different *quality*. We can recognize an individual's voice in the same way. Each voice contains fundamental notes plus higher frequency overtones. No two people have exactly the same overtones because these overtones depend on a large variety of factors—such as size of vocal chords, size of larynx and shapes of these two body parts.

The varied effects of sound

Sound can have a physiological effect as well as a psychological effect on people. On one hand it can damage the ear and cause headaches. On the other hand it can put people into hypnotic states. It is said in the Bible that a king asked a musician to play for him whenever he was possessed by an evil spirit. That cured him.

Sound can also have effects on objects. The sound of supersonic jets can shatter glass panes. International regulations therefore forbid these jets to fly commercially at supersonic speeds overland. Objects whose natural frequency of vibration is equal to the frequency of a particular sound will tend to vibrate with large amplitude when that sound is played. So don't be surprised if one day a string on your guitar starts sounding all by itself—when the radio is playing.

Small amplitude, soft sound

Large amplitude, loud sound

Loudness is related to the amplitude of vibration

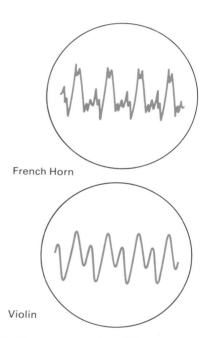
French Horn

Violin

Oscilloscope traces show different qualities for the same note

Questions

1 What two aspects of steel pan design enable notes of high pitch to be produced?
2 Explain in terms of sound frequencies why the same musical note sounds different when played on a steel pan and on a piano.
3 Give *one* example that you have observed where music seems to have put someone into a trance.
4 Name one workplace where workers are exposed constantly to: (a) continuous loud noises; (b) steady, soft noises. Can these two situations affect the behaviour of the workers?

Activities

1 Measure the frequencies of the first pan of a steel band using a signal generator.
2 Use a sonometer apparatus and carry out the three investigations on factors affecting pitch as described above. The investigations can be done qualitatively, i.e. listening for lower or higher pitches when a variable—for instance, length—is changed.
3 Connect a loudspeaker whose cone is visible to a signal generator. By turning up the volume at very low frequencies, observe how the amplitude of the speaker is related to the loudness of the sound. (Alternatively, the bass string on a guitar can be plucked at small and large amplitudes respectively, and the loudness of the sounds emitted compared.)
4 Close your eyes. Get your friends to sing the same tune one at a time. Do their voices sound exactly the same? Can you recognize any of their voices?
5 Observe oscilloscope displays of the same note played on different musical instruments. You can also sing the same note and compare your voice pattern with those of the instruments.

Sounds can be boosted by using microphones or electric instruments with an amplifier. Small amplitude vibrations of the voice or guitar are changed into large amplitude vibrations of the loudspeaker. (Steel Pulse at Reggae Sunsplash, Jamaica)

69

How we hear sounds

The human ear is a sense organ. It is one of a set of organs that gives us information about our surroundings. The information we gather helps us to locate dangers and to find those things necessary for our survival. You only have to close your eyes to notice how much information your ears give you. Like other sense organs, the human ear is also an organ of enjoyment. An understanding of how this wonderful organ works will help you to learn how to care for it.

The human ear

When a person speaks, **sound waves** are produced. These waves travel through the air as rapid pressure changes, and make the objects they strike vibrate.

The outer ear

The outer ear collects these sound waves. It consists of a **pinna** and an **ear canal** which together look rather like a funnel. The sound waves the pinna collects pass down the canal and strike a thin, muscular skin, making it vibrate. This rather delicate skin is called the **eardrum**.

The middle ear

In the middle ear the pressure variations picked up by the eardrum are magnified by a system of three tiny bones (the **ossicles**) which are arranged as levers. These bones are in an air-filled space. The ossicles pass on the pressure variations to another thin membrane, the **oval window**. A fine tube called the **Eustachian tube** runs from the middle ear to the back of the throat. The tube enables us to equalize the pressure on both sides of the eardrum. When the tube is blocked (when you have a cold) you can feel the pressure build up behind the eardrum.

The inner ear

Behind the oval window is a coiled, fluid-filled tube called the **cochlea**. Pressure variations are passed from the oval window to the fluid. Inside the cochlea are nerve cells that are sensitive to pressure changes in the fluid. It is believed that the cells in the wider part of the cochlea respond to low frequency sounds, while those in the narrower part are sensitive to high frequency sounds. The nerve cells are stimulated by the pressure variations and the impulses are carried by an **auditory nerve** to the brain. Here they are interpreted as 'sound'.

The inner ear also contains three **semi-circular canals**, all arranged perpendicularly to each other. These are also fluid-filled, but they are not used in hearing—they help our sense of balance.

The audio spectrum

The range of sound frequencies that the average human being can hear is called the **audio frequency spectrum**. In most humans it ranges from about 20 Hz to 20 kHz. Dogs can hear frequencies higher than 20 kHz. A dog can therefore be called by a dog whistle which a human might not be able to hear. A variable frequency signal generator connected to a good three-way or two-way loudspeaker can be used to test the frequency range that a person can hear. It will be found that older persons

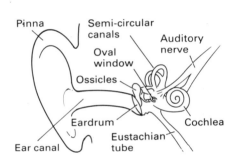

Blind people have to rely mainly on their sense of hearing

Pinna — Semi-circular canals — Auditory nerve — Oval window — Ossicles — Cochlea — Eardrum — Eustachian tube — Ear canal

The outer, middle and inner ear

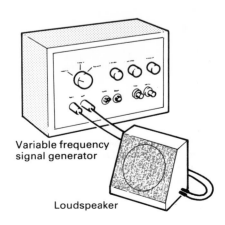

Variable frequency signal generator

Loudspeaker

often do not hear the upper frequencies. Can you guess why this is so? Look at the structure of the ear on page 172 to help you.

High fidelity

Equipment that is **high fidelity** (or hi-fi) can reproduce the entire audio frequency spectrum of sounds. Most medium-priced cassette recorders have a response of about 30 Hz to 12 kHz, which actually is quite good. However when the tape head is clogged with dirt, the sound gets muffled because the high frequency sounds (e.g. violins) are hardly reproduced. There are people who hear sounds muffled like these throughout their life because their ear is not sensitive to high frequencies. They have a difficult time hearing *clearly* what you are saying, because every sound has a mixture of low frequencies and high frequencies and they can't hear the high frequencies. A person with a hearing defect must be taken to an ear specialist. The ear is too delicate an organ to try out home remedies on it. In the case of the defective tape recorder, all that is needed to restore the machine back to brilliant hi-fi is to rub a cotton swab moistened with alcohol on the tape head to clean off the oxide and dirt.

Care of the ear

Here is a list of rules to follow for good ear care.

1 Don't put anything hard or soft into your, or anybody else's, ear. You may puncture your eardrum or introduce an infection. Most reputable cotton swab manufacturers print a warning on the box telling you *not* to put the swabs into the ear canal.
2 Don't swim in dirty water. Don't pour liquids down anybody's ear. The liquids may carry germs.
3 Don't expose your eardrum to very loud noises, e.g. by standing near loudspeakers or noisy machinery. Your eardrum and the delicate nerves in the cochlea can get damaged. Use earmuffs if you must be near to these noises.
4 If your ear must be cleaned out, get it done at a hospital or by a qualified doctor.

Selecting loudspeakers

When buying a good loudspeaker there are three things you must check:

(a) it can reproduce all audio frequencies (20 Hz to 20 kHz);
(b) its ohms specification matches that of the amplifier it will be used with;
(c) its power rating in watts exceeds the power output of the amplifier by at least 25%.

If either of the last two points are not met, your loudspeaker or amplifier may be damaged.

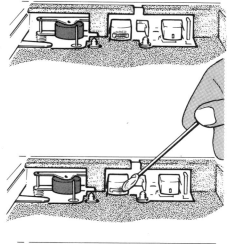
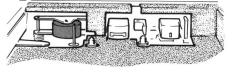

Cleaning a dirty tape head (top) using alcohol on a cotton swab

Ground technician at an airport. Why do you think he is wearing earmuffs?

Activities

1 Examine a model of the ear and identify the parts.
2 Get your teacher to test the hearing range of your class using a signal generator. Do you notice any pattern in the results?
3 Examine the advertisements (in catalogues, magazines and newspapers) to see loudspeaker, tape recorder and amplifier specifications about frequency ranges, ohms impedances (resistances), power outputs or requirements in watts and voltage requirements. How can this type of information be used in selecting your own equipment?

Questions

1 Which two parts of the ear can be damaged by very loud sounds?
2 The average person's ear can detect sounds from about 20 Hz to 20 kHz. Explain how pupils' hearing can be tested to find out the range of frequencies each one can hear. How will this information be useful to teachers?
3 Give *two* reasons why it is not wise to try to clean one's ear by poking cotton swabs down the ear canal.

70

Defence, repair, damage and infection

Transport systems, whether the nervous, blood, or nutrition system, must be protected from damage due to external factors or agents. Attack by microorganisms and foreign substances, or harmful conditions, could lead to malfunctioning of these systems and eventually to death.

The nervous system

The nervous system consists of two main parts: the **central nervous system** (brain, spinal cord) and the **peripheral nervous system** (the other nerves). The peripheral system contains **receptors** which receive the impulses from environmental conditions and sense any changes. It then passes the information to the central nervous system, where it is integrated. The central nervous system is like the 'telephone exchange' which collects and transfers 'calls' received from the various telephone lines (peripheral nervous system).

In man, the nervous system, especially the central nervous system, is well protected by parts of the skeleton. The brain is encased in a bony cage called the **skull** (or cranium). This protects it from injury and shock, especially from external sources. The spinal cord is also encased in a long column of inter-connected bones known as the **vertebral column** (see p. 70).

From the central nervous system nerve fibres radiate to all parts of the body. These fibres, the **motor neurones** and **sensory neurones**, are also well protected, especially from internal injury; they are encased in a thick, fatty sheath known as the **myelin sheath** (see left). The neurones are embedded in body tissue which provides both protection and support.

It has been shown that nerve impulses are like the passage of an electrical pulse, with the axon resembling an electrical wire. An axon is the extension of a nerve cell which conducts nerve impulses away from the cell body. Because of the electrical nature of nerve impulses, lack of protection (or insulation) of the nerve axons could lead to ineffective transmission. This malfunction could result in disaster. The rate of transmission of the nerve impulse always depends on both the cross-sectional area of the axon and the nature of the protective covering. This means that axons with a myelin sheath conduct more rapidly than axons which are uncovered.

The blood and nutrition systems

The blood system consists of organs, e.g. heart, lungs, liver, kidneys, and a series of blood vessels, e.g. arteries, veins, capillaries. All the organs are protected by the **skeleton**, a bony frame designed to protect and support the vital organs. Blood vessels such as veins and arteries are protected by their walls. Moreover, they are embedded in tissues and muscles to avoid damage.

Damage to any part of the blood system could have harmful effects, and could in some cases be fatal. The need for adequate protection is therefore vital.

The nutrition system through which food is taken in (ingestion), broken down into simpler substances (digestion) and diffused into the blood (absorption) is another vital body system. These parts of the body are also protected by skeletal parts and have large muscular external walls. Damage to any part of the alimentary tract could lead to the body's inability to get nourishment. This could lead to death.

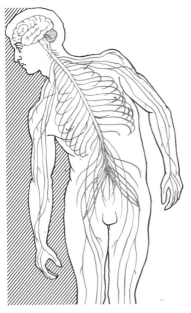

The nervous system

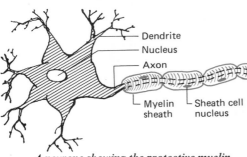

Dendrite
Nucleus
Axon
Myelin sheath
Sheath cell nucleus

A neurone showing the protective myelin sheath

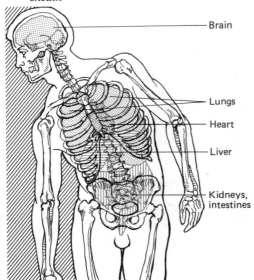

Brain
Lungs
Heart
Liver
Kidneys, intestines

The skeleton protects all the vital organs of the body

Consequences of damaging the transport systems

Nervous system

Damage to or infection of the nervous system generally results in impaired coordination, and neurological disorders, which sometimes lead to varying degrees of paralysis. In the nervous system there is no regeneration of nerve cells to replace tissue loss by degeneration or other changes due to disease. Disability may be reduced, however, by physiotherapy, occupational therapy and speech therapy.

Some of the possible conditions which could result from damage or infection of the nervous system are given below.

Paralysis   This is the loss of ability to contract a muscle or muscles, due to impaired nervous control.

Paralysis may be present in varying degrees of severity. If the disorder is in lower motor neurones it usually results in rapid wasting of muscles. Paralysis due to damage of upper motor neurones causes partial or complete loss of certain types of movement, although the muscle or muscles involved may be still able to carry on other types of movement. Temporary paralysis could result from excessive intake of alcohol and/or drugs (see p. 151). Paralysis, in varying degrees of severity, may result when the brain is damaged as a result of ruptured blood vessels caused by hypertension. This is a common occurrence in Caribbean countries since hypertension and *diabetes mellitus* are the most prevalent diseases.

Parkinson's Disease   This disease is characterized by skeletal muscles becoming rigid, and by tremors which are more prevalent when the body is at rest. There is also a slowness in starting and maintaining voluntary movement.

Ataxia   This is due to lesions on the nervous system which result in uncoordinated movement. In many cases there is staggering while walking, and generally balance is faulty.

Epilepsy   This disease is usually characterized by fits and convulsions; it is caused by a malfunction of the nervous system.

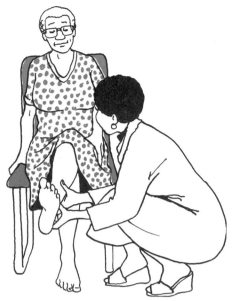

Physiotherapy can reduce the effects of paralysis

Blood system

Most disorders in the blood system are caused by the entry of pathogenic organisms—bacteria, viruses, protozoa, etc. Some disorders may, of course, be caused by nutritional deficiencies (e.g. anaemia) or genetically inherited characteristics (e.g. haemophilia).

Pathogens may enter the body in various ways, e.g. with food and water, through the skin, through the respiratory tract. These organisms may damage body tissue in various ways, especially by the production of poisonous protein substances—**toxins** which are circulated in the blood. The effects of these toxins vary from disease to disease. These foreign proteins, both the toxin and those in the invading organism itself, are called **antigens**, and their entry into the body sets off a defence reaction in the host. Each antigen causes production of specific antibodies in the blood serum, which combine with the antigen and destroy them. This is a similar reaction to the one already discussed on p. 60 on incompatibility in blood transfusion.

Antibodies increase in number over a period of a few weeks, eventually declining very slowly. While antibodies are present, the body is in a state of 'readiness' for defence against the particular antigens that caused the antibodies to be produced in the first instance.

The ability of the body to produce antibodies is used when vaccinations are given to provide acquired immunity to a particular disease. **Immunity** refers to the ability of the body to resist or fight off an infectious disease. Immunity may be **natural** or **acquired**. In the case of natural (inborn) immunity the immunity is due to inherited structures.

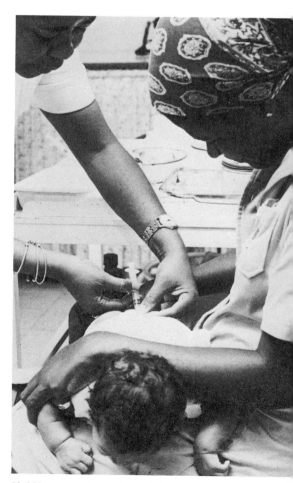

Child being vaccinated in a clinic in Jamaica

Acquired immunity may be **passive** or **active**. Active immunity may result from natural exposure to a particular infection, or it may be acquired artificially by the use of vaccines. Vaccines generally contain dead or weakened pathogens which, when injected into the body, trigger the production of antibodies. These latter remain active for defence should the individual be exposed to that particular pathogen. Vaccination against a disease does not mean that the individual will never contract the disease, but it sets up the body's defence system.

Nutrition system

Most damage to the nutrition system results in impairment of chemical processes.

The vast majority of food we eat is ingested in complex, insoluble form. Digestion, which starts in the mouth and ends in the small intestine, is the process by which these foods are made simpler and soluble. In those states they are then absorbed into the body.

Impairment of digestion results in food being un- and under-digested. In both cases the body loses valuable nutrients. This condition could lead to starvation and possibly death.

Normal sugar metabolism results in the storage of excess glucose as glycogen in the liver. This transformation is due to the presence of **insulin**—a hormone produced by the pancreas. Malfunction of the pancreas could lead to under-production of insulin, and hence to a disorder known as diabetes mellitus.

Questions

1 What effect does the absence of a myelin sheath have on nerve impulses along the axon?
2 Where, in humans, are you most likely to find (a) myelin-covered axons; (b) axons not covered with myelin? Give reasons for your answers.
3 What is meant by the term 'immunity'?
4 Distinguish between active and passive immunity.
5 How has the work of Edward Jenner contributed to our present knowledge about combatting infectious diseases?

Maintaining balance

There are certain principles involved in keeping objects balanced or in **equilibrium**. In this section the principles of parallel forces and the position of the centre of gravity will be explored.

Conditions for equilibrium under parallel forces

Can you balance a metre rule laden with weights and suspended by a spring balance? Careful measurement over a set of tries using different weights will show that *two* conditions must be satisfied for the rule to remain balanced.

1   The sum of the forces in one direction must be equal to the sum in the opposite direction.
2   The sum of the clockwise moments about any point (e.g. at the point of suspension) on the rule must be equal to the sum of the anti-clockwise moments about that point.

Why should you take measurements with the weights in more than one position before agreeing with conditions 1 and 2 above?

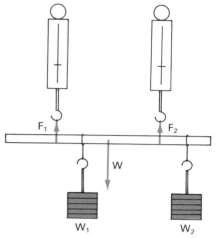

Parallel forces keeping a metre rule in equilibrium

Weight and centre of gravity

If a brick is placed on a table it remains stationary. Yet this same brick falls to the ground if it is placed in the air. This suggests that there is a downward force acting on the brick which pulls it towards the ground. (The table-top provides an equal and opposite *upward* force on the brick when it is put there.) The downward pull on an object is called its **weight**. Weight is caused by the gravitational pull of the Earth on an object. An object's weight can be measured using a spring balance. (Laboratory beam balances don't really measure an object's weight—they measure its mass.)

Every object behaves as though its total weight acts from a single point. The point through which the total weight of an object appears to act is called its **centre of gravity**. The diagrams show two ways of locating the centre of gravity of a rule. One way is to try to balance it on a pencil or the edge of a triangular prism. When balanced, the centre of gravity of the rule will be directly above the pivot. The other is to use the rule, the pencil or prism, and a weight W_1 that can be moved along the rule to make it balance. When the rule is in equilibrium the position x of the centre of gravity from the pivot can be calculated if W_1, x_1 and W are known.

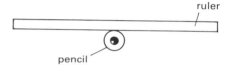

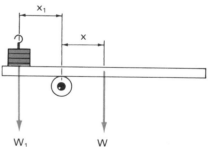

Two ways of locating the centre of gravity of a ruler

Lowest position principle

The centre of gravity of an object always seeks the lowest possible position when that object is suspended. This is called the **lowest position principle**. Thus, a pendulum bob comes to rest vertically under its point of support. This fact can be used to determine the centre of gravity of an irregularly shaped object, e.g. an irregularly shaped cardboard sheet.

Suspend the sheet from a pin and allow it to swing freely until it comes to rest. In this position the centre of gravity must be somewhere along a vertical line (drawn with the aid of a plumb line) under the pin. Repeat the procedure with the pin in a different position. The centre of gravity is located where the two lines cross since it is somewhere along *both lines*. You can verify this by trying to balance the sheet at the point of intersection on the tip of a pencil.

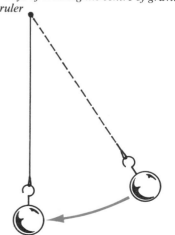

The pendulum illustrates the lowest position principle

Centre of gravity and equilibrium

Did you notice how easy it was to upset the balanced cardboard sheet from the point of the pencil? This type of equilibrium is called **unstable equilibrium**. A ball bearing, a watch glass and a table-top can be used to demonstrate that there are three types of equilibrium.

In **stable equilibrium** the centre of gravity of the ball bearing is at its lowest position. If the ball is moved, the centre of gravity is raised to a higher position. The ball therefore tries to move back to the position of low centre of gravity. In **unstable equilibrium** the centre of gravity is at the highest point. Any movement of the ball therefore causes the centre of gravity to be lowered. Once the position of their centre of gravity is lowered, objects do not usually return to a position where the centre of gravity is higher—they keep going down until the centre of gravity is again as low as possible. In **neutral equilibrium** the height of the centre of gravity remains the same wherever the object moves to. Hence it can find equilibrium in many locations.

Stable equilibrium

Unstable equilibrium

Neutral equilibrium

The centre of gravity and stability

An inclined plane and various lengths of wood cut from the same beam can be used to show how the height of the centre of gravity of an object affects its stability. Stand one end of the beam on the plane, and then increase the angle of incline until the beam topples over. If the centre of gravity is low, the angle of incline can be made very large before the wood topples. The wood is in very stable equilibrium. For high centres of gravity (or for very narrow bases), a small angle of incline will topple the wood. Hence the wood is in unstable equilibrium. What are some of the consequences of low and high centres of gravity?

Children do not grow at steady rates. Sometimes between the ages of 11 and 15 their heights increase greatly over a very short period of time. Their centre of gravity therefore raises suddenly and they consequently fall over more frequently at this time. When their body becomes accustomed to handling their new size they can walk with ease again!

Vehicles also tend to topple over more easily if they are loaded so that their centre of gravity is high. If a lot of people are *standing* in a bus or a truck the vehicle can easily topple, especially when swinging around corners. This is why there are traffic rules such as 'Not more than 10 standees'. If too many people or too much of the load is on one side of the vehicle it will also topple over very easily. This is especially noticeable in boats.

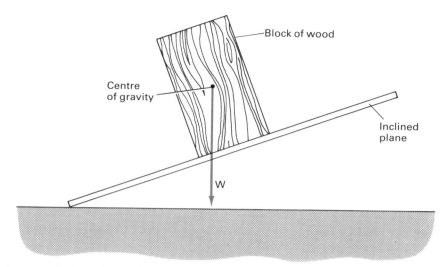

Apparatus for investigating how height of centre of gravity or width of the base of the object affects stability

Activities

1 Verify the two conditions for equilibrium under parallel forces using the apparatus described above.
2 Find the centre of gravity for the following shapes of laminae: (a) square (b) triangle (c) irregular (d) circular. Do the laminae balance when placed so that their centres of gravity are directly on the eraser of a pencil?
3 Demonstrate stable, unstable and neutral equilibrium using the apparatus described above.
4 Using various heights of the same piece of wood on an inclined plane observe how height of centre of gravity affects stability.

Questions

1 What types of equilibrium do the following illustrate:
   (a) an irregularly shaped sheet of cardboard balanced at its centre of gravity on the tip of a pencil;
   (b) the same sheet of cardboard suspended near its edge by a string;
   (c) a person standing with his feet close together.
2 Which is a safer design for a bus, one with an area on top for carrying loads (e.g. farmers' produce) or one with the load-carrying area near the bottom? Explain your answer.
3 Explain in terms of the centre of gravity why passengers should remain seated in a bus and why they should not all sit to one side of the bus.

Where is the centre of gravity likely to be?
What will happen and why?

72

Floating and sinking

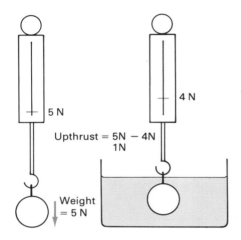

The stone appears to weigh less in water because it experiences upthrust

Why do some objects float while others sink? How are submarines able to stay under water, and then come up again? Does the fluid itself have any effect on whether something will sink or float? What are some of the dangers of diving? These are the kinds of questions that will be discussed in this section.

Why do some objects sink?

All objects experience an upward force called an **upthrust** when they are wholly or partially submerged in a fluid. The diagram shows how to measure the upthrust on a fully immersed stone. The stone sinks because its weight (the downward force of gravity acting on it) is greater than the upthrust provided by the water. The upthrust is equal to the weight of the stone in air minus the apparent weight of the stone in water:

upthrust = weight in air − apparent weight in water

Principle of flotation

Why should a very heavy, large ship float while a much lighter, small stone sinks? This is because flotation is governed by a principle:

'An object will float if the weight of fluid
it displaces is equal to its own weight.'

The ship floats because it is shaped so that the weight of water it displaces is actually equal to the total weight of the ship! The principle of flotation can be verified using a loaded test tube and an overflow can as shown in the diagram. As long as the loaded test tube floats, the weight of fluid displaced by it and overflowing into the little beaker will be found to be equal to the weight of the test tube and its contents.

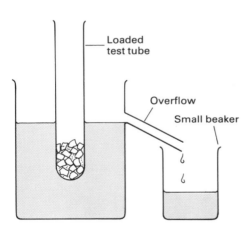

Testing the principle of flotation

Does the fluid matter?

The principle of flotation could be verified using any fluid. The floating object always displaces its own weight of fluid. However, if the same loaded test tube is put into two different liquids (e.g. rain water and a strong salt solution) careful observation will reveal a slight difference. The test tube sinks deeper in the fresh water than in the salt water. A larger volume of fresh water than salt water is displaced. But the same *weights* of both are displaced. This suggests that the denser salt water tends to provide more upthrust than the less dense fresh water. As ships move from the salty ocean into large rivers (where the water is fresher) they sink a little. International regulations therefore require ocean-going ships to be marked with a Plimsoll line which shows the maximum depth they should sink in various kinds of water when they are loaded.

Submarines and fishes

Submarines are able to sink and float by using their **ballast tanks**. When the ballast tanks are empty, the total weight of the submarine is less. The upthrust is enough to make it float. When water is pumped in to fill the tanks, the total weight of the submarine becomes greater than the upthrust. The submarine therefore sinks. To refloat the submarine, all that is needed is to pump water out of the ballast tanks to reduce its total weight. The upthrust will then be greater than its weight, and it will rise.

Bony fishes are able to alter the depth at which they 'float' by using their **swim bladder**. Automatic inflation of the bladder occurs when the fish dive to deep areas where the water pressures are high. High pressures compress the fish and therefore reduce their volume. This makes them sink since it also reduces the upthrust. The inflation of the swim bladder makes the fish swell and so the upthrust is once again restored.

Water safety devices

The discoveries you have made in this section suggest that light objects with a large volume will float best. For this reason, water safety devices are usually light and of a large volume. Life rafts, inflatable life jackets, inflatable car tubes, even low density logs can all help to keep us afloat.

Diving hazards

The main hazards in diving arises from the fact that pressure in a fluid increases the farther you go downwards from the surface. The high pressure deep under the water can produce two effects.

1 The pressure of the water can burst the delicate eardrum.
2 The diver can get the 'bends'. Under high pressure the **nitrogen** in the air supply dissolves in the bloodstream. If the diver rises rapidly to the surface where the pressure is lower, the nitrogen will come out of solution and form bubbles in the blood vessels. This can cause great pain and even death. People who dive therefore need special training and special equipment for such a hazardous undertaking.

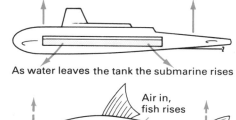
As water leaves the tank the submarine rises

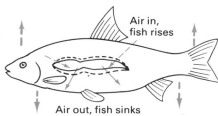
Air in, fish rises
Air out, fish sinks

Floating and sinking. Submarines use ballast tanks; fishes use swim bladders

Deep sea diving requires special equipment to provide air and to withstand the high pressure in deep water

Questions

1 A heavy iron ship floats while a much lighter iron nail sinks. Explain this.
2 On a certain ferry crossing, trucks are weighed before being allowed on the ferry boat, but the cars are not weighed. Explain, in terms of the principle of flotation, why the practice makes sense.
3 What properties must the padding of a water-safety life-jacket have?
4 A battery hydrometer has a heavy base, and a large bulb. (Hydrometers are used to indicate the density of a given liquid.) Explain in terms of stability and flotation how these two features help in the functioning of the hydrometer.

Activities

1 Using a spring balance, twine and a large beaker of water, measure the upthrust of a stone immersed (a) wholly (b) partially.
2 Verify the principle of flotation using the apparatus described in the text. Does the principle hold for (a) water and (b) oil?
3 Use a loaded test tube in fresh water and in salt water to demonstrate the Plimsoll line effect.
4 Get a tall can. Punch small holes in it at various heights on its side. Fill the can with water. From where does the water pitch out the furthest? Does increase in water depth cause an increase or decrease in water pressure?
5 Use a loaded test tube with a paper scale as a *hydrometer* to find out which liquids are denser (provide more upthrust) than which, e.g. milk, milk mixed with water, water, salt water, etc.
6 Make a model submarine (a glass bottle with a screw top will do). Make your submarine go to different depths by varying the amount of water inside it.

Section of the Demerara Bridge, Guyana, showing the floating supports

73

Moving through water

Staying up, moving and keeping steady in the water – Olympic synchro-swimming

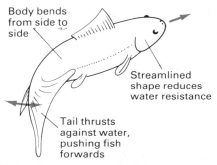

Body bends from side to side

Streamlined shape reduces water resistance

Tail thrusts against water, pushing fish forwards

Swimming movements of a fish

There are four main problems to overcome when trying to move through water. The first is how to stay up in the water. The second is how to produce movement. The third is how to keep steady. The fourth is how to reduce friction.

How to stay up

Boats can float on the surface because their hollow shape displaces a large volume of water and they therefore experience a great **upthrust**. Fishes with swim bladders (bony fish) are able to adjust their volume to keep their place in the water. However, fishes like sharks with no swim bladders must constantly swim slightly upwards to stop themselves sinking. Fishes moving from salt water to fresh water have to work harder to keep their depth since they experience less upthrust in the less dense fresh water.

How to produce movement

Movement through water is usually achieved by action and reaction forces. A backward thrust (**action**) is produced by fish when they lash their tail and tail fins against the water. This produces a **reaction** by the water on the fish, which drives the fish forward. When we swim our arms lash against the water with a backward and slightly downward action. This gives rise to a forward reaction, which moves us along, and an upward reaction, which helps us to keep afloat (like the sharks, we have no swim bladder, so we have to do at least some slight swimming action to keep afloat).

How to keep steady

The diagrams show how various fins on a fish help to reduce rolling, yawing and pitching. Apart from helping to reduce pitch, the pectoral fins act as brakes when they are spread out at right angles to the body. If only one fin is spread out the fish turns, so these pectoral fins can also be used in steering.

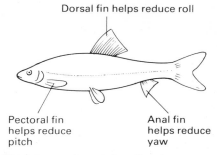

Dorsal fin helps reduce roll

Pectoral fin helps reduce pitch

Anal fin helps reduce yaw

Fins help to reduce pitch, roll and yaw

How to cut down on friction

Viscous frictional forces tend to hinder movement in water. Therefore it is not surprising to find that the surface of a fish's body is very smooth. Boat bottoms need to be kept smooth for the same reason. Salty sea water tends to speed up rusting, which pits the surface of the boat's hull. To retard rusting, pieces of zinc are fixed to the steel hull below the waterline. This helps to prevent rusting and keeps the hull smooth. Painting also retards rusting. Periodically, too, barnacles clinging on to the hull are scraped off. Both of these measures help to reduce friction.

The general shape of fishes also helps to reduce the frictional **drag**. Water flows past the fish's body in smooth **streamlines**. Whenever a fluid flows past an object in smooth streamlines the frictional forces on that object are at a minimum. Boats are therefore designed so that their shape is streamlined. Aeroplanes are also designed using this shape, even though air offers less resistance than water. When the aeroplane travels at high speeds through air, friction will become very large if the vehicle is not streamlined. Nowadays even cars are streamlined. This cuts down on the energy the engine needs to produce to overcome friction between the car and the air.

Navigating at sea

Up to a few years ago, the magnetic compass was widely used on ships to give the direction the ship sailed. The compass makes use of the fact that if a permanent magnet is suspended freely it will align itself in the direction of any magnetic field that is present. The Earth's magnetic field runs approximately North to South. Therefore the compass needle settles in this direction if no other magnetic field is present. Today, gyrocompasses and radar have replaced the magnetic compass as navigation aids on big ships.

Zinc plates attached to the hull of a ship help it to move through the water smoothly

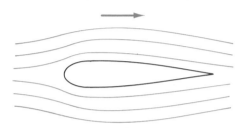

The streamline shape

A magnetic compass aligns itself roughly North to South

Direction-finding equipment on board a ship

Questions

1 Compare a fish with a jet aircraft in the following respects:
   (a) their shape;
   (b) how they produce forward movement;
   (c) how they stay up.
2 Long ago cars were usually square in shape whereas today they are more curved and streamlined. Explain how streamlined cars help to save fuel.
3 How are fishes and ocean-going boats well designed for easy movement through water? Refer to two of their features.

Activities

1 Examine fishes and identify the parts (especially the various fins).
2 Observe fishes swimming (in an aquarium). Note what the various parts we have mentioned do.
3 Suspend a magnet by a thread. Note that it settles approximately North–South. This is the principle of the magnetic compass.

The radar screen is another very valuable aid to navigation at sea and has replaced the use of a magnetic compass

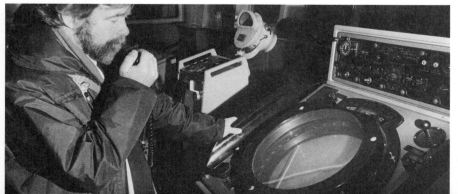

74

Forces and motion

Newton's Laws of motion

Isaac Newton formulated three laws of motion. The first of these can be stated as follows:

If there is no net force acting on a body, then the body either remains at rest or continues to move with the same velocity.

If you are standing in a bus which then comes to a sudden stop, you will notice that you tend to continue in the forward direction; this is an example of the first law of motion.

Newton's second law of motion can be stated as follows:

The acceleration of a body is directly proportional to the force acting on it; i.e. the greater the force to which a body is subjected the greater its acceleration will be.

The second law can also be stated as follows: the greater the mass of a body the smaller will be its acceleration for a given applied force.

Ask a friend to stretch out a hand, palm upwards; and then place a heavy book on the palm. What do you think will happen if you move the book away? This is an example of Newton's second law of motion.

Newton's second law of motion raises questions as to the meaning of the terms mass, force and acceleration.

Mass can simply be taken to mean the amount of matter in the body, where matter is the stuff of which everything in the universe is made. As you already know, the unit of mass is the **kilogram**.

The word **force** comes from the Latin word meaning 'strong'. It can be defined as any action between two objects which tends to change their relative state of rest or motion. Force is measured in **newtons**.

Acceleration is simply the rate at which an object changes its velocity. Acceleration is measured in **metres per second per second** (m/s²). If the object is increasing its velocity we say it is **accelerating**. A force must be applied to accelerate an object. If an object is decreasing its velocity,

Have you ever wondered how acrobats manage to balance?

it is said to be decelerating. A force must also be applied to decelerate an object.

Newton's third law states:

For every action there is an equal and opposite reaction.

The action/reaction principle can be demonstrated by filling a balloon with air and then releasing the air. You will notice that as the air rushes out in the forward direction, the balloon moves back (i.e. in the opposite direction).

What do you think will happen if the air in the balloon in the diagram is suddenly released? What will be the effect on the balloon's speed of increasing the amount of air in the balloon before it is released?

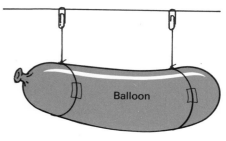
a) Fill a balloon with air

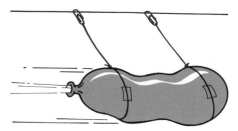
b) Release the air. What happens?

Rocket launch

Multi-stage rockets are used in space flights. Rockets work using the laws of motion, including the action/reaction principle.

Activity

Building a two-stage rocket from balloons.

Work with a partner to build the rocket by following these steps.
1 Inflate one of the balloons and pinch its neck so that the air cannot escape.
2 Let your partner tape a small cardboard cylinder around the open end of the balloon.
3 Now insert the closed end of the second balloon into the open end of the first balloon and inflate the second, tying its end with a suitable knot.
4 Cut the knot and describe what happens. Can you work out how a real two-stage rocket works?

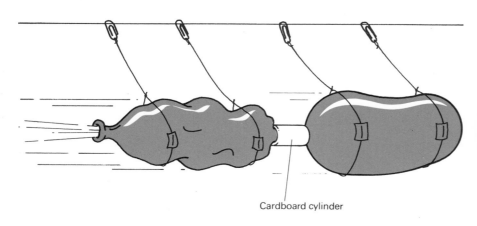
Cardboard cylinder

Making a multi-stage rocket out of balloons

Rocket talk

Thrust is the force which moves the rocket forward. It is obtained by releasing material from the rocket (like releasing air from a balloon).

The **payload** is the part of the rocket or spacecraft that is not expended (got rid of). If the payload is too large the rocket will not take off.

Blast off What do you think is meant by this term?

Artist's impression of rocket blasting away from the Earth

Astronauts in space are able to float because they are outside the pull of gravity. They therefore become 'weightless'

The pull-back of gravity

Every object experiences a force which acts on it and tends to pull it towards the centre of the Earth. This force is known as the **force of gravity**. As the object gets farther away from the Earth, the pull of gravity on it decreases.

An object on the surface of the Moon experiences a smaller gravitation pull than it would near the surface of the Earth. This happens because the 'pull-back' of the Moon's gravity is one-sixth that of the Earth's. For this reason an object weighs less on the Moon than on Earth, although its mass remains the same.

The force of friction

Friction is caused by the ridges and bumps on surfaces, and by the tendency of the particles of materials to stick together. The frictional force slows down moving objects. If you rub your hands together you can feel the frictional force between them. As you walk across the floor there is a frictional force between your shoes and the ground that stops your feet slipping.

Friction reduces the efficiency of machinery which has moving parts. But it can also be useful, as for example in the braking system of motor vehicles.

Satellites

Isaac Newton, in his work *Principia Mathematica*, first suggested that artificial satellites could be made. He showed, by calculation, that if a projectile is raised above the Earth, and at the same time given a velocity of 28 800 kilometres per hour, it would enter an indefinite orbit around the Earth. Such objects are known as **satellites**.

The projectile would be falling continuously, but since it would be moving at such a high velocity, it would fall only as fast as the curved surface of the Earth moved under it.

Satellites vary in size and weight. The basic parts of a satellite are:

(a) the power supply;
(b) the communications subsystem;
(c) the instrumentation subsystem;
(d) the guidance and control subsystem.

Satellites perform many different functions. For example, they are used in weather forecasting; in remoting sensing of the Earth's resources; for military and intelligence purposes; and in navigation.

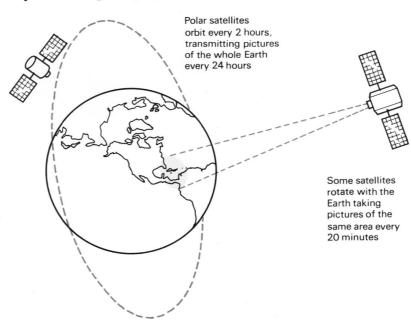

Polar satellites orbit every 2 hours, transmitting pictures of the whole Earth every 24 hours

Some satellites rotate with the Earth taking pictures of the same area every 20 minutes

Weather satellites are used to transmit pictures and other information about the Earth's weather at frequent intervals

Summary

1 The Universe is in continuous motion; nothing stands still.
2 The mass of any object remains the same no matter where the object is located.
3 An object tends to remain at rest or to keep moving in a straight line at a constant speed unless an unbalanced force acts on it.
4 The more massive an object, the greater the force needed to change the motion of the object.
5 A net force results when not all forces on an object are balanced.
6 When a net force acts on an object, the object accelerates.
7 Acceleration is directly related to the force exerted on an object.
8 The greater the mass of an object the smaller the acceleration it experiences when a given unbalanced force is exerted on it.
9 The force of gravitation at or near the surface of a celestial body is called gravity.
10 The gravitational force exerted on any object depends directly on the mass of the object.
11 The force of gravity produces a constant acceleration.
12 Objects of different masses are accelerated at the same rate by the force of gravity.
13 Any object moving in a circular path is continuously accelerated by a continuous force towards the centre of the circle.
14 The Earth's gravitational force keeps the Moon in its orbit.
15 The Sun's gravitational force keeps the planets in their orbits.
16 The effect of the gravitational force between bodies of ordinary size is extremely small and difficult to measure.
17 Every piece of matter in the Universe attracts every other piece.
18 The velocity at which an object is launched is one factor that determines its orbital path.
19 An object is weightless only if the net gravitational force acting on it is zero.
20 The weight of an object is the strength of the gravitational force pulling on it.

Activities

1 Design a model to demonstrate the action of a satellite.
2 Make a working model of the solar system.

75

The carbon, nitrogen and water cycles

The constant activities of all living organisms result in the circulation of chemical elements. Three of the most important cycles in nature are the carbon, nitrogen and water cycles.

The carbon cycle

Carbon is most abundant in the biosphere as **carbon dioxide**. This gas is used by plants in **photosynthesis** to produce **carbohydrates**, with the release of oxygen. Both carbohydrates and oxygen are used by animals in respiration to provide energy, with the release of carbon dioxide. And so the cycle continues. Carbon dioxide is also produced by heating and burning in industrial activities. This adds to the carbon dioxide in the biosphere.

The nitrogen cycle

The atmosphere is the main source of nitrogen in nature. However, nitrogen in the molecular state cannot be used by animals and most plants. Some bacteria can take free nitrogen and convert it into **nitrates**. These bacteria may be living freely in the soil (e.g. *Azotobacter*) or may be present in symbiotic unions in the root nodules of leguminous crops (e.g. *Rhizobium*). Plants convert these nitrates into **proteins**, in which state they are eaten by man and other animals. The animals then convert the proteins into forms most useful to them. When the animals and plants die they are broken down by bacteria (they decay), and form **ammonium compounds**. These compounds are then converted into **nitrates** which could be absorbed by the plant. Certain microorganisms (e.g. *Thiobacillus denitrificans*) transform nitrates to nitrogen gas—a process known as denitrification. And so the cycle continues. Nitrogen may also be transformed into nitrates by chemical methods and by thunderstorms.

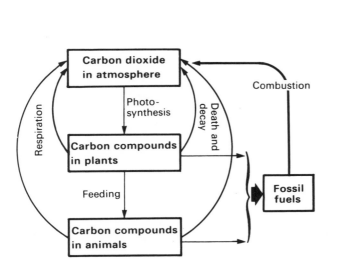

The carbon cycle

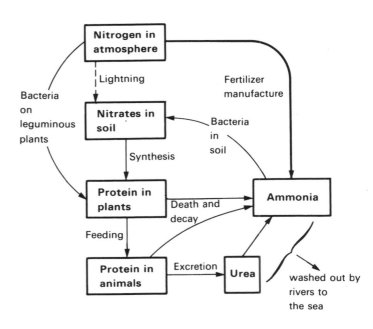

The nitrogen cycle

The water cycle

Water is a compound containing hydrogen and oxygen. It is perhaps the most important liquid known. Water is present in the sea, rivers, lakes, and the soil, from which it is taken in many processes. Water can be changed into vapour by heat (evaporation) so that it rises into the atmosphere. On rising it cools, eventually condensing back to water (condensation), and returning to the ground as rain (precipitation).

Water is also taken in by animals, used in respiration and excretion, and returned eventually as water back to its source. Plants also need water for the proper functioning of their metabolic processes. The water plants take in from the ground is returned to the source in respiration and transpiration. When plants and animals decay, water is released because their bodies are made up of a large percentage of water.

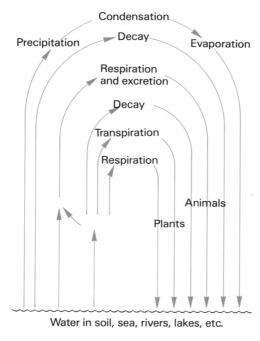

The water cycle

Question

Why are nitrogen-fixing bacteria in root nodules important in maintaining soil fertility?

76

Air masses and their effects

An **air mass** can be defined as a mass of air of relatively uniform character covering a huge area of the Earth's surface and having definite boundaries. Air masses are usually named or classified according to the areas they cover. For example, there are tropical air masses, maritime air masses (i.e. air masses over the sea), polar air masses, etc.

The air mass in contact with a particular area of the Earth eventually acquires the temperature and **humidity** of the area which lies under it. This means that the air masses over different parts of the world have different energy levels as well as differing moisture contents.

When air masses move across one of the area boundaries there is a tremendous flow of energy which gives rise to such natural phenomena as depressions, cyclones and hurricanes.

Fronts

The plane along which two rapidly moving air masses meet is called a **frontal surface**. The line where a frontal surface meets the Earth's surface is called a **front**.

The are four general kinds of fronts:

(a) A **cold front** is the plane along which cold air replaces warmer air.
(b) A **warm front** is the plane along which warm air replaces colder air.
(c) At a **stationary front** there is no replacement of air.
(d) The **occluded front** is found when a cold front overtakes a warm front.

Cloud formation, rainfall and general turbulence are associated with a moving front. Cold fronts usually bring unsettled atmospheric conditions, heavy winds, thunder showers, etc., whereas more stable weather conditions are associated with warm fronts.

Since air masses move large distances they are agents for the large scale spread of pollutants. Here are some examples.

(a) When the volcano erupted on the island of Krakatoa in 1883, dust encircled the world for two years, reaching as far away as Europe, thousands of kilometres distant.
(b) When the Soufriere volcano erupted in 1979, dust showered and covered the neighbouring islands, particularly Barbados.
(c) Sand and dust storms of the Sahara have attained peaks of violence and have moved across the Atlantic as far as the island of Barbados.
(d) Industrial wastes and radioactive fallout are also carried large distances by air masses.

Breezes

Moving air also gives rise to land and sea breezes.

Breezes blow from the sea to the land during the day and in the reverse direction at night. During the day the land heats up faster than the sea and the air over the land rises. Cooler air from the sea rushes in to take its place giving rise to a cooling effect. The flow of air from sea to land is known as sea breeze.

At night the land cools more rapidly than the sea; and cooler air moves from land to take the place of the warm air that rises over the sea. This air movement is called a land breeze.

Day – breezes blow from sea to land

Night – breezes blow from land to sea

Depressions, storms, cyclones and hurricanes

A **depression** occurs in any region in which the atmospheric pressure is lower than in the surrounding air. Depressions vary considerably in size (from 160 km–3200 km) and speed (from almost stationary to more than 1000 km per day).

Storms are the result of disturbances in the atmosphere which arise when air masses move to areas of low pressure. Storms are accompanied by rain clouds and strong winds. Cyclonic storms (cyclones) usually develop when rotating air masses move off their normal course.

Hurricanes are tropical cyclones characterized by very high winds. The hurricane rotates along its axis in addition to the forward movement of the storm itself. (This movement is not unlike that of a spinning top.) The two movements of the hurricane give rise to varying wind speeds. On one side of the hurricane the rotation and the forward movement of the storm are in the same general direction. Here the wind speeds can exceed 350 km per hour. On the opposite side of the hurricane the movements are opposed and the wind speeds are less. Whereas the edge of the hurricane can be a swirling rotating madhouse, the centre can be an area of calm. The centre of a hurricane is called its **eye**. It is not unusual for the rotary speeds of a hurricane to exceed 350 km per hour, and for the forward speeds to lie between 16 km and 32 km per hour.

Although no two hurricanes are alike, the following description of the hurricane which in 1928 wrecked the island of Guadeloupe illustrates very well some of their general features.

Hurricane damage in the Bahamas

Soon after noon on the 11th September, the winds began to blow from the north while the barometer which stood at 1013 millibars, about normal, began to fall—unmistakeable sign of an approaching storm.... At 9.00 pm the pressure was 1008 and the wind was gradually increasing.... At 5 am on the 12th it fell rapidly to 1002 and by 7 am to 1000 millibars. After that the situation rapidly deteriorated. The wind was gaining in strength every moment.... Towards midday the house collapsed and the barometer went down to 960 millibars. Even so, the wind was still increasing in violence and the cyclone growing more intense.

Everywhere there was a fearful chaos of tiles and floors from ruined houses whose walls were crumbling. Waves poured over the quay, and wrecked the docks. The sea swept up to the town and the shops. Then the house where I had taken refuge started to go. The roof was torn off piece by piece.... Everything was swimming in water and the wind had reached prodigious strength. At last, towards 2 pm the eye of the storm passed over us. The sky cleared for 10 minutes, which gave me time to note the lowest pressure I had yet observed, 942 millibars. The wind which had previously been blowing from the north, now swung to south and raged more furiously than ever.... By 4 pm the barometer had risen to 970 millibars and by 10 pm it stood at 990 millibars. By 4 am next day, the 13th September, it rose to 1005 millibars as the last gusts of the dying wind disturbed the ruined town. When we ventured out at 7 am the barometer recorded 1008 millibars.

What a spectacle awaited us! Houses wrecked and gutted! Streets blocked with every kind of debris, trees stripped bare to the trunk.... And worst of all was the isolation. Communications were at a standstill.

From an eye witness account published in *L'Illustration* (Paris), 1928.

The hurricane season usually lasts from July to September. You may have heard the little ditty:

> June too soon
> July stand by
> August come it must
> September remember
> October all over.

Question

Use the eye-witness account of a hurricane to identify the four distinct stages through which it passes. Describe the major features of each stage.

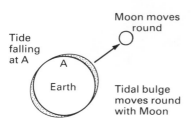

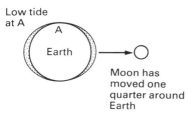

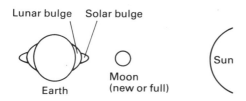

The effect of the Moon on the tides at a point A on the Earth

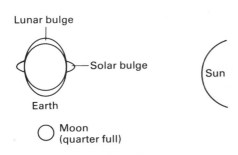

Gravitational pulls producing spring tides

Lunar bulge

Solar bulge

Earth

Sun

Moon (quarter full)

Gravitational pulls producing neap tides

77

Tides and their effects

If you have ever spent time at the seaside you must have wondered why the sea 'goes out' and then 'comes in' again. Did you also wonder why the sea is sometimes so calm and inviting as it gently carresses the seashore, and at other times pounds the seashore with awesome power, making the water all white and foamy?

Questions like these are really asking 'what makes tides?'

How are tides formed?

In the 17th century the great scientist Isaac Newton suggested that every object attracts others with a force which depends both on the masses of the objects, and on their distance apart. Newton expressed these ideas in his famous 'Law of Universal Gravitation'. From his experiments and calculations Newton concluded that:

(a) the greater the mass of the objects the greater the pull they exert on each other;
(b) the greater the distance between the objects the smaller the pull they exert on each other.

This idea of gravitational pull can be used to explain the formation of tides.

Tides are formed as a result of the simultaneous pull on the Earth (more particularly the sea) by the Sun and by the Moon. Since the Moon is nearer to the Earth than the Sun, the pull of the Moon on the Earth is greater than the pull of the Sun on the Earth, even though the Sun is so much larger than the Moon. So the gravitational pull of the Moon on the Earth (and the sea) is the major factor in tide formation.

Let us start by considering the position when the Moon is directly above a point A. The Moon pulls on the water in the sea directly beneath it at A. This gives rise to a tidal bulge. When the Moon moves it pulls the water along with it and so the tidal bulge at A becomes smaller, i.e. the tide begins to fall. The tide reaches its lowest level when the Moon has gone one quarter of the way around the Earth. This smallest bulge of the sea is known as **low tide**; the greatest bulge (when the moon is overhead) is known as **high tide**. The Moon takes about 24 hours 50 minutes to go around the Earth, so that low tide follows high tide after about 6 hours. Some places on the Earth experience two high tides and two low tides each day.

Spring tides and neap tides

Spring tides are extra-high high tides and extra-low low tides. They occur both when the moon is full and when it is new. They are caused by the reinforcement of the Moon's gravitational pull on the sea by the Sun.

When the Moon is full or new the Earth, Moon and Sun lie in the same straight line. The Moon's gravitational pull on the Earth is added to by that of the Sun on the Earth. These combined pulls cause larger tidal bulges and so the tides are higher at high tides and lower at low tide.

At **neap tides** the tidal range (i.e. the difference between high and low tides) is much smaller than at spring tides. Neap tides occur during the first and last quarters of the Moon. At this period the Sun and the Moon are at right-angles to each other and to the Earth. So the gravitational pull of the Sun partially opposes that of the Moon.

Activity

Data on high and low tides for 5 consecutive days in one Caribbean country is given in the table below. Study the data carefully and discover possible patterns.

	DAY 1	DAY 2	DAY 3	DAY 4	DAY 5
Time of 1st low tide	0142 hrs	0301 hrs	0452 hrs	0619 hrs	0730 hrs
Time of 1st high tide	0807 hrs	0925 hrs	1124 hrs	1205 hrs	1245 hrs
Time of 2nd low tide	1428 hrs	1527 hrs	1732 hrs	1832 hrs	2008 hrs
Time of 2nd high tide	2024 hrs	2138 hrs	?	?	?

Predict possible times for the second high tide on days 3, 4 and 5.

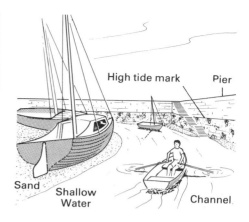

High tide mark — Pier — Sand — Shallow Water — Channel

Variations in the tides

In some places, e.g. the Mediterranean Sea, the tidal range is very small (0·6 m) whereas in places like the Bay of Fundy the tidal range can be of the order of 50 m. In places with a large tidal range the difference in the heights of the tides can be exploited to produce electricity.

Although the Sun and the Moon provide the force that causes the tides, the actual tidal pattern at a given place depends very much on the shape of the shoreline and the depth of the sea bottom, etc. For example where the seabed at the coast is very shallow, a large area is exposed when the tide goes out.

At the mouth of some rivers the incoming tides are held back, at least for a while, by the water flowing out. But the outflow of water from the river can not hold back the incoming tide beyond a certain level. When this is reached the tide rushes in a big surge called a **tidal bore**.

Using the tides

Over the years man has used the tides in a number of ways. The possibility of harnessing the tides to produce electricity has been mentioned, but this can only be achieved where the tidal range is high. We make use of the tides in other ways, e.g.

1 The best time to salvage a ship which has run aground is at high spring tide.
2 The best time to work on a new pier would be at low spring tide.
3 High tide is the best time for ships to enter and leave a harbour.
4 The tides (and currents and waves) wash large quantities of sea shells and parts of plants onto beach areas, especially at spring tide. These are a source of food for birds; and some people delight in collecting the shells.
5 On smooth shallow beaches the receding tide leaves pools of clear water in slight gullies, providing ideal bathing spots.

Can you think of other ways in which the tides serve man?

Sea fans in the intertidal zone, Grand Cayman

Effects of tides on plants and animals

Plants such as algae (seaweed) and animals such as molluscs live on rocks and in the sand in the intertidal zone. At high tide they are completely submerged; at low tide they are exposed. These organisms are usually characterized by their muscular feet and 'holdfast' organs which enable them to cling to the substrata without being washed off during high tides. They can only reproduce sexually during high tide when they are completely immersed.

Questions

1 What adaptations would you expect intertidal organisms to show?
2 Imagine that the Earth had two moons. What changes would this have on the observed tides?

Soufriere volcano, St Vincent, in 1979

Dormant – inside the crater, January 1979 (above)

Six weeks after the eruption, May 1979 (below)

A volcano erupts

These extracts from the local newspaper describe the many faces of the Soufriere volcano, on Guadeloupe, during a period of intense activity in August 1976.

76.08.12
A record of 12 000 tremors was registered in the La Soufriere volcanic zone in Guadeloupe last month.... There is the possibility of an eruption.

76.08.16
Thousands of panic stricken people fled the French island of Guadeloupe by ship and plane today after official warnings of a 'giant' volcanic eruption that could strike anytime after midnight with the force of atomic bombs . . .

'We consider that we are entering a phase that can only end in a giant eruption' said prefect Jean Aurosseau.

76.08.17: We are running headlong into a catastrophe
'All we can say is that the eruption is inevitable' said Alain Brouse, a University of Paris scientist leading the team of vulcanologists. 'We have reached the point of no return. We're moving toward a major eruption in terms of intensity and volume.'

76.08.18
Activity around Soufriere appeared to be decreasing after more than 1000 tremors the previous night shook the island. It could be the calm before the storm. The lull in activity was causing concern among scientists. 'We are still unable to determine whether the volcano is decreasing its activity or whether it is leading up to a big bang.'

76.08.19
Earthquake activity in the volcano-threatened island of Guadeloupe has been declining, . . . but this inactivity should be seen as a temporary lull.

76.08.23
Guadeloupe's simmering La Soufriere volcano could go off with a big bang this evening or tonight. And the catalyst which could set it off with the force of a 30-megaton atomic bomb is Emmy, the season's fifth tropical storm which last night was feared to be developing into a full-fledged hurricane.

It is just possible the change in barometric pressure could trigger the volcano.

76.08.28
Ash and steam continued to come out of the simmering volcano . . . The international team of scientists monitoring the volcano reported yesterday that steam was coming out of a crack on the south-eastern side of the volcano while ash flowed from the crater . . . The report also stated that the number of tremors was decreasing steadily and before midday yesterday only 102 tremors were recorded.

Soufriere did not go off with the bang that was expected, but its activity caused considerable tension on the island during the whole of August 1976.

Some volcanoes have erupted only once within historical time, whereas others have had many eruptions. Mount Vesuvius has erupted more than 40 times since AD 79. Some volcanoes erupt without warning, while the area around others is rocked by a series of earth tremors before the eruption takes place.

Volcanic eruptions are among the most spectacular of natural disasters but they often cause fewer deaths than earthquakes, tidal waves or hurricanes. The damage to agriculture, e.g. to the banana industry of St Vincent after St Vincent's Soufriere erupted in 1979, and the ruin of Costa Rica's coffee crop in 1964 is more often extensive. Since volcanic soils are fertile, farmers return to farm the lower slopes of a volcano after an eruption. This can lead to further loss of life.

Vegetation begins to return after destruction by 1979 eruption, St Vincent

Where are the world's volcanoes?

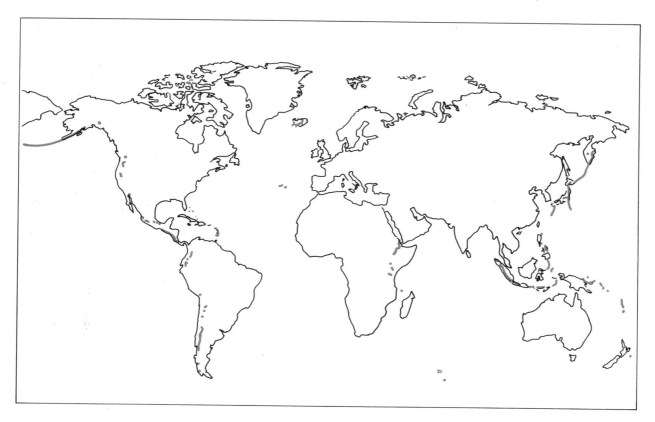

Map of the world showing areas of volcanic activity

What makes volcanoes active?

The Earth's crust is divided into a number of **plates**. These plates float like rafts on the semi-fluid layers below the crust. When two plates meet one may be forced under the other, taking pieces of the Earth's crust towards the centre of the Earth. At the same time molten rock and gas from beneath the crust move towards the surface, and may be released in a volcanic eruption.

Sometimes the molten rock pours out of the volcano as lava; it flows freely and allows the gases to escape. At other times the lava is sticky and forms a dome (cap) at the top of the volcano. If sufficient pressure builds up within the volcano it can blow its top—spreading lava over the countryside. The effect is like opening a bottle of champagne.

What comes out of a volcano?

The material that comes out of a volcano when it erupts include dust, ashes, mud, lava and gases such as hydrogen sulphide, carbon dioxide, methane and carbon monoxide. Small stones, big rocks (rocks having masses of up to 30 tonnes have been thrown out of volcanoes) and water are also ejected. Water, as steam, is responsible for the billowing clouds that are seen above active volcanoes.

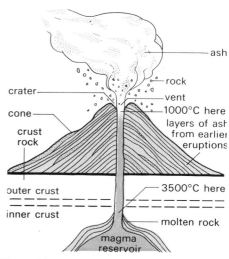

Typical features of a volcano

195

The economic value of volcanoes

The destructive aspects of volcanic activity are usually emphasised and the economic value of volcanoes often ignored. However, volcanoes are a tourist attraction and are therefore money earners. For example, hot springs are a very attractive feature of areas of recent volcanic activity.

Volcanic soils are among the most fertile. Sometimes two, or even three crops can be grown yearly on these soils. Valuable ores are also associated with areas of volcanic activity.

Geothermal energy can be tapped from some parts of the world in which there is volcanic activity.

Earthquakes

Thousands of measurable earth tremors occur daily. Most of these are so small that they are hardly noticed. However, strong earthquakes have claimed on average over 25 000 lives each year since 1914.

Study carefully the map showing the areas where most earthquakes occur. What patterns do you observe? Compare this earthquake map with the map of active volcanoes (p. 195). What further patterns do you observe?

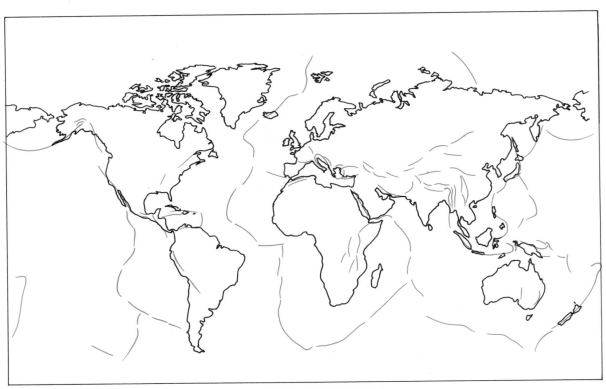

Areas of seismic activity throughout the world

What are earthquakes?

An earthquake is a tremor or ripple-like movement in the rocky crust of the Earth—caused by sharp abrupt movements of rocks (plates). Earthquakes vary considerably in intensity (destructive power). Several scales, e.g. the Mercalli and Richter Scales, have been established to measure their intensity.

The Mercalli scale is a 12-point scale. Here are descriptions of some of the levels:

point 1   detected only by seismographs.
point 5   generally felt by everyone except heavy sleepers, shifting of furniture, bells ring, unstable objects overturn.
point 12   total destruction, objects thrown into the air, much heaving, shaking and distortion of Earth's surface.

Earthquakes (seismic activity) are accompanied by sound waves, ground waves, and tidal waves.

Regions of an earthquake

The **focus** of an earthquake is the place at which there is the greatest intensity. If it lies less than 64 km below the surface, the earthquake is described as shallow. When the focus lies between 64 km and 300 km beneath the Earth's surface the earthquake is described as intermediate. If the focus is greater than 300 km the earthquake is called deep.

Waves move out from the focus of an earthquake. The point at which the wave first 'hits' the Earth's surface is called the **epicentre** of the earthquake. The epicentre is thus the point on the Earth's surface directly above the focus.

The seismograph

The seismograph is an instrument for detecting and measuring earthquake activity. It operates on the principle of inertia or Newton's first law of motion. Seismographs were originally constructed so that portions of the apparatus moved during seismic activity; the disturbances were amplified and then recorded. In one type of seismograph a heavy weight was suspended in front of a cylinder 'on which it racks its movement with a needle' (see *right*). During earth tremors the weight and needle remain fixed, while the cylinder moved, so recording seismic activity. More modern seismographs use a moving film to record the disturbances.

Tidal waves (tsunamis)

Tsunamis are the result of coastal earthquakes which cause very big waves to develop. During tsunamis the sea withdraws for many kilometres along the coastline and then returns in immense waves which can be 25 m high, 100 metres long and travel at speeds of up to 500 km per hour.

Tsunamis cause extensive flooding, and many people drown. In Lisbon in 1755 more than 60 000 persons died during a tidal wave. And in Krakatoa in 1883, more than 35 000 persons died in the tidal wave which accompanied a volcanic eruption.

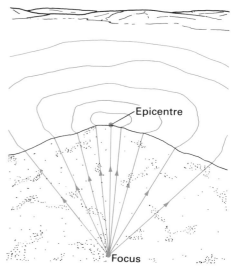

The waves of an earthquake

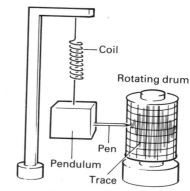

A seismograph

Questions

1 Give the names of three Caribbean islands on which there are active volcanoes.
2 Why are volcanoes considered to be economically important?
3 What is meant by the following terms:
   (a) plate;
   (b) magma;
   (c) crater;
   (d) cone.
4 How is seismic activity detected? Describe the features of the instrument used to detect seismic activity.

79

Energy changes make things happen

It is difficult to say exactly what energy is, but it is possible to show that energy changes make things happen. This section is about some different forms of energy, and it will demonstrate that energy changes (differences) make things happen.

Some forms of energy

1 **Chemical energy** is the energy stored in the molecular bonds of substances. The energy is released when chemical reactions take place.
2 **Internal energy** is the energy associated with the motions of particles within matter.
3 **Heat energy** is energy on the move from hot regions to cooler regions.
4 **Light energy** can be considered as energy which can be seen. It is difficult to store light.
5 **Electrical energy** is associated with the movement of charged particles.
6 **Sound energy** is the form of energy which is received by the ear. Sound energy is produced by a vibrating source and is transmitted from one point to another in a medium such as air. Sound cannot travel in a vacuum.
7 **Nuclear energy** is obtained from the nucleus of atoms. This stored energy can be released during nuclear reactions. There are two types of nuclear reaction: **fission** reactions in which large unstable atoms are split to yield smaller ones; and **fusion** reactions in which small atoms are brought together to yield larger ones. Fusion reactions occur constantly in the Sun to produce light and heat.

Energy changes

(a) move, warm or change matter;
(b) provide valuable clues as to the nature of matter;
(c) are used to convert raw materials to useful products;
(d) do things for us all the time.

Energy is measured in joules (J).

The effect of heat energy

When an object is heated the particles within it gain energy and move around more rapidly. As a result a number of changes may take place:

(a) The temperature of an object may rise.

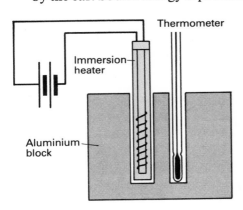

A 1 kg aluminium block is heated with an electric immersion heater, as shown in the diagram. The block receives energy and its temperature rises. This temperature rise is indicated on the thermometer.

The energy changes that take place may be summarized as follows:

electrical energy	→	heat energy	→	mechanical energy
from the power supply		Energy passes from heater, to block, to thermometer		The mercury in the thermometer rises

(b) The substance may undergo a change of state, e.g. from solid to liquid. This is known as **melting** or **fusion** (solid to liquid) or **vaporization** (liquid to gas). The reverse processes (freezing and condensation) will take place when the material is cooled.

solid	melting ⇌ freezing	liquid	evaporation ⇌ condensation	gas

(c) The substance may undergo a change of shape (or volume) when it is heated. Look at the apparatus shown in the diagram. Part (a) shows the height of liquid in the capillary tube before heat was supplied. Part (b) shows the height of liquid after heat was supplied.

Here heating has caused a change of volume.

(d) Materials may undergo a change in chemical composition when heated.

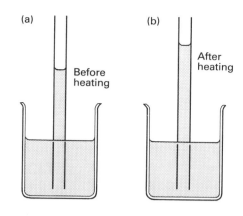

(a) Before heating (b) After heating

Activity A To show the effect of heating naphthalene

Slowly heat some naphthalene in a test tube as shown in the diagram. Note that the crystals begin to melt about 80 °C, and that the temperature remains constant during the melting stage, although the test tube is still being heated.

Clearly the heat supplied during the melting stage was used to change the physical state of the naphthalene; in this case from solid to liquid.

Activity B The effect of heat on copper (II) carbonate

Strongly heat green copper(II) carbonate in a hard glass test tube. Pass the gas given off into lime water, as shown in the diagram. You should notice

(a) the lime water turn milky, indicating that carbon dioxide was evolved;

(b) the starting material was green, whereas the residue is black.

The word equation for this change is:

copper(II) carbonate ⟶ **copper oxide** + **carbon dioxide**
(a green solid)   **(a black solid)**   **(a gas)**

When copper carbonate is heated it is chemically decomposed.

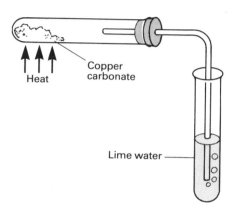

Copper carbonate

Heat

Lime water

From electricity to chemical change

Matter can be decomposed by electrical energy. If an electric current is passed through molten lead bromide, the lead bromide decomposes (breaks down). Brown bromine vapour is given off at one of the plates, and shiny globules of lead are deposited at the other.

From chemical energy to electricity

The dry cell or motor car battery is simply a device that converts the energy of a chemical reaction to electricity.

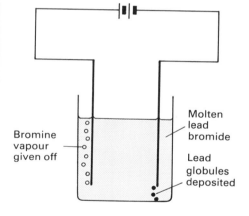

Bromine vapour given off

Molten lead bromide

Lead globules deposited

Activity C Lime power

Obtain a lime, orange or other citrus fruit and stick two different strips of metal (e.g. copper and zinc) into it. Complete the circuit. Is there a reading on the meter?

Light energy produces a chemical change

Activity D

Soak two strips of filter paper in a solution of sodium chloride and allow them to dry. Then dip them in a solution of silver nitrate.

Cover one of the strips with a piece of black paper. Expose the other to direct sunlight or to light from a lamp and observe it for a period of 15 minutes. At the end of this time compare the two strips.

The strip that was exposed to sunlight became dark. This shows that light can produce a chemical change in some compounds.

Questions

1 List the various forms of energy.
2 Name two devices that convert electrical energy to mechanical energy (motion).
3 Solar cells convert light energy directly to electricity. Identify two different uses of solar cells.
4 Describe an experiment you could perform to show that the temperature of water remains constant when it boils. Draw a diagram of the apparatus you would use.
5 Describe a second experiment that would show that heat can change the volume of a substance.

80

Stored energy and energy in motion

The energy forms described in the previous section can be divided into two types:

(a) **potential energy** or stored energy;
(b) **kinetic energy** or energy in motion.

Potential energy

When a lift is on the fourth floor it has more energy than when it is in its rest position in the basement. The extra energy is stored as potential energy. The higher an object above its rest position (or some other position) the more stored or potential energy it possesses.

Consider the two objects with the masses and heights shown in the table. The second object possesses more stored (potential) energy than the first.

	MASS	HEIGHT ABOVE GROUND
First object	1·0 kg	20 m
Second object	1·0 kg	40 m

Now consider two other objects with the masses and heights shown below. In this case the first object has the greater potential energy.

	MASS	HEIGHT ABOVE GROUND
First object	5·0 kg	4 m
Second object	2·0 kg	4 m

The potential energy of an object depends on both its mass and its height above some rest position.

The actual value of the potential energy stored in a body is given by

potential energy = mass × height × acceleration due to gravity

The acceleration due to gravity has a value of 10 m/s².

The higher the lift rises above its rest position (A), the more potential energy it builds up. It has most at B, less at C, none at A. (When the lift is in motion up or down, it also has kinetic energy)

Activity

Consider the 4 objects whose masses and heights above ground are shown in the table below.

OBJECT	MASS (kg)	HEIGHT (m)
A	18	3
B	2	5
C	2	4
D	4	2·5

Object A has potential energy of 18 × 3 × 10 J = 540 J.
(a) Which object possesses the greatest potential energy?
(b) Which object possesses the least potential energy?
(c) Make a statement concerning the potential energies of objects B and D.

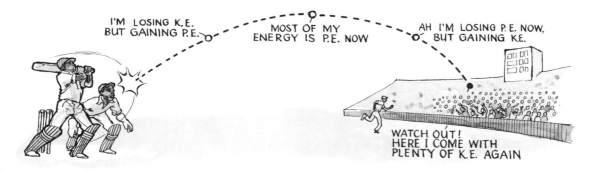

I'M LOSING K.E. BUT GAINING P.E.

MOST OF MY ENERGY IS P.E. NOW

AH I'M LOSING P.E. NOW, BUT GAINING K.E.

WATCH OUT! HERE I COME WITH PLENTY OF K.E. AGAIN

Kinetic energy

The energy in the foods we eat is stored in our bodies as chemical energy. An athlete in a 100 metre race is using up some of this stored energy. The athlete has **kinetic energy** because he is motion. The faster an object moves the more kinetic energy it has.

Consider the first two particles described in the table below. The second particle has greater kinetic energy. Then consider the third and fourth particles. The fourth particle has the greater kinetic energy.

	MASS	VELOCITY
First particle	m	v
Second particle	m	$2v$
Third particle	m	v
Fourth particle	$2m$	v

The kinetic energy of a particle or object depends both on its mass and on its velocity.

What happens when objects collide?

A particle that is moving can produce a change when it comes into contact with another object that is either stationary or moving. **The faster an object is moving the greater the change it can produce.**

Activity

Roll a cricket ball along the floor and allow it to collide with a light cardboard box. The cardboard box moves forward.
(a) Now increase the speed of the ball. Note that the box moves a greater distance along.
(b) Describe an experiment that you can carry out to show that the greater the mass of an object, the greater the change it can produce when moving at a given speed.

Energy in motion (kinetic energy) depends on both the mass and velocity (speed) of an object. The greater the kinetic energy of an object the greater the change it can produce.

Fast-moving vehicles possess a great amount of kinetic energy. What happens to this energy when vehicles collide with a wall or other vehicles? The energy has to go somewhere. Manufacturers so design their vehicles that this energy change causes as little injury to passengers as possible.

Question

Describe at least two ways in which injury to passengers can be reduced during collisions between motor vehicles.

81

Wave motion

Transverse waves

A wave is one means of transferring energy from one point (place) to another. This is best illustrated by water waves.

When the surface of the water in a lake, pond or the sea moves up and down the term **water wave** is used to describe the motion.

When a stone is dropped into a pond, energy moves out from the centre of the disturbance in the form of a wave. After the wave has passed, the water settles back to its original state or level. Strictly speaking, the water has not moved, but the energy has.

Consider waves at sea moving towards the shore. When the wave reaches the shore there is a crashing sound with water splashing all over the place. This has been caused by the energy carried by the wave. Identify the energy transformations that take place when a wave strikes the shore.

When an object floats on the surface of a pond which ripples are moving across, the object bobs up and down. The object moves at right angles to the direction of the wave itself. This type of wave is known as a **transverse** wave. Light and all electromagnetic waves are examples of transverse waves. They can easily be demonstrated with a slinky.

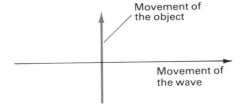

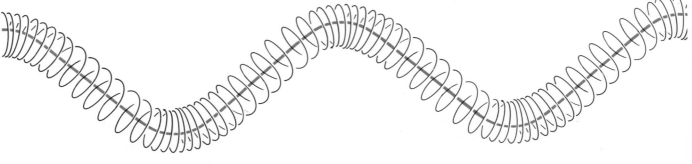

Wave talk

A number of terms are used in describing the movement of waves.

Wave speed is the speed with which waves are moving (m/s). If a wave has a speed of 6 m/s, it means that the wave is advancing 6 metres every second. The symbol for wave speed is v.

Wavelength is the distance between successive crests or troughs of a wave. It is essentially the distance occupied by one complete wave. The symbol for wavelength is λ.

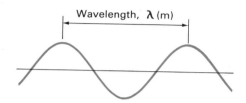

The **amplitude** of a wave is half the distance from a peak to a trough, i.e. the maximum displacement (movement) of a particle from its rest position.

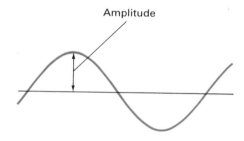

The **frequency** of a wave is the actual number of peaks that pass a given point in one second. The unit of frequency is the hertz (Hz). A frequency of 1 Hz means that only one peak passes a given point every 1 second. A frequency of 2 Hz means that 2 peaks pass a given point every second, i.e. the wave advances by 2 wavelengths every second. The symbol for frequency is f.

The **wave equation** is the relationship connecting wavelength (λ), frequency (f) and wave speed (v).

$$\text{wave speed} = \text{frequency} \times \text{wavelength}$$
$$v \quad = \quad f \quad \times \quad \lambda$$

Problem

What is the wavelength of a wave whose speed is 6 m/s and whose frequency is 2 Hz?

From the wave equation

$$\text{wavelength} = \frac{\text{wave speed}}{\text{frequency}}$$

$$\lambda = v/f$$
$$= 6/2$$
$$= 3 \text{ m}$$

The problem can be tackled in another way:

A wave speed of 6 m/s means that the wave advances 6 metres in one second. A frequency of 2 Hz means that the wave advances 2 wavelengths in one second. So

2 wavelengths advance 6 metres.

1 wavelength advances 3 metres.

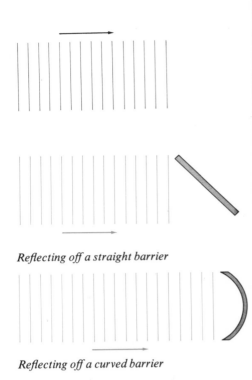

Reflecting off a straight barrier

Reflecting off a curved barrier

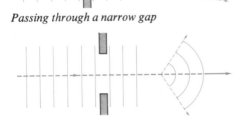

Passing through a narrow gap

Passing through a wide gap

Activities

1 Disturb the surface of the water on a pond by dropping in a small stone. Note that circular waves move out from the point of disturbance.

   The same effect is achieved if you dip one finger into a trough of water.

   Your finger and the stone gave rise to circular ripples on the water. They both acted as **point sources** of a wave.

2 Touch the surface of the water in a trough or pond with a suitable straight edge. Note that parallel waves move away from the point of disturbance. The straight edge is called an **extended** source; and the parallel waves are known as **plane** waves.

3 Generate plane waves in a trough. Allow the waves to fall on a straight solid barrier placed at an angle to the incident waves. Observe the reflected pattern. The angle of incidence of the wave is equal to the angle of reflection.

4 Generate plane waves in a trough and allow them to fall on a curved barrier as shown in the diagram. Copy the diagram and complete it to show the pattern of the reflected waves.

5 Generate plane waves on the surface of water in a trough. Allow the waves to move towards a wide gap as shown in the diagram. Note that the waves continue as plane waves after passing through the gap.

   Now, narrow the gap. Repeat the activity above and record your observations. Continue to narrow the gap and make waves until the gap is very small and the waves pass through.

   When the width of the gap is approximately the same as the wavelength of the waves the wave pattern emerging from the gap should change. It is as if the narrow gap is acting as a point source. This bending of waves around obstacles, or when they pass through a narrow gap, is known as **diffraction**.

Diffraction

Diffraction takes place most readily when the width of the gap is approximately the same as the wavelength of the wave.

Long waves (with a long wavelength) are diffracted more than short waves. Why do you think this is so?

If there is a large amount of diffraction, only a small amount of the wave's energy is received at a point a long way from the source of the disturbance. For this reason long waves are unsuitable for long distance radio transmission, since the signals reaching the receiving station would be weak. Short waves are more suitable for these long distance transmissions, but they cannot be used for local transmissions (see Section 38).

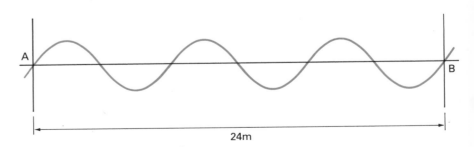

24m

Questions

1 The wave pattern between points A and B in a tank is shown above. Given that the speed of this wave is 12 m/s, determine its frequency.
2 Why are some television antennae dish-shaped?

Glossary

absorption   (of digested food) the taking up of substances by vessels and tissues
acceleration   rate of increase of velocity
acid   a substance with a pH less than 7
adrenaline   a secretion from the pituitary gland which increases the rate of the heart beat and blood pressure
aeration   mixing thoroughly with air
aerobic respiration   type of internal respiration in which digested food is oxidized, energy being liberated
alimentary canal   the canal from the mouth to the anus
alkali   a base which is soluble in water
alloy   a mixture of metals
amino acids   organic acids containing carbon, oxygen, and nitrogen in combination with hydrogen
amnion   the fluid-filled sac surrounding the developing embryo in the uterus
ampere   the unit of electric current
amplitude   the extent of vibrating movement from the top of the crest to the mean position
amplitude modulation   variation of the strength of a carrier wave so music and speech are transmitted
amylases (carbohydrases) enzymes which help digest starch and other carbohydrates
anaemia   decrease in the number of red cells circulating in the blood
anaerobic respiration   internal respiration without absorption of oxygen from outside
anodizing   giving a protective coating to a metal by using it as the anode in electrolysis
antibody   a substance produced in an organism to defend itself against some foreign substance, e.g., a virus
antigen   a substance that stimulates the production of an antibody
aorta   the great artery which takes blood from the heart
aqueous   containing water
artery   a vessel which takes blood from the heart to the body
assimilation   all the processes involved in the use of food material after digestion and absorption
auricle   an upper chamber of the heart
autonomic nervous system   a system of motor nerves supplying muscles and glands
auxins   substances present in small quantities in plants which promote growth

base   a substance which neutralizes an acid to form a salt and water only

capillarity   property of a liquid due to surface tension which causes the liquid to rise in narrow tubes
carbohydrate   a compound containing carbon, hydrogen and oxygen

carrier wave   a radio wave of constant frequency upon which a modulated wave is imposed
cervix   the neck of the womb
chlorophyll   the green colouring matter of plants
chromosomes   parts of the cell nucleus important in mitosis and the passing on of characteristics from parents to offspring
cohesion   attraction between molecules of liquid which causes drops and thin films to be formed
colloid   a suspension of solid particles in a liquid in which the particles are so small that they cannot be separated by ordinary filtration
concave   curved inwards
conduction   a way in which heat is transferred by being passed from one particle to the next
contraceptive   a device for birth control by preventing union of sperm and ovum
convection   a way in which heat is transferred in liquids and gases by the fluid moving
convex   bulging outwards
cotyledon   a leaf in a plant embryo
cortex   the outer layer of an organ

dehydration   removal of water
dentition   the number and arrangement of teeth in the jaw
denitrification   a process whereby nitrates are changed to nitrites or nitrogen by bacteria in the soil
diffraction   the spreading of light waves after passing through a narrow opening or the edge of an opaque body
diffusion   movement of the particles of one substance through another
digestion   process of making ingested food soluble and usable by the body
drag   resistance to motion through a fluid, e.g., air or water

ecology   study of plants and animals in relation to their environment
ecosystem   an area of nature where living and non-living organisms interact with each other, bringing about an interchange of materials
efficiency   the ratio of the energy output of a machine to the input
egestion   elimination of undigested food
elastic limit   the maximum load a wire or string can take and return to its original length when the load is taken off
embryo   a young animal or plant in the earliest stages of development
emulsion   a suspension of one liquid in another where one of the liquids is in the form of very fine drops

endosperm   tissue in a seed which provides food for the growing embryo
enzymes   catalysts produced by living cells used in digestion and other functions of the body
epiglottis   a tough flap or membrane over the entrance to the wind-pipe
equilibrium   a state of balance in which opposing forces neutralize each other
evaporation   changing liquid into vapour
excretion   the getting rid of waste matter from a cell, tissue, or organism

fat   a compound of carbon, hydrogen, and oxygen; an essential ingredient of the diet
fertilization   the union of a male and a female sex cell
fluorescence   the property of emitting light of longer wavelength than that absorbed
focus   the point to which rays of light converge after reflection at a spherical surface or refraction through a lens
foetus   the young animal in the womb after its parts are distinctly formed
food chain   the transfer of food energy from the source in plants through a series of living organisms which successively depend on each other for food
food web   a complex food chain
force   that which changes or tends to change the state of rest or of motion of a body in a straight line
frequency   number of vibrations per second, measured in Hertz
frontal surface   the surface between two masses of air at different temperatures and pressures
fundamental   the frequency of the lowest note emitted by a source of sound

galvanizing   coating sheet iron with zinc to prevent rusting
genes   units of DNA in a chromosome responsible for passing on characteristics from parents to offspring
germination   the beginning of growth of an embryo
gravity   the force of attraction between bodies, e.g. Earth and Moon

habitat   the place where an organism lives
haemoglobin   the red colouring of blood
hermaphrodite   an animal or plant with the organs of both male and female
homogeneous   the same throughout
hormones   internal secretions produced in plants and animals which cause a specific action
host   organism on which a parasite lives

hydrocarbon a compound containing carbon and hydrogen only

indicator a substance which has a different colour when in an acidic solution from that shown in an alkaline solution
ingestion taking food into the body
insulator a substance which will not conduct electricity
ions electrically charged atoms or groups of atoms

joule the unit of energy; 1 newton metre

kilowatt-hour a measure of electrical power; 1000 watts for 1 hour
kinetic energy energy of motion

lipases enzymes aiding digestion of fats
loam soil consisting of a mixture of clay and sand with some organic matter

machine a device for transferring a force applied at one place to another
mammal an animal that suckles its young
mammary gland gland in the female that controls the production of milk
mass the quantity of matter in a body
mechanical advantage the ratio of the load to the effort in a machine
medulla the central part of an organ
meiosis a process of cell division giving rise to sex cells in which the number of chromosomes is reduced to half
melanin dark brown or black pigment occuring in hair and skin
menstruation monthly shedding of the lining of the uterus when a woman is not pregnant
microorganism an organism visible only through a high-powered microscope
mitosis a process of cell division in which each daughter cell has a complete set of chromosomes similar to those in the parent cell
mycelium the mass of thread-like hyphae forming the plant body of a fungus
myelin sheath white fatty substance which surrounds nerve fibres

narcotic a drug which causes sleep, dizziness, euphoria, loss of memory, and lack of muscular coordination
neutralization cancellation of the effect of an acid by adding a base to it
newton the unit of force
nucleus of a cell, a spherical body in a plant or animal cell, which contains chromosomes and controls the growth and behaviour of the cell

ohm the unit of electrical resistance
osmosis diffusion of a solvent through a semi-permeable membrane into a more concentrated solution in order to make the concentrations the same
overtones notes which give musical instruments their particular quality
ovules structures in a plant ovary which contain egg cells, and after fertilization become seeds
ovulation the release of an egg (ovum) from the ovary

pancreas a large gland which discharges digestive juices into the duodenum
parallel circuit a circuit which splits into branches and then rejoins
parturition giving birth
pathogen an organism or substance which causes disease
peripheral nervous system nerves which are on the outside of the body e.g., the skin
peristalsis waves of contraction which push food down the alimentary canal
pH a method of expressing the degree of acidity or alkalinity of a solution. pH 7 is neutral; pH greater than 7 is alkaline; pH less than 7 is acidic
phloem tissue in a plant stem through which food material is carried
photosynthesis the formation of carbohydrates from carbon dioxide and water by green plants using energy from the sun. Oxygen is also produced
pistil the central organ of a flower containing the ovary, the style, and the stigma
pituitary gland major gland producing hormones affecting many actions of the body
placenta dark red disc of tissue in the wall of the womb to which the developing embryo is attached in mammals
plasma colourless part of blood in which the red and white corpuscles float
plastic a substance that can be moulded
platelets minute bodies in the blood involved in clotting
plumule the embryonic shoot of a plant
pollination transfer of pollen (male reproductive cells) from the stamens to the stigma of the same plant (self-pollination) or another plant (cross-pollination)
polymer a large molecule formed by the joining together of a large number of smaller ones of the same kind
potential energy energy possessed by a body because of its position
primary colours colours from which all others can be derived. For lights, red, green and blue; for pigments, red, yellow and blue
protases enzymes which help in the digestion of proteins
proteins nitrogen-containing foodstuffs necessary for growth
puberty the beginning of sexual maturity

radiation a way in which heat is transferred from a hot body to a colder one without heating up the intervening space
radicle the embryonic root of a plant
reflex action an automatic response to a stimulus
refraction bending of waves on passing from one medium to another, or on changing speed
relative humidity water vapour pressure of the atmosphere expressed as a percentage of the saturated water vapour pressure at the same temperature
resistor a material which opposes the flow of an electric current
respiration the oxidation of carbohydrates to carbon dioxide and water within cells to liberate energy

salt the product, together with water, of the neutralization of an acid with a base
sedative a drug which causes sleep
seismograph an instrument for detecting earth tremors
semi-permeable used of a membrane which allows certain substances to pass through it but not others
series circuit a circuit in which the parts are linked up one after the other
solute the substance which is dissolved in a solvent to make a solution
solution a mixture of a solute and a solvent
solvent usually a liquid, although it could be a solid or a gas, which dissolves another substance
spectrum a range of frequencies
spore a single-celled asexual reproductive body
stamen part of a flower which bears pollen
stigma the top of the style in a plant which receives pollen in pollination
suspension a mixture of a fluid with very small particles which do not settle out
symbiosis a partnership between two organisms which is good for both of them

testa the outer coating of a seed
testes sperm-producing glands
tissue a group of similar cells
trachea the wind pipe
transformer an arrangement for changing the voltage of an alternating electrical supply
translocation transference of substances from one place to another in plants
transverse waves wave motion in which the vibration is at right angles to the direction of travel of the wave

umbilical cord the link between the embryo and the placenta
upthrust the upward force exerted on a body when it is immersed in a fluid

vaccines substances which give immunity to disease when given as an innoculation
vagina birth canal. The passage leading from the womb to the exterior
vasectomy cutting of the tube conveying sperm to produce sterility in the male
vegetative propagation asexual reproduction of plants by breaking away of part of the body of the plant
vein a tube taking blood to the heart
ventricle a chamber of the heart which contracts
voltage the pressure of electricity which causes an electric current to flow

watt the unit of power; 1 joule per second
wavelength the distance between two points in a wave motion where it repeats itself

xylem part of a plant stem which conducts solutions and provides support

zygote the product of the union of a male and female gamete

Index